Introduction to ENGINEERING ECONOMY

THE MACMILLAN COMPANY
NEW YORK · BOSTON · CHICAGO · DALLAS
ATLANTA · SAN FRANCISCO

MACMILLAN AND CO., Limited
LONDON · BOMBAY · CALCUTTA · MADRAS
MELBOURNE

THE MACMILLAN COMPANY
OF CANADA, Limited
TORONTO

Introduction to

ENGINEERING
ECONOMY

---

by Baldwin M. Woods, Ph.D.
Professor of Mechanical Engineering

and E. Paul De Garmo, M.S.
Assistant Professor of Mechanical Engineering

UNIVERSITY OF CALIFORNIA

The Macmillan Company

NEW YORK · 1950

" The engineer does for one dollar
what others do for two."

PREFACE

This book is intended to serve as a text for courses which introduce students to the subject of Engineering Economy. The experiences of the authors in teaching this subject to well over two thousand upper division engineering students have convinced them that these students are eager to learn about the monetary side of engineering enterprises. At the same time, the fact that most of them receive little or no training in economics or accounting has become increasingly apparent.

In the existing industrial and social world one is constantly required to have an acquaintance with many subjects which he does not expect to understand completely, but which serve as bases for better understanding of those which he masters thoroughly. Thus a reasonable understanding of the manner in which the various parts of an automobile function enables one to be a more skillful driver. Ability to design these parts of the automobile would probably add little to one's driving ability.

Engineering Economy must, of necessity, cross several fields of knowledge. A single volume cannot pause to harvest all that is in each field. Instead, each field must be sampled so one may know what is in existence and thus appreciate how it will affect any study that is undertaken. Thus an attempt has been made in this volume to show how such subjects as economics, accounting, statistical methods, etc., are related to the economy of engineering enterprises and to give the student a sufficient sample of each field so he will appreciate the relationship of the parts to the whole.

The authors are well aware of the difficulty, and even danger, of attempting to present any portion of such subjects as economics and accounting in abbreviated form. Nothing can entirely take the place of substantial courses in these subjects. But the fact remains that most engineering students at graduation have taken no courses, or at best very few, in these subjects. By giving these students some idea of the proper relationship of these subjects to Engineering Economy, they are able to deal with all economy problems from the viewpoint of fundamentals instead of having to rely on generalized formulas. Such practice is in accord with true engineering procedure. At the same time, these brief introductions to these related subjects may serve to stimulate further study.

In arranging the sequence of the chapters, an effort has been made to supply the student with the tools he will need as he progresses to more difficult problems of investment and selection. Some sacrifice of orderly arrangement has been made to stimulate the student's interest. Thus the subject of Immediate Economy has been placed early in the book to give the student a chance to work on problems that have substance and meaning.

The problems included with each chapter have been designed to require the student to apply the theory which has been discussed. The statements of the problems accompanying the latter portion of the book often contain excess data, and, in a few cases, incomplete data. This will require the student to exercise good judgment in selecting those data which are required for the solutions, whether found in the statement of the problem or in some of the references that are listed.

Limitations of space have forced the omission of certain subjects which are often useful, but not essential. Others have been treated briefly. For example, in discussing statistical methods the subject of correlation is not presented extensively. This is a factor in quality control by sampling. But the student who studies the general process for the first time has a sufficient picture without intensive study of indirect methods, no matter how interesting.

The subject of statistical methods has been given considerable space because of the growing importance of this material. It appears certain that it is going to have a close relationship to economy in many industries in the future.

Every attempt has been made to give credit for all material that has been borrowed from other writers. In many cases it has been impossible to give exact credit where it is due. Many friends and associates have made suggestions and offered ideas and statements through the years which, taken together, have crystallized into many of the thoughts expressed in this volume. To these, for their valuable help, we can only offer this bit of appreciation.

To our many students, who have unknowingly been the proving ground for much of this text, we offer our thanks. They have reacted unfailingly in making us aware of good and bad methods of presentation. It is our hope that they, and those who follow them, will find this book a helpful guide in their study of Engineering Economy.

BALDWIN M. WOODS
E. PAUL DE GARMO

Berkeley, California
August, 1942

TABLE OF CONTENTS

CHAPTER I

CHAPTER II

CHAPTER III

CHAPTER IV

TABLE OF CONTENTS

Introduction to ENGINEERING ECONOMY

Chapter I

INTRODUCTION

As the engineer assumes greater responsibility in the business world he is constantly required to determine the answers to three questions:

1. What is to be done?
2. By what methods may it be accomplished?
3. Which method will give satisfactory results with the least cost?

Engineering economy is concerned with the answer to the third of these questions. It involves the application of certain laws of economics, theories of investment and practices of business to otherwise purely technical problems. At the same time, the application of these laws and practices must many times be seasoned by a judicious amount of common sense.

Alternatives Usually Exist. Most engineering problems may be solved in more than one way. Steam may be obtained just as readily from a gas-fired as from an oil-burning boiler. Either fuel gives the same resultant product — steam. Sometimes the results will not be of equal utility. One result will be superior to all others in quality and technical excellence or will be much cheaper to obtain. Few would find difficulty in choosing between a frame house and one of cut stone construction. The engineer's technical knowledge will enable him to obtain these different results and determine which is superior from the viewpoint of engineering excellence. But is the solution which is technically superior to all others the one which should be used? A reinforced concrete tool shed would undoubtedly outlast one of light, wooden construction. It would afford greater protection to the tools. However, to erect such a concrete shed on the site of a house

1

construction job that would require only three months to complete would obviously be wrong. In this case the wooden shed would be a better solution although it does not possess the fine technical qualities of the concrete shed.

Much of engineering work boils down to making a choice among several possible solutions. This necessity for making decisions is not restricted, of course, to the practice of engineering. Every person must make many choices during his life. In fact, a day does not pass without bringing with it the necessity of choosing between various courses of action. The importance of the decision and the various factors influencing the choice will change with age and viewpoint. The boy of seven, standing before the candy counter trying to decide how to spend the two pennies that he holds in his hand, is faced with the necessity of making a selection from the possible solutions to his problem. His desire for candy may be satisfied by either suckers or licorice. His choice will probably not be influenced to any extent by logical factors. More than likely a realization that the licorice will enable him to emulate his tobacco-chewing grandfather will outweigh all other influences.

Time Changes Viewpoints. Now consider this same boy 30 years later. He is now a trained engineer operating his own business. On a particular job he is faced with the necessity of digging some ditches. He can employ laborers to do the work by the pick and shovel method or he can rent a ditch-digging machine to accomplish the task. His natural desire to do things in a big way will probably tell him to use the machine. His decision now is of considerable importance where as a seven-year-old boy any choice he might have made would have little permanent effect. Now the success of his business demands that he determine which of the two methods will accomplish the task more cheaply. He does some investigating and finds the ground in which the ditch must be dug is full of steam and water pipes so that a ditch-digging machine would be of little value. What appeared to be the slow and inefficient method turns out to be the correct solution to his problem. The error would have been just as serious if conditions had indicated the machine method would have been cheaper and it was not used.

It would seem reasonable to expect that engineers would always take such factors into account in their work. However, there are enough uneconomic structures existing throughout the country to give some support to the contention that some engineers have not always been sufficiently concerned with the economy of their projects and have thus done their share in making the life of the average enterprise in this country only 66 months. The tremendous scope of modern engineering projects makes it essential that all the factors involved in the economy of an undertaking not only be considered but handled in an accurate, approved manner so the results will be satisfactory from all the viewpoints touched by the project. The selection of the final method should never be a matter of guess or be left to the will of the gods. Some will raise their voices to protest that much of the information must be based upon estimates and therefore the final answer can be found by guesswork. Obviously, estimates made after careful study and based on all the information that is available are considerably better than haphazard guesses. It is true that a carefully prepared estimate may also be a guess. However, it is an *enlightened* guess. All the available factors are considered and used. Data that are not entirely available are determined as exactly as possible in the light of the experience of the engineer. Such an estimate is much more exact and useful than a wild guess by some uninformed person. In fact, the accuracy of an estimate is usually limited only by the amount of time and money one wishes to spend in preparing the report.

Engineers Must Work within the Economic System. Under the capitalistic system in operation in the United States it is essential that an enterprise be profitable. While one may question whether or not capitalism is the best economic system, there can be no argument that as long as business is conducted under this system it must earn a return upon the required investment of capital. The million-dollar streamlined trains, 35-million-dollar bridges and 100-million-dollar dams being constructed in this country illustrate the fact that one of the outstanding characteristics of modern enterprise is the great investment of money required to make most engineering enterprises possible. Retooling costs in several automobile plants are over one million dollars for a new year's model.[1] Money is as important a factor as is steel or any of the commonly considered physical materials. The engineer spends much time and effort in learning the properties and behavior of steel, concrete and various alloys so that he may use them intelligently and be able to predict accurately the performance of the machine he is designing. Since money is important and necessary, it is essential that the engineer be acquainted with its properties and the laws governing its use. The modern engineer does not shy away from such factors as creep and fatigue which were formerly disposed of in an "ignorance" factor. It is just as reasonable that in modern engineering money be accounted for in an honest and informed manner.

Whether or not the conclusion is just, or honestly drawn, the prestige of the engineer has suffered in business, banking and lay circles because some engineers have not been cost-minded or concerned with the economic side of their work. It is true that the engineer has often been justified in suggesting that these critics put their own houses in order, but this does not alter the fact that this smoke probably indicates some fire, and housecleaning should begin at home.

If the engineer is to give and obtain the proper cooperation from all phases of the business world and assume a larger share of responsibility in the management of industry, it is essential that he be able to speak and understand the language of the businessman. He must follow established business procedures so that his work may readily fit into its proper place in the larger business scheme. His results and conclusions must be couched in the terminology of business. Recognized factors such as depreciation, valuation, accounting practices, interest and overhead should be used in accordance with good business practice. To do this intelligently the engineer needs a knowledge of the fundamentals of investment, accounting and interpretation of business statistics. It is not necessary or expected that he should be an expert in these subjects. He should, however, be able to use these items in a way that indicates an appreciation of their proper use and importance. Such knowledge will do much to

---

[1] For their 1940 model the Buick Motor Company claims to have spent over $8,000,000 for new dies and equipment.

avoid misunderstanding and increase the business world's appreciation of the engineer.

The engineer is well versed in the physical laws of the universe. He is at all times cognizant of the laws of gravitation, conservation of energy and thermodynamics. He would never think of attempting a project contrary to the rules established by these laws. It is surprising, therefore, that many engineers (and businessmen) remain in ignorance of fundamental laws of economics, or at least refuse to abide by these laws if they are aware of them. A few of these laws are of such importance and apply to so many engineering problems that they should be respectfully considered, since their disregard may vitally affect the economy of an engineering project just as surely as will the neglect of applicable physical laws.

Human Factors Are of Increasing Importance. There is another factor which may exercise a tremendous effect upon the economy of an engineering undertaking. This is the relationship of the human individual to the project. It appears that industry is becoming increasingly conscious of the interdependence of humanity and itself and realizes that business without human beings would be impossible. It is only too true that the effect of the human element cannot be written down in an equation or set of rules, or accurately predicted at all times, yet it may be so great as to outweigh all other factors. Much of the knowledge about this factor can be learned only through long, and sometimes bitter, experience. However, as long as it is present, the engineer can ill afford to close his eyes to it.

At times the reaction of the public to an engineering innovation may be almost immediate. At other times there is a slow, cumulative effect over a period of years. Either case may be beneficial or disastrous. The present situation in automotive design is an excellent example of the effect of immediate public reaction. Engineers are well aware of the advantages of placing the engine of an automobile in the rear of the car and of the need for improved streamlining. Yet no manufacturer dares to attempt to do as well as he knows how in these two matters. The public reaction to the Chrysler Airflow models, introduced in 1934, is too well remembered. These cars embodied many excellent engineering advances which were little known to the average public and which were incorporated into nearly all cars in later years. The change that was probably least perfect from an engineering viewpoint was the change in body appearance. It was quite poor as an example of true streamlining, yet Chrysler engineers felt the public was not ready for the radical change that would accompany good streamlining. Therefore they made only a moderate change. It was soon apparent that the motoring public was not ready to accept even this moderate deviation from conventional body design, and the models were abandoned after a few years. At the same time, manufacturers of vacuum cleaners and household appliances found great consumer acceptance of "streamlining" on their models in spite of the fact that from an engineering viewpoint these changes had no effect upon the efficiency or utility of the equipment. In these instances the human element was an immediate and important factor.

In other instances the human factor acts only after accumulating momentum through a long period of time. This is well illustrated in the attitude of people in recent years toward public utility companies. Neglect of the human factor for a long period of time by some of these companies brought the whole industry into ill repute. As a result they were condemned by many people who knew nothing of the facts concerning a particular company against whom they held a grudge. Such an attitude had a very definite effect upon the economy of these utilities. Many of the companies, despite radical changes in their operating policies, were still unable to overcome public opposition.

The current great turmoil and conflict between labor and management is another example of trouble that may arise through long-time neglect of the human factor. No one will deny that this strife is having a terrific effect upon the economy of the entire nation. One might well paraphrase the old saying, "You can't fool all the people all the time," into, "It is foolish to disregard any of the people any of the time." If the engineer is to take a leading role in the future conduct of industry, he must not neglect the human factor in his application of engineering economy. It is true that the human element may be ignored for a short time without any noticeable reaction. However, since it is so apparent that continued neglect will bring disaster, it is risky to conclude that this factor may be neglected at all without some reaction.

Requirements of an Economy Study of an Engineering Project. In order to justify the expenditure of time and money, an economy study should satisfy the following requirements:

1. It should be based upon consideration of all available factors.

2. When some factors *must* be estimated, these estimates should be made intelligently, in the light of experience and sound judgment.

3. The study should show the annual rate of return that may be expected from the required investment. This is the factor upon which the decision regarding the advisability of investment will usually be based.

4. In so far as they apply correctly, the study should make use of the same factors that the accountant will use in determining the financial efficiency of the investment after it is made.

A study made in this manner will properly consider the effect of time on money and property. Thus, interest and depreciation will be included in the correct manner. If known factors are not neglected or ignored, the result after investment will more nearly coincide with the conclusions of the economy study.

"Rate of return upon the required investment" is a term universally understood by business managers. With this figure for the contemplated project before them, they will have little difficulty in comparing the advantages to be obtained from the investment to those which might be gained by investing the same amount of money in some other enterprise.

Since a study of an engineering project is likely to be somewhat complicated by technical terms not readily understood by the nonengineer, it is important that the engineer follow as closely as possible the language and form of customary business practice in making his reports. His use of the common language and methods of business will do much to further his usefulness and opportunities in the business world. The ultimate purpose of an economy study is to bring about more economic use of engineering principles in business. If it does not serve this purpose it is a waste of time and money.

Chapter II

SOME ECONOMIC LAWS

Economics may be broadly defined as the study of wealth: its value, creation and distribution. The economist is concerned with the meaning of wealth and its place in the existing economic order. He is interested in the various kinds of economic systems, the law of supply and demand, different price systems, wage systems, profits, banking and the distribution of wealth. While a thorough understanding of all of these subjects is of considerable importance to anyone engaged in the conduct of a business enterprise, such a knowledge would require a great amount of study and is outside the purpose of this book.

In the world of finance and trade the laws of economics are of prime importance. They are encountered with such frequency that they become the basis of everyday practice. Many of these principles are not of such immediate concern to the engineer and are handled infrequently. However, certain principles are of such importance to him that they must be considered carefully. Money and materials, forms of wealth that the engineer uses in nearly all his work, are as much subject to economic laws in his hands as in those of the banker or merchant. To use this wealth intelligently and economically the engineer must use it in accordance with these laws.

Law of Diminishing Returns. It is a common experience for a man to set himself up in a small business with capital which he has acquired through saving over a period of years. The capital may amount to less than $1,000, but through hard work he is able to obtain an annual return of $2,000. The condition of his business appears excellent, and he believes that if he could expand he could make a much larger profit. He reasons that if he can make $2,000 on an investment of $1,000 he should be able to make $5,000 or $6,000 annually if he could increase his investment to $3,000. Would his business not be three times as large? To bring about this expansion he borrows $2,000 and invests it in the business. As the months pass he finds he is not making three times as much profit as he was before. In fact, he discovers his profit is actually less than it was before he expanded. Within two years he may be forced to turn the business over to his creditors.

Such an experience is so common in the business world that it is often said that most businesses cannot stand prosperity. In tabulations of the causes of business failures such cases will usually be listed under the heading "Insufficient Capital." The fundamental cause for the failure was the law of diminishing returns.

The *law of diminishing returns* may be stated as follows: When the use of one of the factors of production is limited, either by increasing cost or by absolute quantity, a point will be reached beyond which an increase in the variable factors will result in a less than proportionate increase in output.

An examination of this statement reveals that it applies to two particular conditions:

1. One factor cannot be increased.

2. All of the factors of production can be increased, but only with increasing difficulty.

The first studies of the law were probably made in the field of agriculture. Here the first condition is exemplified. Suppose a farmer has 100 acres of land on which he raises corn. If he is an average farmer and does not employ other labor he will probably get a yield of not over 35 bushels from each acre. The size of his crop is determined by a number of factors. These are (a) sunshine, (b) fertilizer, (c) cultivation, (d) the amount of land, (e) the labor available at the correct time, and (f) rain. All of these factors may be varied except the amount of land. Only 100 acres are available for cultivation. (Of course some of the factors may not vary at the farmer's will, but at least they are not rigidly fixed.) The successful growing of corn depends greatly upon having the ground in the proper condition at a particular time.

The time at which the seed must be planted and the amount of time available for preparation of the soil are determined largely by the weather. Working by himself, the amount of ground which the farmer can prepare, and the quality of the preparation, are limited. If he employs a hired hand more ground will be better prepared and the yield might be increased from 35 to 40 bushels per acre. If he employs a second man to help in the preparation of the ground and in planting the seed he might obtain a further increase of two bushels per acre. It is likely, however, that the addition of a third man would result in little, if any, increase in the crop yield. After sufficient labor is employed to prepare all of the land in a reasonably good manner and plant the seed, there will be very little gain from the employment of additional labor. The amount of land is definitely fixed, and the law of diminishing returns applies to the results obtained from increasing the amount of labor utilized.

An examination of the other factors necessary for the corn crop reveals that increasing them will effect an increase in the yield of the land up to a certain point. Beyond this point the return is less than proportional, and the yield may actually decrease. No rain will result in no crop. A reasonable amount of rain will cause a large increase in the total amount of corn. However, increasing the amount of rain greatly will actually lessen the yield from the 100

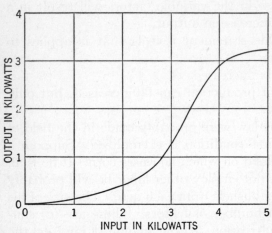

FIGURE 1. Output curve for a $3\frac{1}{2}$ horsepower constant speed motor.

acres. The same results will be obtained from increases in the amount of sunshine, fertilizer and cultivation. Thus, in agriculture the effect of diminishing returns may readily be seen. Its effect is much the same as that obtained by the rider who whips his horse.

A small amount gives a great increase in speed. Too much whipping results in a great decrease in speed — at least in a forward direction. In nonagricultural pursuits the point of diminishing returns is usually not reached so quickly.

A case of diminishing returns that is familiar to the engineer is that of the output of an electric motor which is held at a constant speed. The output curve obtained by testing such a motor is shown in Figure 1. This was a 3½-horsepower motor that was wound to give a constant speed of 1,290 r.p.m. In Table 1 the

TABLE 1. LOAD TEST DATA FOR 3½ HORSEPOWER CONSTANT-SPEED MOTOR SHOWING PROPORTIONAL AND ACTUAL OUTPUT PER UNIT OF INPUT

	Input, kw.	Actual output, kw.	Proportional output, kw.	Output per unit of input
a	b	c	d	e
A	0.5	0.00		0.000
B	1.0	0.10		0.100
C	1.5	0.25	0.15	0.167
D	2.0	0.41	0.33	0.205
E	2.5	0.70	0.51	0.357
F	3.0	1.20	0.84	0.400
G	3.5	2.20	1.40	0.628
H	4.0	2.92	2.52	0.730
I	4.5	3.15	3.28	0.678
J	5.0	3.20	3.50	0.640

results obtained from the test are shown. The test data are shown in the first two main columns. The computed results are contained in the last two columns. The column headed "Proportional output" is computed to show what the output would have been had it continued to increase at the rate shown on the previous reading. Thus,

$$\frac{c_B}{b_D} = \frac{d_C}{b_C}$$

By comparing the actual output with the proportional output one may determine whether an increase in input results in less than proportionate, proportionate or greater than proportionate increase in output.

Two factors of production were present in this experiment — the motor and the input of electric energy. The motor was a fixed factor, but the input could be varied at will. Each increase in input might have given any one of five possible results on output:

1. No increase.
2. Less than proportional increase.
3. Proportional increase.
4. Greater than proportional increase.
5. Decrease.

Three of these conditions are shown in the table, and a fourth was present but did not appear as such. The first reading shows that, although the input was increased from zero to 0.5 kw., no increase in output occurred. From B to H, inclusive, each successive increase in input resulted in a greater than proportional increase in output. At some point between H and I the increase in output was evidently proportional to the increase in input. Starting with I, the increase in output was less than proportional to the increase in input. Danger of "burning out" the motor prevented any additional increase in input where the internal losses might have resulted in an actual decrease in output.

This experiment, of course, shows only a special case of diminishing returns. It does illustrate a condition that is very common — output that continues to increase but with decreasing efficiency. The table shows that maximum efficiency was 73% [1] when the output was 2.92 kw. A maximum output of 3.2 kw. was obtained but the efficiency was only 64%. When such an occurrence is tied up with dollars and cents, it may readily be seen why continued increase in output may result in a smaller rate of return on the investment and possibly in actual loss.

Another example of diminishing returns is found in the performance of the ordinary automobile engine. Here the input is a mixture of gasoline and air. It is common experience that if the ratio of gasoline to air is made too low, by adjustment of the carburetor, the engine will develop very little power. As the ratio is increased, the performance of the motor improves and greater power is developed. If the ratio of gasoline to air is further increased, a point of maximum output is obtained. Increas-

---

[1] This unusually low efficiency for an electric motor is due to this motor being a special constant-speed type.

ing the ratio beyond this point results in poorer performance and an actual decrease in the output of the engine so that it does not run smoothly. The fuel mixture is said to be too rich.

When improvements are to be made upon urban property, the principle of diminishing returns becomes very important. Here, again, the available land is the fixed factor. The amount of money which may be spent in erecting buildings upon a given piece of land is practically unlimited. The return that can be realized from the money invested will be dependent on both the land and the investment. The person investing money in such improvements is interested in obtaining a maximum rate of return. Increasing the amount invested when the returns not only do not increase proportionately but actually decrease, eventually leads to no profit. Such a condition is, however, entirely possible.

Suppose the cost of erecting a four-story building on a given city lot is $500,000. To build a six-story building, instead of one having four stories, would probably cost an additional $300,000. These two additional stories have cost $150,000 each where the originally considered four stories cost only $125,000 each. The difference is due to the fact that the additional two stories must be considered as being built under the original four stories and therefore must be of sufficient strength to support the additional weight. This assumes that each story of the building is the same from the standpoint of ornamentation and physical characteristics. In addition, elevators and service stacks must be provided up through the lower four floors to provide access and service to the fifth and sixth stories. These not only cost money but also take away some valuable space from the first four stories.

If two more stories were added, making an eight-story building, those two additional stories would probably cost around $175,000 each, or $350,000. Again this is due to the necessity of building these additional stories so they will support the previous six and to the fact that the building materials and workmen must be raised a greater distance above the ground. The necessity for additional elevators and service stacks will again decrease the usable space on the lower floors. The results of increasing this building from four to eight stories in height are shown in Table 2.

TABLE 2. COST OF BUILDINGS OF VARIOUS HEIGHTS

Stories	Cost of addition	Total cost
4	$500,000	$ 500,000
6	300,000	800,000
8	350,000	1,150,000

It may readily be seen that increasing the usable space less than 100% increased the cost of the building 130%. The increased income derived from the additional stories would be much less than 100% since the rental rate of the upper levels of nearly all buildings would be considerably less than that of the lower floors. Diminishing returns present a very real problem in this type of project. Results of an actual study of this type are shown on page 191. The conclusions show that the architect who dreamed of designing a building so tall that only the top floor could be used, because all the floors below would be taken up with service stacks and elevators, may not have been entirely insane.

The small businessman who expanded his business until he became bankrupt is an example of diminishing returns where all the factors could be increased, but only with increasing difficulty. While such failures are usually said to result from insufficient capital, additional capital was obtained, but its cost was greater than that of the original $1,000. The original capital represented the man's savings, and the monetary cost to him was only the interest which this money was earning in a bank, some 2 or 3% annually. To obtain the additional capital he borrowed money upon which he had to pay an interest rate of 4 to 6%. Additional capital was obtained only with increasing cost.

The same condition existed in the item of labor. When the business was small the owner did much of the work. He was the supervisor over his few employees. When he expanded the business he was forced to employ additional labor and supervision. When the business was small, much of the labor cost was his own effort. After expansion most of the labor cost was actual money. Thus this factor was increased with greater than proportionate cost. Diminishing returns, where all of the factors of production may be increased by increased rates of cost, are often encountered when expansion of existing facilities is attempted.

It should be remembered that the law of diminishing returns is stated for "equilibrium" conditions. An increase in one factor might be accompanied by a change in method or by new equipment which would materially alter the whole picture. Instead of an expansion of existing conditions there would actually be an inauguration of an entirely new undertaking. Just as the engineer does not design a bridge to be made of steel and then construct it of wood without changing his design, the economist does not attempt to rigidly apply the law of diminishing returns where changes in conditions and technique have obliterated the original hypothesis. In a large proportion of the cases with which the engineer is concerned there are new and modifying factors. It must be recognized that these will modify the effect of the law of diminishing returns, delaying, speeding up or even eliminating its application. It cannot, however, be ignored.

Minimum Cost Point. Knowing that the principle of diminishing returns affects the return obtained from a unit of input, one needs to be able to determine the results in terms of dollars. The input to most enterprises is most easily measured in money. The investor of capital is interested in getting the maximum rate of return from his investment. The return per unit of input (efficiency) may increase or decrease with additional input. Determination of the point of maximum efficiency, or the point of

TABLE 3. MONETARY COST OF UNITS OF OUTPUT OF A 3½-HORSEPOWER CONSTANT-SPEED MOTOR

	Input, kw.	Output, kw.	Input per unit of output		Monetary unit cost		Total unit cost, cents
			Variable factor	Fixed [a] factor	Fixed factor, @ 8 cents	Variable factor, @ 2 cents	
A	0.5	0.00	—	—	—	—	—
B	1.0	0.10	10.00	10.00	80.00	20.00	100.00
C	1.5	0.25	6.00	4.00	32.00	12.00	44.00
D	2.0	0.41	4.88	2.44	19.52	9.76	29.28
E	2.5	0.70	3.57	1.43	11.44	7.14	18.58
F	3.0	1.20	2.50	0.83	6.64	5.00	11.64
G	3.5	2.20	1.59	0.45	3.60	3.18	6.78
H	4.0	2.92	1.37	0.34	2.72	2.74	5.46
I	4.5	3.15	1.43	0.32	2.56	2.86	5.42
J	5.0	3.20	1.56	0.31	2.48	3.12	5.60

[a] Number of motors to give 1 kw. output.

the lowest unit cost, becomes of prime importance in most engineering work.

To study the effect of diminishing returns upon unit cost where two factors of production are involved and one is fixed, examine Table 3. The first two columns of figures are the same as in Table 1 and concern the same test of a constant-speed electric motor. The fixed factor in this case is the motor. The third column shows the number of units of the variable factor which would be required in order to obtain one unit (1 kw.) of output. Thus in line B, since 1 kw. of input produced an output of only 0.1 kw., to obtain 1 kw. of output 10 kw. input would be required.

In the fourth column similar data are tabulated for the fixed factor, the motor. Thus in line C, since one motor produced only 0.25 kw. of output, four motors would be required to produce 1 kw. of output if all were operated under the assumed conditions of load and efficiency.

In order to determine the monetary cost of obtaining one unit of output, it is necessary to know the monetary value of the required units of input. In this case the variable input factor, electric energy, was assumed to cost 2 cents per kw.-hr. The cost of the fixed factor — the motor — was more difficult to determine. This cost is made up of the depreciation of the motor, rent on the building where it is housed, taxes, insurance and other overhead costs. In this case it was assumed that the total of these costs was 8 cents per hour for one motor.

A study of this table shows that the lowest cost per unit of output for the fixed factor occurs at J corresponding to an output of 3.2 kw. For the variable factor the most economical point of operation is at H, where the output is only 2.92 kw. Least total operating cost, however, is at I, where 3.15 kw. of output are obtained and the unit cost is 5.42 cents. This shows the method that may be used to determine the least cost point where both fixed and variable production factors are involved. Information can usually be obtained from which the unit costs of the several production factors may be determined. This example also shows why the proper operating point for a machine or structure may be at neither the point of maximum mechanical efficiency nor the point of maximum output. The ultimate goal is to have these three points coincide, but this optimum condition is seldom achieved. In fact, in many actual cases it may not be desirable. For example, when a motor operates 90% of the time at three-fourths load, but must be capable of furnishing full load, it would obviously be desirable to have maximum efficiency at three-fourths load rather than at full load.

The example just cited involved only two input factors. Many cases will involve three or more factors, any or all of which may be fixed or variable. If a unit value can be determined for these various factors, such problems can be solved in a similar manner. Additional factors only serve to make the solution more complex. The following example illustrates a common problem of this type.

In the curing (vulcanization) of automobile tires by the use of pot heaters it is desirable to operate the correct number of heaters and use the proper number of laborers to give the lowest curing cost per tire for any particular curing time. The number of tires that can be cured per hour, using various combinations of heaters and men in the curing unit crew, is shown in Table 4. Each

TABLE 4. NUMBER OF AUTOMOBILE TIRES VULCANIZED PER HOUR IN A POT HEATER TYPE UNIT

Heaters used	Men in crew				
	2	4	6	8	10
1	16	24	28	30	31
2	20	44	50	60	63
3	22	50	70	90	94
4	22	54	94	120	125
5	21	56	105	150	157
6	20	55	110	170	179
7	18	53	112	175	190

heater will hold 30 tires, and the curing time is 50 minutes. Any saving in time must be made by decreasing the time consumed in placing the tires in and removing them from the molds and in pushing the molds into and taking them out of the heaters. Certain limitations are put upon physical effort by the heat in which the men must work, making a definite amount of rest necessary.

The production factors may be considered to be three in number: the building and its fixed charges, heaters and their steam consumption, and labor cost. These three items were found to have the following hourly costs:

Building and fixed charges	$2.00 per hour
Heaters and steam	$3.00 per hour per heater
Labor	$0.90 per hour per man

Table 5 gives the total cost per tire cured for each combination of heaters and men. These were computed in the following manner (case of six heaters and eight men):

Cost for building (fixed)	$ 2.00
Cost for heaters and steam (variable) 6 × $3.00	18.00
Labor (variable)	7.20
Total	$27.20
(From Table 4) Tires cured per hour	170
Cost per tire	$0.160

In the solution of most problems of this type it is not necessary to compute all of the figures shown in Table 5. A few calculations and a little inspection will show about which combination will give the lowest unit cost, and only one or two more compu-

TABLE 5.   UNIT COSTS FOR VULCANIZING AUTOMOBILE TIRES IN A POT HEATER TYPE UNIT WITH VARIOUS COMBINATIONS OF HEATERS AND MEN

Heaters used	Men in crew				
	2	4	6	8	10
1	$0.425	$0.358	$0.364	$0.407	$0.452
2	0.490	0.264	0.268	0.253	0.270
3	0.582	0.288	0.234	0.202	0.213
4	0.718	0.326	0.206	0.177	0.184
5	0.895	0.368	0.213	0.161	0.166
6	1.090	0.429	0.231	0.160	0.162
7	1.378	0.502	0.254	0.173	0.168

tations will reveal the best combination to use. Table 5 also shows what happens to unit costs when a plant that is designed for large scale, single-purpose production is forced to operate at fractional capacity.

Increasing and Decreasing Cost Industries. All the examples of diminishing returns thus far considered lead to a single conclusion, namely, a change in the output of a business may increase, decrease or not affect unit costs. The effect of diminishing returns to the farmer who raised corn was noted when only a small increase in output was attempted. The automobile engine and the electric motor showed an increasing rate of output per unit of input when the output was first increased beyond zero. A decrease in the rate of output per unit of input did not come until a large increase in output was attempted. In the curing of automobile tires a relatively small change in the combination of men and equipment caused a great change in unit costs. It is thus apparent that certain types of enterprises are affected more than others.

If various industries are examined, it will be found that certain types have characteristic tendencies in respect to increase or decrease of unit costs with changing rates of production. These tendencies are closely tied up with the industry's use of durable goods. These durable instruments of production represent fixed, or approximately fixed, factors of production. Compared with a steel mill, a tailor makes very little use of durable goods. If the tailor operates at low capacity he has only a small amount of capital tied up in unused goods. The large steel mill, operating at 20% of capacity, has a tremendous sum invested in unproductive equipment. Doubling output would cause a great decrease in the unit costs of the steel mill but would lower the tailor's unit costs little, if any.

Another influence upon the tendency of costs to increase or decrease is the dependence of the industry upon natural factors. A coal mine has only one source from which to obtain its product. As more coal is produced, the supply will probably become more scarce and difficult to obtain. The farmer or stock raiser is again very subject to the influence of natural factors. The producer of Mickey Mouse pictures, however, is very little affected by such conditions.

A third condition that will influence the effect of diminishing returns upon an industry is the extent to which it may be able to utilize mass production methods. Mass production methods are usually accompanied by important savings which will overbalance or at least lessen the effect of diminishing returns. Manufacturing industries are notably different from agriculture in this respect.

It is thus apparent that industries may be operating in such a condition that increased production will give increased costs, constant costs or decreased costs. It is characteristic for certain types of business to show some one of these three tendencies under ordinary operating conditions. For this reason agricultural industries are often referred to as increasing cost industries while manufacturing enterprises are known as decreasing or normal cost industries. It must be remembered that this is a broad classification which applies only to normal industries operating at normal capacity. Under other conditions, and even at times under ordinary conditions, industries may be in other classes. The classification does, however, indicate a tendency worth remembering.

Maximum Return. Another economic consideration, which is closely related to diminishing returns, is that of maximum profit from sales. If the price of a certain slide rule were reduced from $15 to $10 an engineer might buy two of them instead of one in order to have one at home as well as at his office. If the price were further reduced to $8 the same engineer might possibly buy a third rule, although this would be very doubtful. Lowering the price to $5 would probably not cause the engineer to buy four slide rules.

In this case the market for slide rules was considered to be limited to one engineer. Of course, the market for most products is not limited to one person, but nevertheless it is limited. Lowering the selling price of an article will broaden the market somewhat. But there comes a point where a further decrease in selling price will produce little, if any, additional market. Each decrease in selling price will probably mean less profit per article sold, although the profit may not decrease as rapidly as the selling price, owing to a decrease in production cost through larger production.

The manufacturer is interested in obtaining the maximum return from the sale of his product. Table 6 shows what one producer found from a careful survey of the market for his product. One thousand articles could be sold in a given area when

TABLE 6.   RELATION BETWEEN SELLING PRICE AND
MAXIMUM PROFIT

Selling price	Sales	Unit costs	Unit profit	Total profit
$1.00	1,000	$0.60	$0.40	$400
0.80	2,500	0.58	0.22	550
0.75	3,800	0.60	0.15	570
0.70	4,200	0.61	0.09	378

the selling price was $1. A profit of 40 cents could be made on each article at this price. Reducing the price to 75 cents decreased the unit profit to 15 cents, but since the sales increased 280%, the resulting profit was over twice as much. A further decrease in selling price to 70 cents brought only 400 additional sales and resulted in a decrease in total profits. It should also be noted that the point of greatest profit does not come where the lowest unit cost was obtained. This illustrates three important points which must not be neglected.

1. The point of greatest total profit may not correspond with the point of maximum unit profit.

2. The point of greatest return does not always coincide with the point of lowest unit cost.

3. In a given market, continued reduction of the selling price of an article will not produce proportionate increase in sales. Where the producer has a monopoly on the market, he may adjust his selling price to obtain the maximum return. Just what this price must be is difficult to determine and must be found by experiment or by a very careful market analysis. But ordinarily a complete monopoly does not exist, and competition will affect the selling price of the product. Even under competitive conditions, however, the producer will have considerable freedom in adjusting his price and production to obtain a more favorable return.

Kelvin's Law. In 1881 Lord Kelvin originated an economic law of particular interest to the engineer. In determining the size of electric conductor which would be most economical to conduct a given current, the following rule was established:

The most economical area of conductor is that for which the annual cost of energy lost is equal to the investment charges for the copper used.

In this particular case each increase in the size of the conductor causes a decrease in the loss of electric energy owing to the resistance of the conductor. On the other hand, each increase in the size of the conductor involves additional cost for copper, depreciation, interest and tax charges and often for extra poles and equipment. An example of this exact problem is shown in Chapter XV.

The original derivation of Kelvin's law did not consider the effect of increased wire size upon the cost of supports and insulation. Thus the law in its simple form is not of great value. However, it forms the basis of more refined methods of analysis and comparison when the conditions which will produce the minimum annual cost must be determined. A number of these problems will be considered in detail in later chapters.

REFERENCES

Bowers, E. L., and R. H. Rowntree: "Economics for Engineers," McGraw-Hill Book Company, Inc., New York, 1938.

Johnson, A. S.: "Introduction to Economics," D. C. Heath and Company, Boston, 1922.

Kimball, D. S.: "Industrial Economics," McGraw-Hill Book Company, Inc., New York, 1929.

Taussig, F. W.: "Principles of Economics," The Macmillan Company, New York, 1939.

PROBLEMS

1. Give three reasons why an engineer needs a knowledge of economics.
2. Is a small business more likely to be affected by the law of diminishing returns than a large industry? Why?
3. Would the law of diminishing returns affect improvements on property in a small suburban community as greatly as it would improvements on property in the business district of a large city? Why?
4. What effect does a change in process have upon the law of diminishing returns?
5. Explain why it is not always desirable to operate a machine at the rate which gives maximum mechanical efficiency.
6. A large company reports that doubling their output from 20 to 40% of capacity lowers their unit costs 19.5%. Doubling the output from 50 to 100% of capacity reduces unit costs only 14.5%. Explain this.
7. Classify the following as increasing, decreasing or normal cost industries: (a) automobile manufacturing; (b) department stores; (c) banking; (d) petroleum refining; (e) motion picture theaters.
8. Where a complete monopoly of the market exists, is it always the best policy to adjust prices so as to obtain the greatest return? Why?
9. Explain how Kelvin's law applies to a pipe line for transporting oil.

Chapter III

SELECTIONS IN PRESENT ECONOMY

Factors Affecting Present Economy. If one were assigned the task of excavating 50 cubic yards of dirt, he would be vitally concerned about a number of factors that would affect the ease and cost of completing the work. Probably the first thought would be about the shape of the required excavation. A ditch 3 feet wide by 6 feet deep and 75 feet long would require the removal of 50 cubic yards of material. Similarly, a trench 6 feet wide by 3 feet deep and 75 feet long would require the same amount of excavation. One might also remove the same amount of earth by excavating to the depth of one foot over an area 27 by 50 feet.

In each case the amount of material removed is exactly the same. Yet very little thought is required to realize that each shape of excavation would require a different amount of effort. A considerable portion of the material for a ditch 6 feet deep would have to be raised several feet in order to effect its removal. This would obviously require a greater expenditure of effort, and therefore be more costly, than the trench that is only 3 feet deep. In the case of the excavation 27-by-50-by 1 foot the material is raised only a few inches vertically. However, it would be necessary to do considerable moving horizontally in order to get the material clear of the 27-by-50-foot area.

Thus it is seen that the cost in energy, or the equivalent cost in money, of excavating the 50 cubic yards of earth is greatly affected by the physical dimensions or *design* of the excavation.

A second item that would have to be considered would be the method to be employed in removing the dirt. For example, if the excavation were to be 3 feet wide and 6 feet deep, various

23

methods might be used. A number of men using picks and shovels could be employed. By equipping a lesser number of men with pneumatic spades for breaking up the dirt one might complete the same ditch in a shorter length of time. Again, one could rent a ditch-digging machine and complete the task in a few hours with only a couple of men to operate the machine.

Each of the above methods would accomplish the task in a satisfactory manner. However, they would not cost the same. For a particular job one would show a smaller cost than the others. Here, again, is a factor that affects the economy of obtaining the required excavation, namely, *method*.

The third factor that would affect the cost of excavating is the material to be removed. The task was to remove 50 cubic yards of earth or dirt. Whether this dirt were a loose, sandy soil which could be shoveled up easily, or hardpan, which would require a great amount of work with a pick, would make a considerable difference in the cost of excavating. Thus the *materials* dealt with in a project may have considerable bearing upon the costs.

The above example illustrates how the economy of a project may be influenced by methods, design or materials. Such a choice must be exercised in many engineering operations, and the success of the undertaking will depend upon the correct selection.

Time Not a Factor. Many problems involving economic selection are similar to the excavation example in that time is not a factor that must be considered. While it might require a few more hours to complete the excavation by pick and shovel methods than by the use of a ditch-digging machine (although this is not necessarily true if sufficient men were employed) the difference would be relatively slight and would not ordinarily affect the choice which must be made. One is interested only in obtaining a certain amount of excavation. Regardless of the method employed, the hole obtained through the removal of dirt is the same. After the result is obtained, the effect of time is the same regardless of the means of getting it. Thus, the choice is solely between two or more methods of obtaining identical results.

A similar situation exists when a choice must be made in materials or design. The hole remaining after 50 cubic yards of material have been removed would not be altered by the kind of dirt.

Since the result would be the same, the effect of time need not be considered. Neither is time a factor when the results are dependent only upon a change in physical dimensions or design. A 50-cubic-yard hole would remain regardless of the dimensions of the excavation.

This fact, that time is not an element in the choice, distinguishes this type of economic selection. In each case the choice is between two or more factors involved in an immediate result. For this reason such problems are referred to as cases of *immediate* or *present economy*.

Results Must Be Identical. The excavation example illustrates another important requirement in cases of present economy. *Results must be identical.* In this case the result was a 50-cubic-yard hole regardless of the method, material removed or shape. If the pick and shovel method had resulted in a hole 50 cubic yards in size, and that obtained through the use of a ditch-digging machine were 80 cubic yards, the choice between these two could hardly be considered to be selection between equivalent methods.

This does not mean, however, that two articles, one of which is vastly superior to the other in unit qualities, cannot be compared and a proper selection made. For example, a mild steel bolt with a cross sectional area of 1 square inch has an ultimate strength in tension of approximately 60,000 pounds. A nickel-steel alloy bolt of the same size would have a strength of 90,000 pounds. If strength were a factor in the design, it would not be correct to compare the cost of mild steel and nickel-steel bolts of the same size. Yet a fair selection could be made between a mild steel bolt with a cross sectional area of 1 square inch and a nickel-steel bolt having a cross section of only 0.667 square inch, since both would have identical strengths.

Thus, in setting up the data for selection in present economy one must be certain that the immediate results are identical. In most such problems there is little difficulty in making the correct choice after the facts have been properly assembled. However, the task of obtaining the necessary information and arranging it so a correct comparison may be made often requires a great amount of work and considerable knowledge and experience.

Selection of Methods or Processes. The financial success of many projects depends upon the use of the most economical method of accomplishing a desired end. Modern large scale production is built upon the principle of utilizing manufacturing processes that will enable an article to be produced in the cheapest possible way. Just as the ditch-digging machine and the pick and shovel method will produce identical ditches, alternate methods of manufacture will often produce identical products, yet one method may be much more economical than the other. One need only to consider what it would cost to produce the modern automobile without the aid of any machinery to realize the significance of this statement. The engineer must be able to determine the facts about each available method and select the proper one. His work then becomes economically, as well as mechanically, efficient.

If one were required to determine the stresses in the various members of a roof truss, two methods of solution would be available. Either mathematical or graphical solution would yield sufficiently accurate results. Yet it would be found that if the mathematical solution required four hours the same answers could be obtained by graphical means in about two hours. If one were paying a designer to determine the stresses and his rate of pay were $1.50 per hour, the two methods would have to be compared as follows:

Mathematical solution, 4 hours @ $1.50	$6.00
Graphical solution, 2 hours @ $1.50	3.00
Saving through the use of the graphical method	$3.00

With the two methods yielding identical results, it would be rather foolish to use the more expensive method.

This same type of problem is encountered in determining the proper method to use in the production of certain machine parts. Figure 2 shows two equivalent sheave housings which were produced by different methods — casting and welding. The cast housing was produced by the use of a rough casting which required considerable machining to obtain the holes and mounting surfaces. The welded housing was made from steel plate and bar stock. All the parts were cut by the use of a shear and torch. The main body was formed by cutting a single plate to shape and bending in the form of a U. All holes except one were cut with a torch. The costs of the two methods were found to be:

	Casting	Welded
Rough casting	$1.85	$——
Steel		0.85
Cutting and forming		0.66
Cost of welding		0.26
Machining	0.80	0.03
Total cost	$2.65	$1.80

Saving $2.65 − $1.80 = $0.85

Thus a saving of 32% is possible by using the welding process in producing this sheave housing. Such a saving is well worth the effort required to assemble the data necessary for the proper selection.

FIGURE 7 Cast iron and welded sheave housings. (From *Procedure Handbook of Arc Welding Design and Practice*. Courtesy Lincoln Electric Co.)

As in most cases of immediate economy, the correct choice was apparent when the facts were properly assembled. This type of problem is constantly before the industrial world. In some instances the required information is readily obtained, while in others much calculating and careful estimating are necessary to get the information upon which a decision may be based. In either case care must be exercised to assure that the information is accurate and that the results are identical.

Selection of Material. Another case of selection in engineering work occurs when more than one material is available for a specific use. Usually one material will be more economical than the others. Determining cost of using each material and selecting the most economical is a problem in engineering economy. As an example, consider the problem of making the small part shown in Figure 3. This was a part of a time-recording device.

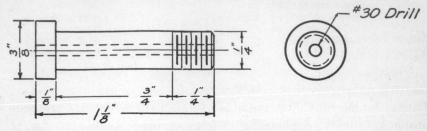

FIGURE 3.   Small screw machine product.

The strength required was relatively small, but the piece could not have any of its dimensions changed. It was produced on a small, high speed turret lathe. In the past, 1112 screw machine steel, costing 7 cents per pound, had been used. A study was made to determine if the part might be produced more cheaply by using brass screw stock which cost 27 cents per pound but could be machined at a much higher rate. A time study of the production process using the two materials showed the following:

Operations	Time in seconds	
	1112	Brass
Feed stock to a stop and lock chuck	5.	5.
Index turret	2.	2.
Turn ¼ in. diameter and center drill	17.5	5.
Index turret	2.	2.
Drill #30 hole	16.5	7.
Index turret	2.	2.
Cut ¼ in. thread	5.	3.
Index turret	2.	2.
Cut off piece	3.5	2.
Reverse cross turret	2.	2.
Total	57.5	32.
10% allowance	5.5	3.
Standard time	63.0	35.
Pieces per hour	57.1	102.9

The labor cost for making this part was at the rate of $1.00 per hour. Overhead was figured at the rate of $0.98 per hour. The weight of material required was 0.0353 pound of 1112 steel or 0.0384 pound of brass screw stock. Using these figures, the cost per piece with each type of stock was:

	1112	Brass
Overhead	$0.01717	$0.00952
Labor	0.01751	0.00971
Material	0.00247	0.01038
Total cost per piece	$0.03715	$0.02961
Saving per piece by using brass		$0.00754

Since several thousand pieces were to be made, the saving of $7.54 per thousand was an appreciable amount.

This particular type of selection is of vast importance in our modern industry where articles are produced in very large quantities. To gain an impression of the significance of the previous statement, it is only necessary to remember that a saving of 0.1 cent per piece means $1,000 when one million pieces are produced. In making a selection between different materials one must be careful that they are exactly equivalent in results. The low-carbon and nickel-steel bolts previously mentioned are examples of this. If two materials are not exactly equivalent in results, they cannot be compared on as simple a basis. If one material has superior qualities but these qualities cannot be taken advantage of owing to size or design limitations, the superiority becomes of no value and may have to be ignored in the solution of the problem at hand. If the superior material should be found to be more economical, even though it would not be used to the limit of its possibilities, it should be used. Such a material merely carries a handicap in cost comparisons with other materials. The important point to remember is that each material being considered must satisfy the minimum requirements. Qualities above those required may have no value.

Alternate Proposals with Different Lives May Be Problems in Present Economy. The results of such calculations may be greatly in error if the products do not have the same life. For example, a wood building would be much cheaper to construct than one of reinforced concrete. Obviously the life of the structures will not be the same, and they cannot usually be compared without considering the effect which the passage of time will have upon them. Thus time is an important factor. Such cases are outside the scope of this chapter, but will be considered later. An exception to this, however, is where the need for the article or structure is not expected to be as long as the actual physical life. For example, a number of companies have constructed wooden buildings in making certain additions to their plants. There was no doubt that steel or concrete structures would have lasted much longer and have required less expenditure for maintenance. However, the companies did not believe they would have any use for the buildings for a period greater than six years. Since either wood or the more expensive forms of construction would provide adequate facilities for this long a period, time was not a factor in the problem and a direct comparison of the annual costs of the two types could be made. The costs to be compared were found by determining the sum of maintenance, taxes, insurance, interest on the required investment and depreciation charges where the life of each structure was six years. It is thus observed that it is not always economical to use a material that has an extremely long life. Each particular set of circumstances has its own correct solution. With new materials constantly becoming available, and new uses for old materials being developed, one must always keep this type of selection in mind. There are few articles which do not offer considerable choice in the selection of materials either to improve quality or to lower cost.

Selection of Design. Consider the problem of selecting a wood beam to support a uniformly distributed load of 2,200 pounds over a span of 12 feet. The beam is to be of common grade Douglas fir and the deflection limited to $\frac{1}{300}$ of the span. From suitable handbooks it is found there are three common sizes of beams which will support the load under these conditions. These sizes and their safe loads are:

Nominal size	Safe load
4 by 8 inches	2,270 pounds
3 by 10 inches	2,630 pounds
2 by 12 inches	2,390 pounds

Thus, from the standpoint of ability to support the desired load each of these sizes is satisfactory.

When one attempts to determine the cost of using each of these beams he finds that the three sizes do not cost the same per unit volume. The 4-by-8-inch and 3-by-10-inch sizes list at $32.00 per thousand board feet while the 2-by-12-inch size costs only $31.00 per thousand board feet. This difference is due to the fact that some sizes are more readily obtained in the cutting of the tree into lumber and that certain sizes are more widely used and as a result are produced in greater volume.

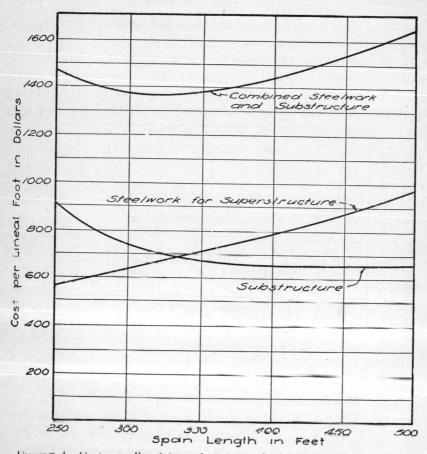

FIGURE 4. Costs per lineal foot of structure for low-level combined bridges on sand foundations 200 feet deep. (Reprinted by permission from "Economics of Bridgework" by J. A. L. Waddell, published by John Wiley & Sons, Inc.)

Another factor that affects the cost of the various sizes of beams is the actual volume of material in them. The 4-by-8-inch beam contains 32 board feet. The 3-by-10 has 30 board feet, while the 2-by-12-inch size contains only 24 board feet. The final cost figures for the three sizes appear as follows:

Nominal size	Cost per M. board feet	Board feet	Cost per beam
4 by 8 inch	$32.00	32	$1.02
3 by 10 inch	32.00	30	0.96
2 by 12 inch	31.00	24	0.74

From this table it can be seen that there is a decided advantage in using the 2-by-12-inch beam.

In the case of the wood beam each successive size contained a smaller volume of material and was more economical to use. Also the cost per unit volume of material decreased as the depth of the beam increased. Thus both factors which affected the cost de-

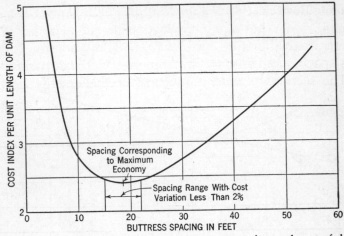

FIGURE 5. Typical relation between buttress spacing and cost of dam.

creased. In many cases where design selection is involved this is not true. Usually some of the cost factors increase while others decrease. The problem then becomes one of selecting that design which gives the lowest total cost. An excellent example of this type of problem is seen in Figure 4, which shows a set of cost curves taken from J. A. L. Waddell's classical work, "Economics of Bridgework." These curves show the cost per foot of structure for low-level combined bridges on sand foundations 200 feet deep. In this case the cost of the substructure decreases slightly. The cost of the steelwork of the bridge increases rapidly as the span length is increased, owing to the necessity for heavier construction. With these conditions one would expect that one particular length of span should be more economical than all others. The curves show that this condition exists at approximately 325 feet. Thus if a bridge of this type, 1,200 feet in length, were to be built, one might use a design of either 300- or 400-foot spans and have all spans of the same length. However, the curves of Figure 4 show that the cost of the two designs would be as follows:

Length of spans	Number of spans	Cost per foot	Total cost
300 feet	4	$1,380	$1,656,000
400 feet	3	$1,440	$1,728,000

The saving of $72,000 through the use of 300-foot span lengths is well worth the time required to make the necessary computations and comparison.

Economic Buttress Spacing for Multiple-Arch Dams. Selection of economic design has many applications in the planning of permanent structures. Figure 5 shows a typical relationship between buttress spacing and cost for an Ambursen flat-slab dam 20 feet high. The sections of such a multiple arch dam are shown in

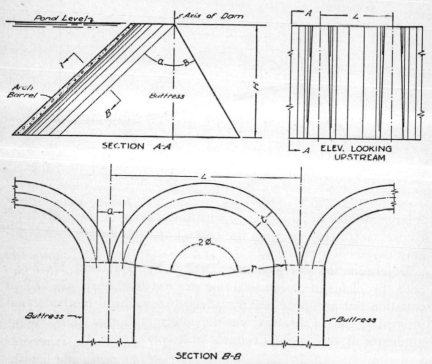

FIGURE 6. Sections of multiple-arch dam.

Figure 6. F. C. Rogers [1] has derived an equation which allows one to compute the most economical spacing for such structures. This equation is:

$$L^2 = a^2 + \frac{4\,K_f \sin \phi\,(HB - aA)}{K_c A z}$$

where
L = buttress spacing in feet
a = horizontal dimension between mean arch radii at upstream face of buttress
K_f = cost of forms per square foot
ϕ = one-half of central arch angle, in degrees
H = height of dam, in feet (pond level to foundation)
B = $\tan \alpha + \tan \beta$ (see Figure 6)
A = $\dfrac{\pi\phi}{90 \sin \phi \cos \alpha}$ (see Figure 6)
K_c = cost of concrete and included steel, per cubic foot of concrete
z = arch design constant = t/r (see Figure 6)

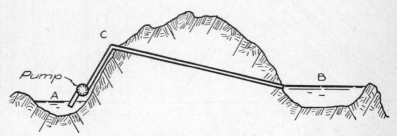

FIGURE 7. Fundamental problem in determining economic balance between pump and tunnel sizes.

A large number of factors vary with the spacing of the buttresses. By the use of this equation the correct spacing for greatest economy may be determined.

Determination of Economic Design by Graphical Methods. Some problems in design selection are not readily reduced to an equation but are quite readily solved by graphical methods. An interesting case of this type was the determination of the economic gradients of the various tunnels and conduits in the Colorado

[1] F. C. Rogers: "Economical Buttress Spacing for Reinforced Concrete Dams," Civil Engineering, August, 1938.

River Aqueduct which supplies water to the Los Angeles area. Here the problem is essentially balancing the cost of obtaining greater hydraulic head by pumping against the cost of the required

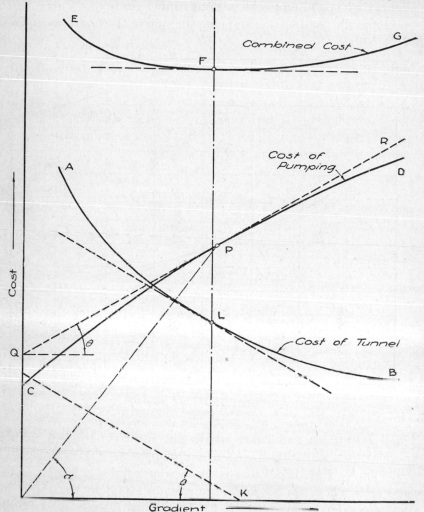

FIGURE 8. Method of determining economic tunnel size for an aqueduct.

size of conduit. The problem is simply illustrated in Figure 7. If greater head is obtained, a smaller size of conduit will transport the required amount of water because of the greater gradient which may be utilized. Figure 8 shows relative cost curves for the cost of pumping and tunneling. Curve AB represents the total construction cost of the tunnel for varying gradients. CD represents the capitalized cost of perpetually pumping the water to the heights corresponding to the various tunnel gradients. Curve EFG represents the combined cost, being the sum of the first two curves.

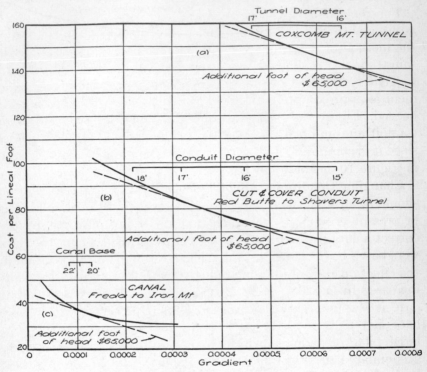

FIGURE 9. Cost curves for aqueduct types.

Thus point F on this curve marks the most economical tunnel gradient.

The curve EFG is not needed if one determines point L on the curve AB where the slope is numerically equal to the slope on curve CD. To do this, QR is plotted tangent to curve CD at some estimated point P. CK is then drawn at the same inclination as QR, but reversed. By moving upward parallel to CK a tangent to AB is found at point L. If P and L do not lie on the same vertical line, the process is repeated with a new assumed position for P.

In terms of the coordinates of the diagram, the slope of QR is equal to the cost of an additional foot of head at point P. If this can be computed directly, it is not necessary to plot curve CD in order to determine line CK. Curve AB may be plotted to represent the cost of one foot of tunnel. With curve AB, and tan θ = cost of one foot of head, point L and the corresponding most economical gradient can be determined.

For the Colorado River Aqueduct the capitalized cost of an additional foot of head was found to be $65,000. Figure 9 shows the method of determining the diameter of the Coxcomb Mountain tunnel. A line representing tan θ = $65,000 was drawn tangent to the cost-of-tunnel curve. This gave the correct gradient as approximately 0.00060. For this slope a 16-foot funnel is needed. Figure 9 also shows this method applied to cut and cover conduit and an open canal. This was necessary on the aqueduct since it is composed of all three types of conduits, as may be seen in Figure 10 on the following page.

Changing Conditions Affect Selection. One word of caution should be added concerning the results obtained through selections in present economy. The correct result today may not be the correct solution tomorrow if the conditions upon which the data were based have changed. An excellent example of this is found in the effect on the gold mining industry when the price of gold was increased from $20.67 to $35.00 per ounce in 1934. Prior to that date it was not profitable to use certain processes which were necessary to recover the gold from low-grade ores. As a result, large piles of tailings, which were considered worthless, were accumulated at many mines. After the price of gold was increased it was found that a considerable portion of the low-grade ores and tailings could be put through these more expensive recovery processes so the gold could be recovered and a substantial profit earned.

Thus, because one has made a correct analysis of a problem today and selected the proper method, material or design, he should not be unmindful of new methods, materials and processes which are developed and which may have a vital effect upon the economy of his operation. It is indeed rare that anything is done so efficiently that time will not reveal more efficient methods.

Limitations of Present Economy. While selections involving

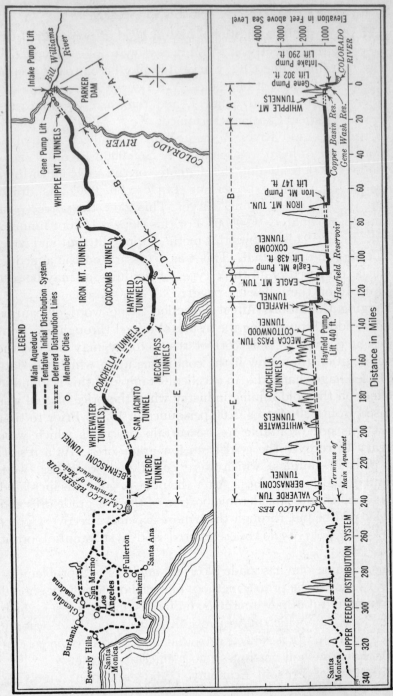

FIGURE 10. The Colorado River Aqueduct.

present economy have many applications, as indicated in the various examples which have been mentioned, the larger proportion of selection problems are outside the scope of present economy because time is a factor. In many cases the dividing line between present economy and long-term economy is not distinct. A slight change in conditions or viewpoint may shift the problem from one classification to the other. As a result each set of conditions must be carefully handled to assure that all the controlling factors are considered. Since the engineer is vitally concerned with all types of economic selection, it is necessary for him to understand how investments, in the form of structures and equipment or their equivalent, money, are affected by time. The two factors which are most important as the result of the passage of time are interest and depreciation. For this reason the next few chapters are devoted to these subjects so that all of the necessary tools may be available for use in solving all types of problems in economic selection.

REFERENCES

Grant, Eugene L.: "Principles of Engineering Economy," The Ronald Press Company, New York, 1938.

Harding, C. Francis, and Donald T. Canfield: "Business Administration for Engineers," McGraw-Hill Book Company, Inc., New York, 1937.

Hinds, J.: "Economic Water Conduit Size," Engineering News-Record, January 28, 1937.

Hinds, J.: "Economic Sizes of Pressure Conduits," Engineering News-Record, March 25, 1937.

McCullough, C. B.: "Economics of Highway Bridge Types," Gillette Publishing Company, Chicago, 1929.

Rogers, F. C.: "Economical Buttress Spacing for Reinforced Concrete Dams," Civil Engineering, August, 1938.

Waddell, J. A. L.: "Economics of Bridgework," John Wiley & Sons, Inc., New York, 1921.

PROBLEMS

10. A low-level combined bridge, on sand foundations 200 feet deep, is to be constructed which will have a total length of 2,000 feet. It is necessary to have a span of not less than 350 feet near the center of the bridge. Two designs are being considered: (a) five equal spans of 400 feet each; (b) a center span of 350 feet and three equal spans on each side of the center. Using the curves shown in Figure 4, determine which of the proposed designs is the more economical.

11. A construction company has a contract to build a 2.2-mile irrigation canal.

They estimate that if a special machine is constructed for use in lining the canal, they can save $1 per foot of canal. The machine will cost $12,000 to construct and can be used only on this one job. It is estimated that $2,000 can be recovered from the sale of the machine as junk when the job is completed. Would you advise the construction of the machine? What would be the saving by the method selected?

12. Type A concrete has 15% greater strength than type B. When used in pavement in correct amounts to give equal strengths they will last equally long. A specification calls for a 4-inch thickness of type A, or its equivalent in type B. If type B costs $7.00 and type A costs $8.00 per cubic yard, which will be more economical?

13. A man who has invented a new type of garden tool wishes to interest some manufacturer in purchasing his patent. He desires to send some type of illustration of the tool to 100 manufacturers. Two possible methods of doing this are being considered.

   a. Have a draftsman make pictorial drawings of the tool on tracing cloth. From the drawings, black and white prints can be made. The draftsman will charge $10 for his work. Black and white prints cost 6 cents each for the first 50 prints and 4 cents for each additional print.

   b. The inventor has several small photographs of the tool, which can be enlarged and photographed as one larger picture. Enlargement will cost $2.50. Prints from the enlarged photograph will cost 15 cents each. Which method would be the more economical?

14. In the previous problem, what other factors should be considered, besides cost, in making a decision as to the better method to use?

15. In the annealed state, 18–8 stainless steel has a yield strength of 33,000 pounds per square inch. 17S Duralumin has a yield point of 10,000 pounds per square inch. For a particular job a company finds that either material is equally suitable if the design is based upon the yield strength of the material. Stainless steel will cost 70 cents per pound and the Duralumin 51 cents per pound. The specific gravities of stainless steel and Duralumin are 7.77 and 2.79 respectively. Which material will be the more economical?

16. In manufacturing an electric heater it is necessary to make two ⅜-inch holes in #22 gage metal. If these are drilled with the aid of a jig, each hole will require one minute. The jig will cost $20. The drill press operator receives $0.80 per hour.

   The holes could also be made on a punch press. By this method they could be produced at the rate of two holes each two seconds. A die would be required which would cost $40. Punch press operators receive $0.70 per hour. All other costs by the two methods are assumed to be equal.

   If 1,000 heaters are to be produced, and the jig or die would be of no further use, which method should be used for this job?

17. The ore of the Jumping Gopher gold mine contains 0.4 ounce of gold per ton. One method of mining and processing costs $4.89 per ton and recovers 94.5% of the gold. A second method costs only $3.51 per ton and recovers 81.4% of the gold.

   a. If gold is worth $35.00 per ounce, which method should be utilized?

   b. Would a decrease in the price of gold to $25.00 affect the answer?

Chapter IV

INTEREST

Origin and Definition. Interest, like taxes, appears to have existed from the time of man's earliest recorded history. Records reveal its existence in Babylon in 2000 B.C. In the earliest instances interest was paid in grain or goods. The principal, or amount which had been borrowed, was likewise often repaid in this manner. History also reveals that the idea of interest became so well established that a firm of international bankers existed in 575 B.C. with home offices in Babylon. Its income was derived from the high interest rates it charged for the use of its money for financing international trade. Interest is not only one of our oldest institutions but its uses suffered little change through the years.

In spite of its age and history, and its ever-presence in business transactions, interest is often misunderstood, and many times ignored, in engineering and industrial calculations. The term "interest" is often applied to items which in reality are not interest but *profit*. Such use of the term is not at all disastrous, if understood, and it is doubtful if such misuse will ever be entirely eliminated. Whenever two factors of a problem under consideration are money (or its equivalent) and time, interest automatically also becomes a factor.

Interest may be defined in several ways. It is the money paid for the use of borrowed capital. Interest is the income produced by money which has been loaned. It may be illustrated in another way. Suppose John Jones comes to Henry Smith and wants to borrow $100, saying he will pay it back one year from now. Henry has $100 in his pocket with which he had planned to purchase a few luxuries which he does not now possess, but which he could do

41

without. The thought of those quickly passes through his mind. He decides that it would not be too bad to go without these luxuries if John Jones would promise to pay him something extra for his doing without these personal pleasures for a year. He thinks that $5 would be a fair price for this year of sacrifice on his part.

He quickly remembers that, although he has known John for some time and believes he is entirely honest, human nature has its weaknesses and there is some possibility that John might run off and not repay what he has borrowed. Also he remembers how many innocent people are killed by automobiles each year and realizes that this might happen to his friend while he owes him money. So he feels that he should also be paid something for these risks he will be taking by loaning his money and thinks he is entitled to an additional $5 because of this. He tells John Jones he will be glad to let him use the $100 for one year if John will promise to give him back $110 at the end of the year. John agrees to do this and the deal is made.

These extra $10 which Henry receives at the end of the year are said to be the *interest* which he earns from his $100 investment. One can see that the interest received represents payment for the use of the money by the borrower, and payment to the lender for foregoing the use of his money and for the risk he took in permitting another person to use his possessions. Thus interest may represent payment for several factors. This is usually the case in business transactions.

In the transaction between John Jones and Henry Smith, John Jones promised to repay Henry Smith the amount he borrowed and in addition agreed to pay a specified rate of interest. Thus the amount of principal to be repaid, and the rate of interest, were guaranteed by the borrower. These facts are fundamental conditions where interest is involved. Repayment of the principal is guaranteed by the borrower, and the rate of pay for the use of the borrowed funds is specified. Thus there is a clear distinction between *interest* and *profit*, since profit accrues from the investment of capital in business ventures where there is no guarantee of return of the capital and no assurance as to what the rate of return will be, if any.

Simple Interest. In the example cited, the capital involved was $100. This amount, for the use of which interest is paid, is known as the *principal*. The *rate of interest* is the amount of interest earned by a *unit of principal* in a *unit of time*. In common practice the unit of time is taken as one year, unless otherwise specified. Thus in our example 100 units of principal earned 10 units of interest in one unit of time, or the rate of interest was $^{10}\!/_{100} = 0.1$ or 10% per annum. This is the customary way of expressing interest rates — per cent per annum.

In the simplest type of time-money transaction, a given principal is invested for a stated period of time at a designated rate of interest. The debt is to be repaid at the end of the period of time, which may or may not be the same length of time as that upon which the interest rate is based. The interest, however, is directly proportional to the time which the loan runs.

If one wishes to know how much interest will be earned during the time of such a transaction, it may be found in the following manner. Let P represent the principal, i the interest rate, and n the number of units of time or the interest periods. The interest I is found by the formula

$$I = Pni \qquad\qquad (1)$$

since the interest earned is directly proportional to the principal involved, the interest rate and the number of interest periods for which the principal is loaned.

Thus if $100 is loaned for three years at an interest rate of 5% per annum, the interest earned will be

$$I = \$100 \times 0.05 \times 3 = \$15$$

If one wishes to know the entire *amount*, S, due (principal plus interest)

$$S = P + I = P + Pni = P(1 + ni) \qquad\qquad (2)$$

Interest computed in this manner is known as *simple interest*.

Ordinary and Exact Interest. Ordinarily the unit of time for the interest period is considered to be one year and the resulting interest rate is the rate per year. When it is necessary to calculate the interest due for a fraction of one year it is often the practice to assume that a year is made up of 12 months of 30 days each, or

360 days. The exact number of days involved is used. Thus 51 days is considered to be $^{51}\!/_{360}$ of one year. Interest computed on this basis is called *ordinary simple interest*.

If, however, the interest is computed on the basis of a 365-day year, the result is called *exact simple interest*. Table I of the Appendix, "The Number of Each Day of the Year," makes it easy to determine the number of days between any two dates. Ordinary interest is commonly used unless otherwise specified.

Compound Interest. In the case of simple interest the interest does not become due until the end of the loan period and is directly proportional to the time involved. Now consider a loan that is made for a length of time equal to several interest periods. Provision is made that the earned interest is due at the end of each interest period. However, the borrower is allowed to keep the earned interest but must thereafter pay interest upon these amounts, just as he does upon the principal. Thus, interest that has been earned, but is not paid, is assumed to be converted into principal. This procedure takes place at the end of each interest period. The borrower at the end of the first interest period has the use of the original principal P plus the interest I earned during this period, all of which belongs to the lender. Thus the total amount of money due the lender at the end of the first period, and used by the borrower during the second interest period, is

$$P + Pi = P(1 + i)$$

Similarly, since the lender is entitled to interest upon all the money due him, the interest earned during the second interest period is

$$(P + Pi)i = Pi + Pi^2$$

The amount due the lender at the end of the second interest period and available to the borrower at the beginning of the third period is

$$P + Pi + (Pi + Pi^2) = P(1 + i)^2$$

Thus, because of interest, one unit of principal at the beginning of an interest period will amount to $1 + i$ units at the end of the period. The results may be shown as follows:

Period	Principal at beginning of period	Interest earned during period	Amount at end of period
1	P	Pi	$P + Pi = P(1 + i)$
2	$P(1 + i)$	$P(1 + i)i$	$P + Pi + P(1 + i)i = P(1 + i)^2$
3	$P(1 + i)^2$	$P(1 + i)^2 i$	$P + Pi + P(1 + i)i + P(1 + i)^2 i = P(1 + i)^3$
n	$P(1 + i)^{n-1}$	$P(1 + i)^{n-1} i$	$P(1 + i)^{n-1} + P(1 + i)^{n-1} i = P(1 + i)^n$

Thus the formula for the amount due at the end of n interest period is

$$S = P(1 + i)^n \qquad (3)$$

In this process, where earned interest is added to the principal and interest is thereafter paid on the total amount, the interest is said to be *compounded* or *converted* each interest period. In the most general case where the interest period is one year the interest is said to be compounded annually.

In Column 1 of Tables II to XXI inclusive, of the Appendix, values of $(1 + i)^n$ for various values of i are tabulated so that problems involving this factor may be readily solved. These columns are titled "Amount at Compound Interest." Thus if $100 principal is loaned for a period of three years with interest at 5% compounded annually, the total sum due at the end of the three years may be found by Equation (3) as follows:

$$P = \$100$$
$$i = 5\% \text{ compounded annually}$$
$$n = 3$$

From Table XVIII, $(1 + i)^n$ for these values $= 1.157625$ and

$$S = \$100 \times 1.157625 = \$115.76$$

Very often the interest period, or time between successive conversions, is something less than one year. It has also become customary to quote interest rates upon an annual basis and designate the conversion period. If the interest rate is 3% per interest period and the interest period is six months, it is customary to speak of this rate as "6% compounded semiannually." Interest rates quoted in this manner are known as *nominal interest rates*. The actual annual rate of return upon the principal is not 6% but something greater. For instance, consider $100 to be invested at a nominal rate of 6% compounded semiannually. The interest earned during the year would be

First 6 months

$$I = \$100 \times 0.03 = \$3.00$$

Total principal at beginning of the second period

$$P + Pi = \$100 + \$3.00 = \$103.00$$

Interest earned second 6 months

$$\$103 \times 0.03 = \$3.09$$

Total interest earned during year

$$\$3.00 + \$3.09 = \$6.09$$

Actual annual interest rate

$$\left(\frac{6.09}{100}\right) \times 100 = 6.09\%$$

This actual rate of return upon the principal during one year is known as the *effective interest rate*.

If nominal interest rates are quoted and the length of time involved is given in years, any problem can easily be solved by the general formula, $S = P(1 + i)^n$, by converting the nominal rate into rate per interest period and determining the number of actual interest periods. Thus, if $100 is invested for 10 years at 6% compounded quarterly, there are 4 conversions per year and the interest rate per interest period is $6/4 = 1.5\%$. The total number of interest periods is $10 \times 4 = 40$. Using these values in Equation (3),

$$S = \$100 \ (1 + 0.015)^{40}$$
$$= \$181.40$$

In this manner problems involving nominal interest rates can very easily be solved. It is only necessary to remember that in Equation (3) n is the *actual number of interest periods* and i is the *rate per interest period*.

The use of this method and Equation (3) gives a simple means of determining the effective rate corresponding to any given nominal rate of interest. For example, in the case just cited the nominal rate is 6% compounded quarterly. What is the effective rate?

Rate per interest period = $6/4 = 1.5\%$
Number of periods per year = 4
Amount of 1 unit per year = $S = P(1 + i)^n$

From Table XI, for $n = 4$:

$$(1 + i)^n = 1.06136$$

and

$$S = 1 \times 1.06136 = 1.06136$$
$$\text{Interest earned in 1 year} = S - 1 = 0.06136$$

Since effective rate has been defined as the interest earned by one unit of principal in one year, 0.06136, or 6.136%, represents the effective rate corresponding to a nominal rate of 6% compounded quarterly. Therefore

$$\text{Effective rate} = S - 1 \qquad (4)$$

when S is the amount of 1 for one year at the nominal rate.

Present Value. From Equation (3), $S = P(1 + i)^n$, it was shown that P units of principal invested at rate i will amount to S units at the end of n periods. Thus at rate i, P is the *present value* of S.

If, in Equation (3), $S = 1$ and v is defined as the present value of 1 due one interest period hence,

$$1 = v(1 + i)$$

and

$$v = \frac{1}{1 + i} \qquad (5)$$

Since

$$P = S \times \frac{1}{(1 + i)^n}$$
$$P = Sv^n \qquad (6)$$

Column 2 of Tables II to XXI inclusive, of the Appendix, titled "Present Value of 1," gives values of v^n so problems involving present value may be readily solved. To find the present value of $100 due five years hence with interest at 6% per annum:

$$S = \$100$$
$$n = 5$$
$$i = 6\%$$

from Table XIX:

$$v^n = 0.747258$$
$$P = \$100 \times 0.747258 = \$74.73$$

For a nominal rate of 6% compounded semiannually the solution would be:

$$n = 5 \times 2 = 10$$
$$i = \tfrac{6}{2} = 3\%$$
$$v^n = 0.744094$$
$$P = \$100 \times 0.744094 = \$74.41$$

Discount. In numerous financial transactions the holder of negotiable paper, such as a note or contract which is not due and payable until some future date, desires to exchange this paper for cash. In order to do this he will accept a sum of cash smaller in amount than the face value of the paper. The difference between the present value (the amount received for the paper in cash) and the worth of the paper at some time in the future (the face value of the paper) is known as the *discount* for the period involved. The *rate of discount* is defined as the discount on one unit of principal for one unit of time. If the rate of discount is designated by d, it is equal to the difference between 1 and its present value, v.

$$d = 1 - v = 1 - \frac{1}{1 + i} = iv \qquad (7)$$

and

$$i = \frac{d}{v} = \frac{d}{1 - d} \qquad (8)$$

Then for any discount rate the corresponding interest rate for the discount period may be determined. For example, if a 60-day note having a face value of $100 is discounted $1.00, the rate of discount for the 60-day period is

$$d = 1 - 0.99 = 0.01$$
$$i = \frac{d}{1 - d} = \frac{0.01}{1 - 0.01} = \frac{0.01}{0.99}$$
$$= 0.01010 \text{ per 60-day period}$$

For the effective rate [from Equation (4)]

$$n = 6$$
$$i = 0.01010$$
$$S - 1 = (1 + 0.01010)^6 - 1$$
$$= 1.0622 - 1 = 0.0622$$
$$= 6.22\%$$

Interest vs. Profit. Considerable confusion is caused by the fact that the term "interest" is used by various persons to denote entirely different things. Such a situation has led to much misunderstanding.

The difficulty arises from attempting to apply the old-time classical economist's definition of interest to present-day practice. This definition stated that interest was the money returned to the owners of capital for the use of their funds. Thus, whatever was received because capital was employed was considered to be interest.

Modern business seldom uses the old definition of interest. In fact, modern economists are turning from the old definition. In common business practice, interest is considered to be the rental paid for the use of borrowed capital. In most cases business considers interest to be at a rate agreed upon at the time the money is borrowed. In addition there is a promise or guarantee that the capital will be returned to the owners at some specified time. Thus interest arises from the borrowing of capital, and the rate of interest is established at the time of borrowing and will not vary from the stated rate.

Differing from interest, in modern business usage, is the idea of *profit*. When the owners of capital (individuals or companies) invest their funds in an enterprise where there is no specific guarantee that the capital will be recovered or that any additional return will be had, any amount recovered beyond the original investment is said to be *profit*.

In some aspects, interest and profit are identical; in others they differ considerably. Most outstanding of the differences is the fact that when interest is earned there is relatively less risk involved, there is little need for business judgment, and the return will not exceed a specified rate. The two are alike in that they are payment for the utilization of capital. Without their existence there would be little incentive for people to accumulate capital and use it for business ventures. Both, to an extent, represent payment to the owners of capital for foregoing the use of their funds.

It is thus easy to understand why the two terms are often used interchangeably. In many cases no confusion results. In others, the result is far from good. Since the vast majority of business uses the terms in the manner explained above, it appears desirable to confine their usage to the more precise definitions and thus avoid misunderstanding wherever possible. If this is not done one must be certain that he knows exactly what is meant when the term "interest" is used in the broad manner that is sometimes employed.

It is well to point out that modern economists are tending to drop the broad usage of the term "interest" and are substituting the terms "gain" or "return to capital." [1]

In the chapters which follow, "interest" will be used only when speaking of borrowed capital. Gain from the use of owned capital will be called "return" or "profit." In this manner it is hoped that greater clarity and understanding will result.

When Must Interest Be Considered? There are very few, if any, economy studies where interest is not a factor which has to be considered. Since economy studies are made in terms of money, interest automatically enters the picture.

If the capital necessary to finance an enterprise must be borrowed, the cost of obtaining this capital is an expense of the venture. If the person, or corporation, owns sufficient capital to finance the proposed project, there is no borrowed money involved, and in the true meaning of the term there is no interest expense. However, in this case one must decide if the expected rate of return (profit) is sufficient to justify the investment. In order to do this it is usually necessary to compare the expected profit with the rate of interest which could be obtained from lending the same capital at a specified rate. Thus interest is a factor that must be considered although not as an expense in the strict sense.

It is, and will probably remain, a quite common practice to include profit on owned capital as though it were an item of expense. While from a strict interpretation of the definition of interest such inclusion is not correct, it is justified by saying that in order to invest capital in an enterprise one must forego lending this money at guaranteed interest rates, and thus one of the ex-

---

[1] See "Principles of Economics" by F. W. Taussig for an example of this. (Vol. I, 4th edition.)

penses of investment is the return that has been sacrificed. What is actually meant is that the person does not wish to invest capital where risk is involved unless he will receive a rate of return in excess of what he could obtain from a conservative investment at guaranteed interest rates. When profit upon owned capital is included in such a manner, the results may be confusing unless one understands exactly what is meant and realizes that correct interpretation of the results is necessary. As long as the usage is understood and correctly interpreted, there is no serious objection to it. In fact, inclusion of such "interest" (profit) in this manner gives a very convenient and useful method of comparing the cost of alternative investments. Such methods will be discussed in later chapters. However, if return on invested capital is to be included as if it were an expense, it is desirable that it be shown under a true name such as "Profit," "Required Profit" or "Minimum Required Profit."

There are, obviously, some cases where interest may be neglected in certain portions of economy studies without affecting the accuracy appreciably. If the time involved is only one or two years and the interest rate is not more than 2 or 3%, the error introduced by omitting these factors would not be serious. In nearly all cases it would be less than the error due to other factors that are included. However, good judgment must be exercised in deciding whether interest can be neglected in any particular situation. Except in the most obvious cases the safer course is to consider all the factors that might affect the results, and interest is one of these.

What Interest Rate Should Be Used? Much has been written about what interest rate should be used in economy studies. If one is speaking about interest in accordance with the definition, the answer is simple. One should use the rate that has been, or would be, paid for the use of the borrowed money. In comparisons of expected profits with the rate of interest that could be obtained from investment of capital funds in some other manner, one should again use the rate that could be obtained from such investment.

Comparison is often made between predicted rate of profit and another possible profit, such as would be obtained from leaving capital in its existing place in a business instead of using it for expansion or to buy new equipment. In such instances the basis for comparison is the average rate of profit of all the capital invested in the business. This would usually be different from, and greater than, ordinary interest rates.

If one speaks of "Return on the Investment" as "interest," the question of what rate to use becomes complex since the real question is, "What return is sufficient to justify the investment of capital?" One must decide upon a rate of profit rather than a rate of interest. For this reason this question will be discussed in detail in a later chapter.

REFERENCES

Putnam, T. M.: "Mathematical Theory of Finance," John Wiley & Sons, Inc., New York, 1925.
Rietz, H. L., A. R. Crathorne, and J. C. Rietz: "Mathematics of Finance," Henry Holt and Company, Inc., New York, 1921.
Skinner, E. B.: "The Mathematical Theory of Investment," Ginn and Company, Boston, 1924.

PROBLEMS

18. Find the number of days between February 4, 1937, and October 21, 1937.
19. What is the annual interest due on a $700 loan bearing 3% simple interest?
20. How long will a $1,500 note, bearing 5% simple interest, have to run to amount to $1,605?
21. What is the exact simple interest on $2,250 at 4% from May 3 to September 15 of the same year?
22. If $1,500 earns $41.25 in six months, what is the rate of interest?
23. What principal will amount to $1,038 in one year, three months and six days if the interest rate is 3%?
24. What will be the amount of $500 for 14 years, four months with interest at 5%, compounded semiannually?
25. Find the amount of $1 at 4%, compounded annually, at the end of 17.67 years.
26. What rate of interest, compounded semiannually, will have to be earned by $1,000 in order to amount to $2,097.57 in 15 years?
27. Compare the interest earned in 10 years by $500 at 6% simple interest with that earned by the same amount at 6% compounded annually.
28. How long will a $1,200 note, bearing interest at 5% compounded semiannually, have to run to amount to $1,966.34?
29. Find the effective rate of interest earned by money which earns 8%, compounded quarterly.
30. What nominal rate of interest, compounded semiannually, must be earned to be equal to an effective rate of 4%?
31. Find the present value of $500 due five years hence, if interest is 4% compounded semiannually.

32. Find the present value of $500 due in five years. Interest is at the rate of 4% effective.

33. What investment would be required at 3%, compounded semiannually, to amount to $4,000 in 20 years?

34. A man loans $1,000 for three years at 6% simple interest. At the end of this time he invests the entire amount (principal plus interest) at 5%, compounded semiannually, for 12 years. How much will he have at the end of the 15-year period?

35. On his fifth birthday a boy inherits $10,000 which will be paid to him on his twenty-first birthday. What is the present value of his inheritance if interest is figured at 3%, compounded semiannually?

36. A man owes a debt of $2,000 which is to be paid four years hence. What three equal payments, made one, two and three years from now, would satisfy this obligation? Interest at 4%.

37. A note of $200 due in six months was sold for $190. What was the rate of discount?

38. A negotiable paper due in 90 days was discounted to yield an effective interest rate of 8%. What was the nominal discount rate?

39. A man signs a 60-day note for $1,000. The bank deducts interest at the rate of 6% per annum. What was the rate of discount? What effective rate of interest did the bank obtain from its money?

Chapter V

ANNUITIES

A type of transaction which is very common in business is that in which a person makes or receives a series of equal, periodic payments. Such transactions arise when a person (a) discharges a debt by making a series of equal, periodic payments; (b) makes a series of equal, periodic deposits in order to accumulate a desired sum; (c) receives a series of equal, periodic payments in lieu of a single lump sum which is due. All of these transactions involve annuities, but are more commonly known by other names.

An *annuity* is a series of equal, periodic payments. The name was derived from the time when the common period for such payments (as well as for most other financial transactions) was one year. It should be remembered, however, that the period of time between successive payments may be any length of time desired, provided all the periods are equal. Obviously, any rate of interest which may be involved must be the rate per period.

Example (a), cited above, is commonly encountered in "installment buying," "deferred payments," or so-called "buying from income." This method is used to a great extent in the purchase of automobiles, homes, radios and many other familiar items. In this case the buyer is in debt to the seller for a definite amount and is to discharge this indebtedness by making a specified number of equal, periodic payments. This method of payment at once makes the transaction a form of an annuity. The seller is entitled to interest on any amount due.

Case (b) arises where one wishes to have a definite amount available at some future date. He wishes to accumulate this amount by setting aside smaller, uniform amounts at equal intervals which, with the interest they will earn during such time as they are set aside, will add up to the desired amount at the time of the last deposit. This type of transaction, while clearly a form of an annuity, is more commonly known as a *sinking fund*. Its use is common in connection with the retirement of bonds and in providing for depreciation reserves. Both of these cases will be considered later.

The case mentioned as (c) is, perhaps, most often encountered in life insurance and old-age retirement plans. These are often known as *income annuities* or *retirement annuities*. In this case, instead of accepting a lump sum which belongs to him and is due him, the person elects to receive a series of equal, periodic payments. He also receives interest upon the balance of the amount due him so that a portion of each periodic payment is interest and the remainder is part of the principal.

Now consider the general form of an annuity. *In any ordinary annuity the payments are considered as being made at the end of each*

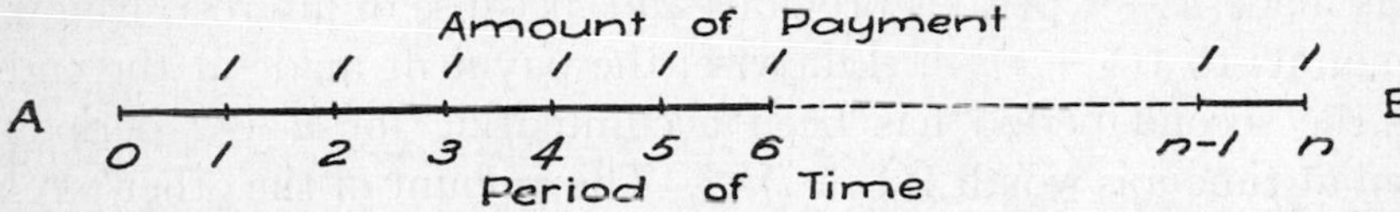

FIGURE 11. Graphical representation of an ordinary annuity.

period. Figure 11 illustrates an ordinary annuity having payments of 1 made for n periods. First consider this annuity from position A and assume the payments are going to be made to a person at this position. At the end of each period, up to and including period n, a payment of 1 is to be made. Since the receiver of the payments is at time 0, a payment of 1 is to be received one period from now and has a present value of v^1 (v being dependent upon the rate of interest, i). Similarly, the payment of 1 to be made two periods from time 0 has a present value of v^2. The present value, $a_{\overline{n}|}$, at time 0, of all the future payments is:

$$a_{\overline{n}|} = v^1 + v^2 + v^3 \cdots v^{n-1} + v^n$$

This is a geometrical series, having a common ratio of v, whose sum is:[1]

$$a_{\overline{n}|} = \frac{v - v^{n+1}}{1 - v} = \frac{1 - v^n}{\frac{1}{v} - 1}$$

[1] Obtained by multiplying both sides of the previous equation by $1 - v$ and simplifying.

Since $1/v - 1 = i$ [Equation (5)]

$$a_{\overline{n}|} = \frac{1 - v^n}{i} \tag{9}$$

Thus an equation for the present value of a series of future equal, periodic payments of 1 is obtained. If the payments are R, instead of 1, the present value, A, of such an annuity is:

$$A = Ra_{\overline{n}|} \tag{10}$$

Column 3 of Tables II to XXI, inclusive, headed "Present Value of an Annuity of 1," gives values of $a_{\overline{n}|}$ for various rates of interest and may be used in the solution of problems involving the present value of annuities.

Now consider the same annuity, represented by Figure 11, but this time consider a person at position B who has made payments of 1 at the end of each period indicated. The first payment of 1 was made $n - 1$ periods previous and, because of interest, it now amounts to $1(1 + i)^{n-1}$. Likewise, the payment made at the end of the second period has been accumulating for $n - 2$ periods and at time n is worth $1(1 + i)^{n-2}$. The amount of the other payments can be determined in the same manner. The amount, $s_{\overline{n}|}$, of this annuity of n payments of 1 each is

$$s_{\overline{n}|} = (1 + i)^{n-1} + (1 + i)^{n-2} + (1 + i)^{n-3} \cdots$$
$$+ (1 + i)^{n-(n-1)} + (1 + i)^{n-n}$$

Again this is a geometrical series, the common ratio being $(1 + i)^{-1}$ and [2]

$$s_{\overline{n}|} = \frac{(1 + i)^{n-1} - (1 + i)^{-1}}{1 - (1 + i)^{-1}}$$

Simplifying by multiplying numerator and denominator by $(1 + i)$

$$s_{\overline{n}|} = \frac{(1 + i)^n - 1}{i} \tag{11}$$

This gives an expression for the *amount of an annuity* of 1. The amount, S, of an annuity having payments of R will then be:

$$S = Rs_{\overline{n}|} \tag{12}$$

Values of $s_{\overline{n}|}$ for various rates of interest are given in Column 4 of Tables II to XXI, inclusive, "Amount of an Annuity of 1."

[2] To obtain, multiply both sides of the previous equation by $1 - (1 + i)^{-1}$.

Equation (11) may also be obtained in another way. $s_{\overline{n}|}$ is the amount of a series of payments, the present value of which is $a_{\overline{n}|}$. In other words, $a_{\overline{n}|}$ will amount to $s_{\overline{n}|}$ in n periods. Therefore

$$s_{\overline{n}|} = a_{\overline{n}|}(1 + i)^n$$
$$= \frac{1 - v^n}{i} \times (1 + i)^n = \frac{(1 + i)^n - 1}{i(1 + i)^n} \times (1 + i)^n$$
$$= \frac{(1 + i)^n - 1}{i}$$

It is convenient to have another set of tables for working annuity problems. What annuity can be purchased by a single payment of 1? This is known as the *annuity whose present value is 1*. The value may be found by solving Equation (10) for R when $A = 1$.

$$R = \frac{1}{a_{\overline{n}|}} \tag{13}$$

Column 5 of Tables II to XXI, inclusive, gives values of $1/a_{\overline{n}|}$ for various rates of interest.

With the formulas which have been derived, solution of problems arising from the various types of annuities mentioned in the opening paragraph will now be considered. In all annuity problems it must be remembered that the interest rate is the rate per period between successive payments. Thus, if nominal rates of interest are given they must be converted into the corresponding rate per period.

Applications and Solutions

Example 1. What is the present value of a 10-year annuity paying $100 at the end of each year? Interest at 4% per annum.

From Equation (10),
$$A = Ra_{\overline{n}|}$$
From Table XVII,
$$a_{\overline{10}|} \text{ for } i = 4\% \text{ is } 8.1108958$$
$$A = \$100 \times 8.1108958 = \$811.09$$

Example 2. What would be the present value of a 10-year annuity paying $50 every six months with interest at 4% nominal?
In this case,
$$n = 2 \times 10 = 20$$
$$i = \tfrac{4}{2} = 2\% \text{ per period}$$

From Table XIII,
$$a_{\overline{n}|} = 16.3514333$$
$$A = \$50 \times 16.3514333 = \$817.57$$

Example 3. If a man buys an automobile and is to pay for it by making 20 monthly payments of $40 each, with interest on the unpaid balance at 6% nominal, what is the purchase price?

This is case (*a*) cited in the opening paragraph. The cost of the car is the present value of the series of equal, periodic payments which is to be made.

$$A = Ra_{\overline{n}|}$$
$$R = \$40$$
$$n = 20$$
$$i = \tfrac{6}{12} = 0.5\% \text{ per period of one month}$$

From Table V,
$$a_{\overline{20}|} = 18.9874192$$
$$A = \$40 \times 18.9874192 = \$759.50$$

It should be noted that in this example interest is charged on only the unpaid balance due. This is the condition for a true annuity. However, in many cases of installment buying interest is charged on the entire principal involved throughout the entire time of payment, resulting in an effective interest rate about double the quoted nominal rate.

Example 4. A man purchases a car for $1,000 and pays $400 in cash. He wishes to pay the balance in 12 monthly payments. What must each payment be if interest on the unpaid balance is charged at the nominal rate of 6%?

The balance to be paid = $1,000 − $400 = $600. This is the present value of the series of 12 payments which he must make. Therefore,

$$\$600 = Ra_{\overline{12}|}$$
$$R = \$600 \times \frac{1}{a_{\overline{12}|}}$$
$$i = \tfrac{6}{12} = 0.5\% \text{ per month}$$

From Table V
$$\frac{1}{a_{\overline{12}|}} = 0.0860664$$
$$R = \$600 \times 0.0860664 = \$51.64$$

Example 5. After the man in Example 3 has made 10 payments, what single cash payment would be required to pay the remainder of the obligation?

If 10 payments have been made, 10 additional monthly payments of $40 each would be required to settle the debt. Thus there remains a 10-payment annuity of $40 per month. The single cash payment must be equivalent in value to this 10-payment annuity — in other words, the present value of an annuity of 10 monthly payments of $40 each with interest at 6% nominal. Therefore,

$$A = \$40\, a_{\overline{10}|}$$
$$a_{\overline{10}|} = 9.7304119$$
$$A = \$40 \times 9.7304119 = \$389.22$$

which is the single cash payment which would pay the remaining debt.

Example 6. A company wishes to accumulate $10,000 by making equal, annual deposits over a period of 5 years. If the money will earn interest at the rate of 4% per annum, what must the annual payment be? This is case (b). From Equation (12),

$$R = \frac{S}{s_{\overline{n}|}}$$
$$n = 5$$
$$i = 4\%$$

From Table XVII,

$$s_{\overline{5}|} = 5.4163226$$
$$R = \frac{\$10,000}{5.4163226} = \$1,846.27$$

Example 7. After three payments of the above sinking fund have been made, what is the amount accumulated in the sinking fund?

If the amount to be accumulated in n periods is K, the annual payment is $\frac{K}{s_{\overline{n}|}}$. This becomes the annual payment R of Equation (12) and

$$S = K \frac{s_{\overline{3}|}}{s_{\overline{n}|}}$$

$$= \$10,000 \times \frac{3.1216000}{5.4163226} = \$5,763.32$$

From this the equation for the amount in a sinking fund after a payments have been made is

$$S = K \frac{s_{\overline{a}|}}{s_{\overline{n}|}} \tag{14}$$

Example 8. To provide for his son's college education a man wishes to deposit a sum of money in a bank and have the bank send the boy checks of $300 four times each year for four years. The bank will pay 4% nominal interest on all money on deposit. How much must the father deposit if the first check is to be sent three months later?

This is case (c). The plan provides for a 16-payment annuity with equal payments of $300. The amount deposited is the present worth of such an annuity.

$$A = R a_{\overline{n}|}$$
$$n = 16$$
$$i = \tfrac{4}{4} = 1\% \text{ per period of three months}$$

From Table IX,

$$a_{\overline{16}|} = 14.7178733$$
$$A = \$300 \times 14.7178733 = \$4,415.36$$

Deferred Annuities. In the case of ordinary annuities the first payment is made at the end of the first period. If the first payment does not begin until some later date, the annuity is known as a *deferred annuity*. If the annuity is deferred m periods it is designated by the symbols $m \,|\, a_n$, indicating the present value of an n period annuity of 1 with payments deferred m periods. *It must be remembered that in an annuity deferred m periods the first payment is made at the end of the $(m + 1)$ period.* In an ordinary annuity the first payment is made at the end of the first period. Deferring the annuity defers the entire procedure and therefore will defer the first payment until the end of the $(m + 1)$ period.

The present value of an annuity of 1 at the time zero (one period before the first payment is made) is $a_{\overline{n}|}$. The value of $a_{\overline{n}|}$ at time $0 - m$ (m periods previous to time 0) will be $v^m a_{\overline{n}|}$. Therefore

$$m \mid a_{\overline{n}|} = v^m a_{\overline{n}|} \tag{15}$$

Example 9. How much would the father in Example 8 have had to deposit at the time the son was born if the first payment to the son was to be made at age 20¼ years? Assume interest at 4% compounded quarterly.

$$Ra_{\overline{n}|} = \$4{,}415.36 \text{ (from Example 8)}$$
$$m = 20 \times 4 = 80$$
$$i = \tfrac{4}{4} = 1\% \text{ per period}$$

From Table IX,

$$v^{80} = 0.4511179$$
$$m \mid A = 0.4511179 \times \$4{,}415.36 = \$1{,}992.12$$

Annuities Due. Another special form of annuity is one where the *payments are made at the beginning of each period instead of at the end.* This is called an *annuity due*. The present value of such an annuity, having payments of 1, is represented by $a_{\overline{n}|}$ and the amount by $s_{\overline{n}|}$.

If we have an annuity of this type and neglect the first payment of 1, the remaining payments make an ordinary annuity of 1 running $n - 1$ periods. Therefore

$$a_{\overline{n}|} = 1 + a_{\overline{n-1}|} \tag{16}$$

The amount, $s_{\overline{n}|}$, of an annuity due, having payments of 1, may be obtained by considering it an ordinary annuity having $n + 1$ periods with the final payment omitted. Then

$$s_{\overline{n}|} = s_{\overline{n+1}|} - 1 \tag{17}$$

Perpetuities and Capitalized Cost. One other type of annuity of interest to the engineer, known as a *perpetuity*, is a series in which the payments continue indefinitely. The present value of a perpetuity may be determined by reasoning that to yield a perpetual income of 1 per period $1/i$ units of principal must be invested. This can be seen from Equation (9), which is

$$a_{\overline{n}|} = \frac{1 - v^n}{i}$$

by letting n approach infinity. Since v is always less than 1, v^n approaches zero and the expression becomes $1/i$.

The present value of a perpetuity having payments of R is equal to R/i and is often spoken of as the *capitalized value* of R.

In providing for the perpetual care of some structure, or the maintenance of endowed foundations, a special type of perpetuity is often encountered. A certain amount S may be needed every k periods to provide for replacement or maintenance. The owner, or founder, wishes to provide a fund of sufficient size so that the earnings from it will provide for this periodic demand.

To be available perpetually, S must be accumulated in k periods from the interest I which is earned by some amount of principal X, which is invested at rate i. Thus the periodic deposit toward this accumulation will be Xi. And

$$S = Xis_{\overline{k}|}$$
$$X = \frac{S}{i} \times \frac{1}{s_{\overline{k}|}} \qquad (18)$$

If the first cost of the structure, or project, is added to X, the sum is known as the capitalized cost. Thus the capitalized cost of an article is the amount of sufficient size to purchase the article and also provide for its perpetual maintenance.

By substituting for $s_{\overline{n}|}$ and $a_{\overline{n}|}$ their equivalent values in terms of i, it can easily be shown that

$$\frac{1}{s_{\overline{n}|}} = \frac{1}{a_{n|}} - i \qquad (19)$$

This gives a convenient method of determining the factor $1/s_{\overline{n}|}$ for solution of problems involving this term.

From Equation (18) we can obtain a convenient equation for the capitalized cost of an article which must be entirely replaced periodically at a cost equal to the first cost. Thus the *first cost and the amount required for periodic replacement are both equal to S.* The capitalized cost is

$$S + \frac{S}{i} \times \frac{1}{s_{\overline{E}|}} = S + \frac{S}{i}\left(\frac{1}{a_{\overline{E}|}} - i\right)$$

$$= \frac{Sia_{\overline{E}|} + S - Sia_{\overline{E}|}}{ia_{\overline{E}|}}$$

$$= \frac{S}{i} \times \frac{1}{a_{\overline{E}|}} \tag{20}$$

Example 10. Machine A costs $100 and has a life of 5 years. Machine B costs $150 and will last 8 years. Assume an interest rate of 5% per annum. Both machines can be replaced at the end of their useful lives at a cost equal to that of their original purchase price. Determine which machine is cheaper by comparing their capitalized costs.

For machine A:

$$\text{Capitalized cost} = \frac{\$100}{0.05} \times 0.2309748$$
$$= \$461.95$$

For machine B:

$$\text{Capitalized cost} = \frac{\$150}{0.05} \times 0.1547218$$
$$= \$464.17$$

Machine A is found to be cheaper since its capitalized cost is $2.22 less than that of machine B.

REFERENCES

Putnam, T. M.: "Mathematical Theory of Finance," John Wiley & Sons, Inc., New York, 1925.
Rietz, H. L., A. R. Crathorne, and J. C. Rietz: "Mathematics of Finance," Henry Holt and Company, Inc., New York, 1921.
Skinner, E. B.: "The Mathematical Theory of Investment," Ginn and Company, Boston, 1924.

PROBLEMS

40. Find the present value of a 20-year annuity of $500, payable at the end of each year, with interest at 4%.

41. What annual interest rate will have to be obtained in order for $702.36 to purchase a 10-year annuity of $100?

42. What monthly annuity, running for five years, can be purchased for $1,000 if the nominal interest rate is 6%?

43. Find the present value of a semiannual annuity of $600 which is to run for 10 years with nominal interest of 5%.

44. What will be the amount of $700 deposited at the end of each year for 12 years, if interest is earned at the rate of $3\frac{1}{2}\%$ per annum?

45. Determine the amount of an annuity of $25 per month for four years with nominal interest of 6%.

46. If an annual deposit of $300 per year is made for 30 years, what monthly annuity, to begin at the end of the first month of the 31st year and running

for 100 months, can be purchased with the accumulated funds? Nominal interest of 6% on all funds.

47. A man purchased a car for $1,049.74, paying $200 in cash and agreeing to make monthly payments of $40 per month for two years to settle for the balance. What nominal rate of interest is he paying?

48. After the man in Problem 47 has made 10 monthly payments, what single cash payment will discharge the debt?

49. What payment will be required to purchase an annuity of 20 semiannual payments of $50 each, the first payment to be received in $12\frac{1}{2}$ years? Interest at 4% compounded semiannually.

50. If $500 is deposited in a savings bank at the beginning of each half-year for eight years, and interest is paid at the rate of $3\frac{1}{2}$% compounded semi-annually, what is the total on deposit at the end of the eighth year?

51. What is the cost of a perpetuity of $800 per year if money is worth 6% per annum?

52. Determine the capitalized cost of a structure which required $2,000 to build and has an upkeep expense of $300 per year. Interest at 6%.

53. What amount will be required to endow a research laboratory which requires $40,000 for original construction, $20,000 per year for operating expenses and $10,000 every three years for new equipment and replacement? Interest at 4% per annum.

54. If $33,550 is paid for mining property which yields a return of $5,000 per year for 10 years and is then worthless, what was the uniform rate of return on the investment?

55. The 1938 revision of the National Housing Act makes it possible to build and own a house by making a down payment equal to 10% of the value of the house and lot and paying the balance in monthly installments, with interest upon the unpaid balance at $5\frac{1}{4}$% nominal. In addition, the owner must pay the taxes and insurance by paying $\frac{1}{12}$ of the annual charges each month. Taxes and insurance are estimated to be $17.40 per year for each $1,000 of the value of the house and lot. Determine the total monthly cost of buying a $5,000 home under this plan if payments are to be made over a period of 25 years.

56. A loan company advertises that one may borrow $70 and repay the loan by making 10 monthly payments of $8.82. What rate of interest are they actually receiving on their money?

Chapter VI

FINANCING ENGINEERING ENTERPRISES

Nearly all engineering projects require the expenditure of considerable sums of money. It is essential that the engineer understand the various methods by which such capital may be obtained and realize the effect of the several methods upon the economy of a project.

Individual Ownership. The bootblack on the corner requires only a few dollars to establish his business. He will usually obtain this money through saving. Similarly, most small businesses obtain the capital necessary for their beginning from the savings of the owner. Funds for expansion are ordinarily accumulated from the earnings of the business. The utilization of the savings of one individual is the method by which a large portion of American business is financed. It is a very satisfactory method for small enterprises and has worked as well for a few very large concerns. In this type of organization the owner has entire control of the operations and receives all the profits which may accrue therefrom.

The Partnership. If the amount of capital required for an enterprise is very great, a single individual will seldom possess sufficient savings to supply the needed money. The obvious solution would be to have two or more persons become partners and pool their resources so that the required capital would be obtained. This method was used to a great extent in this country during the nineteenth century.

The partnership has a number of advantages. It is bound by few legal requirements as to its accounts, procedure, tax forms and other items of operation. Dissolution of the partnership may take place at any time by mere agreement of the partners with practically no consideration of outside persons. It provides an easy method whereby two persons of differing talents may enter into business, each carrying those burdens which he can best handle. This is often the case where one partner is a technician and the other a salesman.

The partnership has four serious disadvantages. First, the amount of capital that can be accumulated is definitely limited. Second, the life of the partnership is determined by the life of the individual partners. When any partner dies the partnership automatically ends. Third, there is often serious disagreement among the individual partners. Fourth, each member of the partnership is liable for all the debts of the partnership. This particular disadvantage is one of the most serious.

The Corporation. The corporation is a form of organization which attempts to avoid the handicaps connected with a partnership. It is a fictitious being, recognized by law, which can engage in nearly any type of business transaction in which a real person could occupy himself. It operates under a charter which is granted by a state, most states requiring three or more persons to sign the charter application and be interested stockholders. It enjoys certain special privileges, important among which is perpetual life without regard to any change in the person of its owners, the stockholders. In nearly all cases, the individual stockholders are not liable for any of the debts of the corporation or the other stockholders, beyond the equity represented by their stock. In payment for these privileges and the enjoyment of legal entity the corporation is subject to certain restrictions. It is limited in its field of action by the provisions of its charter, which define the activities in which it may engage. In order to enter new fields of enterprise it must apply for a revision of its charter or obtain a new one. Special taxes are also assessed against it.

The capital of a corporation is acquired through the sale of stock. The purchasers of the stock are part owners of the corporation and its assets. In this manner the ownership may be spread throughout the entire world and as a result enormous sums of capital can be accumulated. The ultimate example of this type of organization is the American Telephone and Telegraph Company, which has common stock with a par value of nearly

$2,000,000,000, owned by over 500,000 stockholders. No single stockholder owns as much as 1% of the total stock. With few exceptions, the stockholders of a corporation, while they are the owners and entitled to share in the profits, are not liable for the debts of the corporation. They are thus never compelled to suffer any loss beyond the value of their stock. The life of a corporation, being continuous, enables long-term investments to be made and allows the future to be faced with some degree of certainty.

Certificates are issued as evidence of stock ownership. Actual proof of ownership is shown only on the record books of the corporation. In most states stock certificates are not negotiable in the strict legal sense although they may be treated as such in commercial practice.

Three measures of a stock's value are commonly found. *Par value* is the value stated on the stock certificate. This is often $100 per share but may be any sum desired. Some stocks have no stated par value and are known as *no-par-value* stocks. *Market value* is the price a willing buyer will pay a willing seller for stock. It may be less or more than the par value, depending on the earnings of the business and general market and business conditions. *Book value* is determined by subtracting the corporation's debts from its assets to obtain its net worth and then dividing this net worth by the number of shares of stock outstanding. This assumes that the stock is all of one type. There are a considerable number of types of stock, but two of these are of major importance. These two are common and preferred stocks.

Common Stock. Common stock represents ordinary ownership without special guarantees of return. Its ownership usually grants the following rights to the stockholder:

1. Vote at stockholders' meetings.

2. Elect directors and delegate to them power to conduct the affairs of the business.

3. Sell or dissolve the corporation.

4. Make and amend the bylaws of the corporation.

5. Subject to state approval, amend or change the charter or capital structure.

6. Participate in the profits.

7. Have reasonable access to corporate records.

Common stock represents ownership of a portion of the corporation's assets, and the stockholder has a claim on a certain percentage of the net worth of the corporation at all times. While the corporation is a going concern he receives a portion of the profits which may have resulted from operations. In case of failure of the business he is entitled to share in what remains of the corporation's assets after all legitimate debts have been paid. An increase in the outstanding common stock results in increasing working capital for the corporation but does not set up fixed obligations that must be met from earnings since no return is guaranteed to the common stockholders. The ownership is usually spread over more persons by such an increase, but the new owners must look to net earnings for their reward.

A rather recent development is the sale of nonvoting common stock. This stock usually carries all the rights of ordinary common stock except the privilege of voting at stockholders' meetings. This type of stock is ordinarily issued when a new company is being organized. The organizers of the company, usually a small group, wish to obtain additional capital without relinquishing any control over the affairs of the company. Such stock is obviously not of as great value as ordinary common stock. The holders have been guaranteed neither return nor power to exercise any control over the affairs of the company in which they have invested their funds.

Nonvoting preferred stock is sometimes issued for a similar purpose. In this case, however, the stockholders have a definite rate of return promised to them.

A few old and respectable companies have sold nonvoting stock to obtain additional capital. In these cases the dividend-paying policies of the companies were well established. The investors had great confidence in the officers of the companies and were willing to invest their savings without having any voice in the management.

Since the value of common stock must be a measure of the earnings that will be received through ownership of the stock, it is dependent upon several factors. However, these can probably all be summed up under two headings — dividends and market price. The market price will be affected by dividends as well as by general business conditions, future prospects of the corporation, the general money market and the investing public's fancy. In addition it may be drastically altered by speculation, which may bring about a market price that is in no way a true measure of the actual worth of the stock. Likewise, the mere payment of a large dividend is not proof that the stock has great value. Corporations have the unfortunate habit of suddenly failing to make their dividend payments, doing this too often on those stocks which have paid abnormally large returns. If the corporation does a consistently profitable business and is well managed, the holder of common stock will likely realize a handsome return on his investment. If this is not the case, he may not only fail to get any profit but may lóse part or all of his capital. Because of these possible fluctuations in value, common stocks are considered to be somewhat speculative — the degree being dependent upon the particular stock and the past record of the corporation.

Preferred Stock. Preferred stock also represents ownership, but the owner has certain additional privileges not afforded to the holder of common stock. Preferred stockholders are guaranteed a definite dividend on their stock, usually a percentage of its par value, before the holders of the common stock may receive any return. In case of dissolution of the corporation the assets must be used to satisfy the claims of the preferred stockholders before those of the holders of the common stock. Preferred stockholders often have no voting rights. Other corporations grant preferred stockholders the same voting rights as those enjoyed by owners of common shares. Voting rights are automatically granted to holders of some preferred stocks if the dividends are not paid for a specified period. They may be allowed to elect one or two representatives on the board of directors.

Because the dividend rate is fixed, preferred stock is a more conservative investment than common stock. For the same reason, the market value of such stock is less likely to fluctuate. In some corporations the preferred stockholders are permitted to share in the profits beyond their guaranteed returns if the dividends on the common stock exceed a prescribed amount. This is, however, not the usual case.

Bonds. There comes a time in the life of most corporations when there is a need for more working capital. This need might be met by selling more stock. However, this would spread the ownership over more people and thus thin the equity of the original owners. To obtain additional capital and at the same time keep the ownership intact, it is desirable to borrow money from some source at a fixed rate of interest, pledging some of the corporation's assets as security. Such action, of course, puts the corporation in debt. However, if through the use of capital costing only 4 to 6% a profit of 10 to 15% can be made, it would undoubtedly be a wise business transaction to borrow the needed capital. Before embarking on such a course, however, one should always remember that once the debt is incurred fixed costs, in the form of interest, must thereafter be paid regardless of whether or not the venture is successful. In addition the debt must someday be repaid.

If the additional capital is needed for only a short time it will usually be obtained through signing a note at a bank or other lending agency. The note is merely a promise to repay the amount borrowed, with interest, at a fixed future date. The bank will require something of tangible value as security for the loan. Such loans usually do not run for more than two years and are known as short-term notes.

If capital must be secured through short-term notes, the corporation is faced with the necessity of refinancing these loans every two years or oftener. Obviously, this prevents long-range planning of operations since there is always some uncertainty as to whether or not the needed capital will be available when required. The refinancing may also involve extra expense. For these reasons corporations resort to bond issues to obtain long-term additions to working capital without thinning ownership.

A bond is essentially a long-term note, giving as security a trust deed upon certain of the corporation's assets. In return for the money loaned, the corporation promises to repay the loan and interest upon this amount at a specified rate. In addition, the corporation gives a deed upon certain of its assets which becomes effective if it defaults in the payment of interest or principal as promised. Through these provisions the bondholder has a more stable and secure investment than does the holder of common or preferred stock. Since the bond merely represents corporate indebtedness, the bondholder has no voice in the affairs of the business as long as his interest is paid, and of course is not entitled to any share of the profits.

Bonds are usually issued in units of from $100 to $1,000 each in order to facilitate obtaining the desired capital from a wide source. As a rule every bond should show the following items:

1. Acknowledgment of the indebtedness for value received.

2. A promise to repay the principal and pay a stated rate of interest until such repayment, with time, place and method of payment of each stipulated.

3. A description of the entire bond issue of which the bond is a part.

4. A description of the security behind the bond issue.

5. Rights of the bondholder in case of default.

6. Endorsement by an authorized authority.

The amount named on the bond is known as the *face* or *par value* of the bond. This is to be repaid the lender at the end of a specified period of time. When the face value has been repaid, the bond is said to have been *retired* or *redeemed*. The interest rate quoted on the bond is called the *bond rate*.

Interest may be paid in either of two manners. The name of the owner of *registered bonds* is recorded on the record books of the corporation and interest payments are sent to the owner as they become due without any action on his part. *Coupon bonds* have a coupon attached to the bond for each interest payment which will come due during the life of the bond. When an interest payment is due, the holder clips the corresponding coupon from the bond and can convert it into cash, usually at any bank. A registered bond thus requires no action on the part of the holder, but it is not so easily transferred to new ownership as is the coupon bond.

Classification of Bonds. Bonds may be classified in many ways. Perhaps one of the best, and yet simple, methods is to classify them according to the security behind them. In this grouping we have:

1. *Mortgage bonds*. This is the most common type of bond. As security for the money borrowed the corporation gives the lender a mortgage upon certain of its assets in the form of a trust deed.

Title to the property never passes to the bondholders unless the corporation defaults on the payments called for in the bond. In case of default the bondholders, through proper court orders, may obtain possession of the mortgaged property and sell it to obtain the money which was loaned and the accrued interest.

These bonds may be issued as *first mortgage* bonds, in which case the holders have first claim upon the mortgaged property. Second, third or fourth mortgage bonds may also be issued. The claims of holders of these bonds are not satisfied until after those of the holders of prior mortgage bonds. These latter bonds are, of course, not as good an investment as the first mortgage bonds of the same corporation. They usually pay a slightly higher rate of interest and are often called *junior lien* bonds. Second or third mortgage bonds of certain corporations, however, are better and more conservative investments than the first mortgage bonds of some other corporations. The particular case must govern the rule.

Mortgage bonds may contain clauses that require the corporation to maintain the mortgaged property in a certain condition. Clauses may also prevent further mortgages upon the property. The corporation may be restricted from purchasing or disposing of any property or from issuing any additional bonds of any kind. Such clauses are desirable from the viewpoint of the bondholders but are a damper upon the activities of the corporation. They are included in order to make the bond issue more attractive to the investing public and possibly permit a lower interest rate.

2. *Collateral bonds.* In this type of bond the security is some form of recognized commercial security such as the stocks or bonds of a well-established subsidiary. Thus the security for these bonds is essentially a second mortgage upon certain assets of the subsidiary. Therefore the buyer must look to the subsidiary for his security unless the bonds contain provisions giving additional claims upon the parent company in case of default. They are usually issued only by a well-established corporation, and the reputation of the parent is of some value.

3. *Debentures.* These are really long-term notes since they have no security behind them except a promise to pay. Until recently they were not very common and unless issued by a cor-

poration having an excellent credit rating are not a particularly good form of investment. Quite a few issues of debentures have been sold by the larger corporations of this country during the last two years. This has been possible because of the oversupply of investment funds which are available. In order to make them more attractive they sometimes give the holder the right to convert them into stock at a fixed price at some future date. In case of liquidation they usually rank just ahead of preferred stock.

Bond Retirement. Since stock represents ownership, it is unnecessary for a corporation to make special provision for payments to the stockholders. If profits remain after the operating expenses are paid, these are divided among the stockholders. Bonds, on the other hand, represent debt, and the interest upon them is a cost of doing business. In addition to this periodic cost, the corporation must look forward to the day when the bonds become due and the principal must be repaid to the bondholders. Provision may be made for repaying the principal by two different methods.

If the business has prospered and general market conditions are good when the bonds come due, the corporation may be able to sell a new issue of bonds and use the proceeds to pay off the holders of the old issue. If conditions are right the new issue may bear a lower rate of interest than the original bonds. If this is the case the corporation maintains the desired capital at a decreased cost. On the other hand, if business conditions are bad when the time for refinancing arrives, the bond market may not be favorable and it may be impossible to sell a new bond issue, or possible only at an increased interest rate. This would probably be a serious handicap to the corporation. In addition, the bondholders wish to have assurance that provision is being made so there will be no doubt concerning the availability of funds with which their bonds will be retired. A serious weakness of this method of retirement is the fact that the corporate indebtedness is not reduced through this "borrowing from Peter to pay Paul." From their continued use of this method of financing it appears that some corporations never expect, or desire, to cease operating on borrowed capital — in other words, get out of debt. Some of the railroads of this country are striking examples.

To avoid the uncertainties of the method just described, to give assurance to the bondholders and to allow the indebtedness to be reduced, a second method of bond retirement is commonly used. The corporation periodically sets aside definite sums which, with the interest they earn, will accumulate to the amount needed to retire the bonds at the time they are due. Since it is convenient to have these periodic deposits equal in amount, the retirement process becomes a sinking fund. This is one of the most common uses of a sinking fund. By its use the bondholders know that adequate provision is being made to safeguard their investment. The corporation knows in advance what the annual cost for bond retirement will be.

If a bond issue of $100,000 in 10-year bonds, in $1,000 units, paying 6% interest in semiannual payments, must be retired by the use of a sinking fund which earns 4%, compounded semiannually, the annual cost for retirement will be:

From the sinking fund formula,

$$R = \frac{S}{s_{n\rceil}}$$
$$S = \$100,000$$
$$i = \tfrac{4}{2} = 2\% \text{ per period}$$
$$n = 2 \times 10 = 20 \text{ periods}$$

From Table XIII,

$$s_{\overline{20}\rceil} = 24.2973698$$
$$R = \frac{\$100,000}{24.2973698} = \$4,115.67$$

This will be the semiannual cost for retirement. In addition, the semiannual interest on the bonds must be paid. This would be:

$$I = \$100,000 \times \frac{0.06}{2} = \$3,000$$

Total semiannual cost = $\$4,115.67 + \$3,000 = \$7,115.67$
Annual cost = $\$7,115.67 \times 2 = \$14,231.34$

The total cost for interest and retirement of the entire bond issue will be:

$$\$7,115.67 \times 20 = \$142,313.40$$

Callable Bonds. In the problem just considered none of the bonds were retired until the end of 10 years. The money in the sinking fund earned interest at the rate of 4% compounded semi-annually. At the same time the corporation was paying 6%, compounded semiannually, upon the money it had borrowed. It would obviously be advantageous to be able to buy back its outstanding bonds with the money in the sinking fund and obtain an interest saving of 2%. Since bonds usually have a higher rate of interest than can be obtained on sinking fund deposits in a bank or in short-term investments, it is an advantage for the corporation to be able to retire bonds whenever it has money available in the sinking fund. This procedure is usually not desired by the bondholders since they do not wish to relinquish a good bond which pays a good yield. Thus, what is advantageous for the corporation may not be desired by the bondholder. In order to make bonds which may be retired before maturity more attractive to the investor, provision is often made that a price above par will be paid if they are redeemed before the maturity date.

Bonds that contain clauses permitting repayment before maturity are known as *callable bonds*. One method is to retire a certain number of bonds each interest date, selecting the bonds to be retired by lot. Some bond issues definitely state that those having certain serial numbers will be retired at specified dates. If no provision has been made to make the bonds callable, the issuer may obtain nearly the same advantage by buying back its bonds on the open market, giving the effect of investing its sinking funds at the bond interest rate. The market price of the bonds must be approximately par to make this true.

Now consider what saving would be effected if the bond issue cited on the previous pages had been callable. Since the interest rate on the sinking fund would be the same as the bond rate, the total semiannual cost would be:

$$R + I = S\left[\frac{1}{s_{\overline{n}|}} + i\right] = S \times \frac{1}{a_{\overline{n}|}}$$

To retire the issue in 10 years,

$$S = \$100,000$$
$$i = \tfrac{6}{2} = 3\% \text{ per period}$$
$$n = 10 \times 2 = 20 \text{ periods}$$

From Table XV,

$$\frac{1}{a_{\overline{20}|}} = 0.0672157$$

$$R + I = \$100,000 \times 0.0672157 = \$6,721.57$$

The interest which must be paid the first period is $3,000. The amount left for bond retirement would be:

$$\$6,721.57 - \$3,000 = \$3,721.57$$

Since the bonds are in units of $1,000, any retirement must be in a multiple of this amount. The multiple of $1,000 nearest to $3,721.57 is 4. Thus at the end of the first six months the bond interest would be paid and in addition four $1,000 bonds would

TABLE 7. AMORTIZATION SCHEDULE FOR A $100,000 BOND ISSUE

Interest period	Principal	Interest at 3% per period	Number of bonds retired	Principal repaid	Total payment for period
1	$100,000	$3,000	4	$4,000	$7,000
2	96,000	2,880	4	4,000	6,880
3	92,000	2,760	4	4,000	6,760
4	88,000	2,640	4	4,000	6,640
5	84,000	2,520	4	4,000	6,520
6	80,000	2,400	4	4,000	6,400
7	76,000	2,280	4	4,000	6,280
8	72,000	2,160	5	5,000	7,160
9	67,000	2,010	5	5,000	7,010
10	62,000	1,860	5	5,000	6,860
11	57,000	1,710	5	5,000	6,710
12	52,000	1,560	5	5,000	6,560
13	47,000	1,410	5	5,000	6,410
14	42,000	1,260	5	5,000	6,260
15	37,000	1,110	6	6,000	7,110
16	31,000	930	6	6,000	6,930
17	25,000	750	6	6,000	6,750
18	19,000	570	6	6,000	6,570
19	13,000	390	6	6,000	6,390
20	7,000	210	7	7,000	7,210
				$100,000	$134,410

be retired. If a similar procedure is carried out at the end of each interest period the results will be as shown in Table 7. From the $6,721.57 set aside each period the interest on the outstanding bonds is first paid. With the money remaining as many bonds as possible are retired — using the number of bonds which have a redemption value nearest to the amount remaining. In some cases this will require slightly more than the normally provided amount and at other times less will be required. The difference will never be greater than one-half the price of one bond. Such a process of bond retirement is known as *amortization*,[1] and a tabulation like that shown in Table 7 is called an *amortization schedule*.

From the amortization schedule it is seen that the total cost of interest and bond retirement by this method is $134,410. By comparing this with $142,313.40, which was the total cost of the $100,000 issue of noncallable bonds, it can be seen that the different method of retirement resulted in a saving of $7,903.40. This is almost 8% of the face value of the bond issue. The advantage of callable bonds to the corporation is thus quite apparent.

In many cases provision is made in the amortization schedule so that no bonds will have to be retired during the first few years after the bonds are first issued. This is done to allow the corporation to get the new equipment, which was financed by the proceeds from the bond issue, into operation and earning a return before the expense of retirement begins.

Bond Value. The value of a bond is the present value of all the money which the holder of the bond will receive from it in the future. Let

F = face, or par, value
C = redemption price (usually equal to F)
r = the bond rate per interest period
n = the number of periods before redemption
i = the investment rate per period
V_n = value of the bond n periods prior to redemption

The value of a bond is made up of two parts. The first part is the present value of the redemption price at a time n periods before redemption. This is equal to Cv^n. The second part is the present value of all the future interest payments. These constitute an annuity with a periodic payment of Fr. At a time n periods before

---

[1] The term *amortization* may be applied to any method of extinguishing a debt, principal and interest, on outstanding principal, by a series of equal payments at equal intervals.

redemption these are worth $Fra_{\overline{n}|}$. The present value of the bond is therefore

$$V_n = Cv^n + Fra_{\overline{n}|} \tag{21}$$

Example. Find the cost (present value) of a 10-year 6% bond, interest payable semiannually, which is redeemable at par, if bought to yield 5%. Par value is $1,000.

$n = 10 \times 2 = 20$ periods
$r = \frac{6}{2} = 3\%$ per period
$i = \frac{5}{2} = 2.5\%$ per period
$C = F = \$1,000$
$V_n = Cv^n + Fra_{\overline{n}|}$

From Table XIV ($i = 2.5\%$),

$v^{20} = 0.6102709$

From Table XIV ($i = 2.5\%$),

$a_{\overline{20}|} = 15.5891623$
$V_n = \$1,000 \times 0.6102709 + 0.03 \times \$1,000 \times 15.5891623$
$\quad = \$610.27 + \$467.67 = \$1,077.94$

Investment Rate. By use of the bond value formula, Equation (21), the price to be paid for any bond to correspond to an investment rate of i can be determined. Since bond prices are subject to fluctuations on the market, the purchaser of a bond may pay more or less than the par value for it. He then wants to know what rate of interest he is earning on his investment. If he has paid other than par for the bond the rate of return on the investment will obviously not be the same as the bond rate, which is based on the par value.

If Equation (21) is written in terms of i it becomes

$$V_n = \frac{C}{(1 + i)^n} + Fr \frac{(1 + i)^n - 1}{i(1 + i)^n} \tag{22}$$

In terms of i this equation is of the degree $n + 1$ and therefore cannot be solved for i by direct methods. It can be solved by "cut-and-try" methods or to a fair degree of accuracy by interpolation methods. The latter method is ordinarily of sufficient accuracy, and the results are obtained quickly.

Consider a $1,000 bond which is to mature in 12 years, having a bond rate of 4% with interest payable semiannually. If the bond sells for $1,025 and is to be redeemed at par, what is the actual investment rate? By using Equation (21) the price corre-

sponding to various investment rates can be found. For a rate of
$3\frac{1}{2}\%$ this would be:

$$F = C = \$1,000$$
$$n = 12 \times 2 = 24 \text{ periods}$$
$$r = \tfrac{4}{2} = 2\% \text{ per period}$$
$$i = \frac{3.5}{2} = 1.75\% \text{ per period}$$

From Table XII,

$$v^{24} = 0.6594380$$

From Table XII,

$$a_{\overline{24}|} = 19.4606856$$
$$V_n = \$1,000 \times 0.6594380 + \$1,000 \times 0.02 \times 19.4606856$$
$$= \$659.44 + \$389.21 = \$1,048.65$$

In the same manner the other values shown on Figure 12 can be
found and plotted. It can be seen that the line drawn through
the various plotted points is a curve which is slightly concave up-

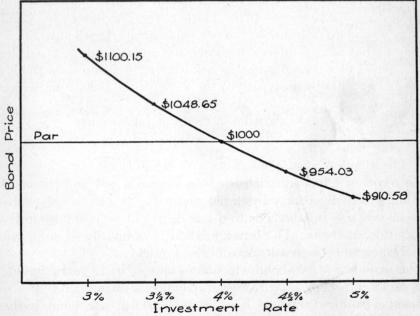

FIGURE 12. Method of determining bond yield.

ward. However, between any two adjacent points it is so near to a straight line that straight-line interpolation between adjacent points will cause very little error.

For the problem being considered, the bond price lies between the prices corresponding to 4% and 3½%. This can be illustrated as follows:

Price	Investment Rate (Nominal)
$1,000.00	4%
1,025.00	X%
1,048.65	3½%

Therefore, by interpolation,

$$(4 - 3\tfrac{1}{2}) : (4 - X) = (1,048.65 - 1,000) : (1,025 - 1,000)$$

and

$$X = 3.74\%$$

The results obtained by this method will be slightly greater than the true value. However, if one does not interpolate over a range greater than ½% the error is so small that for amounts under $100,000 it may be ignored.

The Use of Borrowed Funds. Consider the following case. The Blank Co., a privately owned business, has an opportunity to buy the Small Co. from which it purchases a large amount of its raw materials. The purchase price is to be $50,000. It is estimated that the Blank Co. can realize a saving of $5,000 annually from operating the Small Co. instead of having to purchase their raw materials from it. The anticipated profit of $5,000 is exclusive of any financial expense which might be involved in the transaction but includes provision for writing off the investment over a 20-year period.

The Blank Co. does not have $50,000 available which it can use to buy the Small Co. However, it can sell a $50,000 bond issue and use the proceeds for this purpose. The bonds will be issued as 20-year 7% bonds. Should the Blank Co. issue the bonds and buy the Small Co.?

The correct solution of this problem requires a careful consideration of the effect of the method of obtaining the required capital upon the economy of the project. This effect is best revealed by first determining what the results would be if the Blank Co. had sufficient funds available to consummate the deal without borrowing. This result is readily determined. Since there was provision for a 20-year write-off of the investment, computed by a 7% sinking fund method, included in the determination of the $5,000 saving, this figure is the net saving which should be realized. Thus the return on the required investment of $50,000 would be 10%.

Now determine what additional expenses would be involved if bonds were issued to finance the purchase of the Small Co. In the first place, payment of the bond interest would require $3,500 annually. This would be an actual expense of operating the Small Co. if borrowed funds are used.

A second item is a consideration of the method that will be used to retire the bond issue when it becomes due. The principle of maintenance of capital requires that the Blank Co. have as much capital at the time the investment in the Small Co. is completely written off as they had when they made the investment. So far as their investment in the Small Co. is concerned, this amount of capital is *zero*. They are not using *their* capital to purchase the Small Co. Instead, they are using some other person's capital. Therefore there is no necessity for them to provide for capital maintenance on their own funds through depreciation. They are required only to repay the money which they have borrowed. In other words, they must maintain the other fellow's capital which has been entrusted to them. Thus, the amounts that were included as depreciation expense may be used to retire the bonds. Since the time provided for write-off is the same as the period of the bond issue, and the interest rates are the same, the expense of retiring the bond issue has already been included in the study and adds no additional expense. By a proper consideration of the principle of maintenance of capital, one can avoid the double write-off of investments through providing for both depreciation and retirement of borrowed funds. At the same time one can be certain that all the legitimate expenses have been included.

If the bond interest expense is subtracted from the saving of $5,000, the net saving, or profit, is found to be $1,500. This amount cannot actually be related to the required investment to determine the percentage return on the capital outlay, since the

Blank Co. really has none of its money invested in the proposition. However, in practice it should be related to the amount of borrowed capital involved so as to show the percentage of profit above the actual expense. In this case this figure is

$$\frac{\$1,500}{\$50,000} \times 100 = 3\%$$

This means that the Blank Co. will receive a return of 3% upon the $50,000 which they have borrowed and for which they are liable. They may use this figure for comparing this project with some other they might undertake with the same borrowed funds.

A more significant fact about the figure of 3% is that if conditions change so that this profit of 3% is wiped out, they will then lose money on the proposition. Thus, there is only a 3% margin between profit and loss. This figure becomes the one on which the decision as to investment must be based. There are few industrial projects where a prospective margin of 3% between the maximum profit and possible loss would be sufficient to justify the investment of borrowed funds. Especially is this true if the pay-out period is more than a year or two. It may thus be seen that the use of borrowed capital may change the entire economy of a project. Whenever borrowed funds are to be used it should always be remembered that a reversal of conditions may wipe out the expected profit but the debt will still remain.

Other Effects of the Use of Borrowed Capital. The source of the investment funds influences the economy of engineering projects in numerous ways. Most of these occur because of the necessity of obtaining additional capital. The first effect which might be mentioned under this heading is where it is impossible to obtain additional capital. Many projects are economically feasible if one has the required capital to finance the undertaking. This means that a proposition that is economically desirable for one person may not be so for another who does not possess the necessary capital. Thus, small companies and municipalities often find that they can obtain lowest unit cost by performing certain operations by manual labor. A larger company would obtain lowest unit cost by having an expensive machine to do the same work.

Transportation companies are often unable to sell additional stocks or bonds to obtain funds to purchase new rolling stock. This difficulty is surmounted by issuing equipment trust certificates, by which the certificate holders own the equipment and the company pays for the use of the rolling stock by an annual rental fee. By the end of the life of the equipment the rental fees will have paid for it as well as interest on the certificates.

Construction projects are sometimes financed by the contractors taking bonds of the owner in payment for the work. They in effect have a mortgage on the structure which they have erected. These bonds usually bear a very high interest rate so that the contractor may dispose of them in small lots by discounting them.

When it is necessary to issue bonds to finance some projects, it is often easier to dispose of a large amount of bonds than a small amount. Such financing is usually done through investment bankers who buy the entire bond issue and then sell it in small lots to the investing public at slightly higher prices. The necessary investigation and selling expense of the investment banker is considerable. For a small amount of bonds these would be prohibitive.

Where an undertaking is being financed by public funds, such as a municipal, state or federal project, the money is ultimately to come from taxation. Municipal governments ordinarily issue bonds to cover each project, such as water district bonds, sewer bonds, etc. State and federal governments, however, usually provide for the necessary capital out of fiscal appropriations. Thus in state and federal projects there is usually no attempt to provide for direct repayment of the borrowed capital out of the earnings of the project, even if it is of the self-liquidating type. Many government projects, of course, are not intended to earn direct monetary returns.

Considering the Source of Capital in Economy Studies. It is often advisable to make an economy study in the usual manner, determining the possible return from the required investment, before considering the source of the required capital and its effects.[2] This is because the true merits of the project will then

---

[2] This statement applies to ordinary industrial studies. If the study is for a government project, this fact may be considered at the time the study is made. This is discussed at greater length in a later chapter.

be known. If the proposition has definite possibilities when sufficient capital is available, one will be justified in making proper efforts to finance it in the correct manner. The effects of the source of the capital are financial matters which should be considered as such. While they may make the undertaking not desirable, it should be definitely known that these were the limiting factors. At a later date the capital may be available and the true economy of the project will be known so it may be acted upon.

If capital has to be procured, all the possible methods should be considered and the advantages and disadvantages weighed carefully. The serious difficulty that may arise in times of depression when fixed obligations on borrowed capital must be met, probably from severely reduced revenues, should always be remembered. The attendant advantages and disadvantages of each method should be understood and used to the best advantage. Only after the effects of the source of capital have been considered can an economy study lead to a correct decision.

REFERENCES

Bowers, E. L., and R. H. Rowntree: "Economics for Engineers," McGraw-Hill Book Company, Inc., New York, 1938.

Goldman, O. B.: "Financial Engineering," John Wiley & Sons, Inc., New York, 1923.

Harding, C. F., and D. T. Canfield: "Business Administration for Engineers," McGraw-Hill Book Company, Inc., New York, 1937.

Kimball, D. S., and D. S. Kimball, Jr.: "Principles of Industrial Organization," McGraw-Hill Book Company, Inc., New York, 1939.

Lester, Bernard: "Applied Economics for Engineers," John Wiley & Sons, Inc., New York, 1939.

PROBLEMS

57. What does a share of stock represent?
58. What rights does the holder of preferred stock ordinarily have?
59. Distinguish between the par value and the market value of a share of stock.
60. What degree of control does the bondholder ordinarily have over the normal conduct of a business?
61. How does a debenture differ from a mortgage bond?
62. Explain the difference between callable and noncallable bonds.
63. A bankrupt corporation is being liquidated. List the claims of the holders of the following securities according to the priority of their claims: debentures, common stock, bonds, preferred stock.
64. What is the use of equipment trust certificates?

65. Why does preferred stock usually pay a higher rate of return than a bond of the same company?

66. If you desired to finance a large-scale expansion of a business and did not wish to acquire new owners, what methods of securing capital might you use? Discuss the advantages of each.

67. What price should be paid for a $1,000, 6% bond which is to mature in 17 years, interest being paid semiannually, if the redemption price is par and it is bought to yield 4%?

68. A 20-year, $1,000, 5% bond is callable after eight years at $1,050. It is expected that the bond will be retired as soon as permitted. Interest is paid semiannually. What price should be paid so that a yield of 5% will be obtained?

69. A company issues $200,000 in 7% bonds, to be retired in 20 years. Interest is to be paid semiannually. The bonds are not callable. Repayment is to be made by means of a sinking fund, upon which interest at the rate of 3% will be received. The bonds are in units of $1,000. What amount must be paid annually for interest and retirement? What will be the total cost of the $200,000 for the 20-year period?

70. If the bonds in the previous problem were callable, what would be the total cost of the issue? Determine this by setting up an amortization schedule.

71. What is the yield of a 7% bond which is purchased for $1,170? The bond is to mature in 12 years. Interest is paid semiannually.

72. A $1,000, callable bond, which was purchased 17 years previously for $970, has been retired for $1,050. Interest at the rate of 5% was paid annually. Determine the actual yield of the bond.

73. An irrigation district intends to finance a new project by a $200,000 bond issue. The bonds are to be due in 40 years with the provision that they are callable by lot after 10 years. The bond rate is 6%. A provision in the bonds provides that the district shall set aside equal annual sums throughout the life of the bond issue to provide for interest and retirement. Any excess funds may be invested in a 3% sinking fund. If interest payments on the bonds and the sinking funds are made annually, what will be the amount of the annual deposit which must be made?

Chapter VII

VALUATION AND DEPRECIATION

It is a common experience that physical properties suffer a decrease in value as they grow older.[1] An automobile purchased today is worth less tomorrow, despite the fact that it may actually operate more smoothly and efficiently at the later date. In industrial property and equipment the same decline in value with age is experienced. As a machine ages the costs for operation and maintenance become greater. Wear necessitates a reduction in speed to prevent excessive breakdowns. Newer and improved equipment will give lower unit costs. Changes in the design of the manufactured product decrease the need for the original machine. All of these factors tend to reduce the value of the machine. This decrease in the value of a property is known as *depreciation*.

That the realization of the fact that physical properties suffer a decrease in value with time is not a new one may be seen by an examination of the following statement from the writings of Vitruvius,[2] probably written before A.D. 27.

"Therefore when arbitrators[3] are taken for party-walls, they do not value them at the price at which they were made, but when from the accounts they find the tenders for them, they deduct as price of the passing of each year the 80th part, and so — in that from the remaining sum repayment is made for these walls — they pronounce the opinion that the walls cannot last more than 80 years. There is no deduction[4] made from the value

---

[1] Notable exceptions are liquors and rare antiques.
[2] "Vitruvius on Architecture," translated by Frank Granger, Vol. I, p. 117.
[3] For building laws.
[4] This could only come in when the improved methods of brick building were established under the empire.

of brick walls provided that they remain plumb; but they are always valued at as much as they were built for."

Definitions of Value. Since depreciation is defined in terms of decrease in value, it is desirable to consider the meaning of the term "value." A little thought reveals that the business world gives several meanings to the term. Which is the one to be considered in talking of depreciation? A very common measure of value is the price for which an article can be bought or sold on the open market. This is called *market value* and assumes that there are a willing buyer and seller, each with equal advantage.

A second kind of value is known as *fair value*. This is usually determined by a disinterested party in order to establish a price that is fair to both seller and buyer.

A third type of value is that which is established as the base for the setting of rates for public utilities. Value for this purpose is usually different from market value.

Book value is the worth of a property as shown on the accounting books of a company. It may thus be any amount that the company desires to show. Ordinarily it is considered to be equal to the cost of the property less the amount that has been charged off as depreciation.

Salvage, or resale, value is the price that can be obtained from the sale of the property second hand. It is affected by several factors. The reason of the present owner for selling may influence the salvage value. If the owner is selling because there is very little commercial need for the property this will affect the resale value. Change of ownership will probably not increase the commercial utility of the article. Salvage value will also be affected by the present cost of reproducing the property. Price levels may either increase or decrease the resale value. A third factor which may affect salvage value is the location of the property. This is particularly true in the case of structures which must be moved in order to be of further use. The physical condition of property will also have a great influence upon the resale price that can be obtained. A structure which has been well maintained and is in good condition will obviously be of greater value than one which has been neglected and would require considerable repair before it could be used.

Scrap value is ordinarily considered to be the amount that the property would bring if sold for junk. The utility of the article is assumed to be zero.

A consideration of all of these different measures of value, and the factors affecting them, gives a clue to the true meaning of value. Probably the best general definition of value is that it is a measure of the present worth of all the future profits to be obtained from possession of the property. One possesses a property in order that he may receive profits therefrom. The value which he places upon the property is a measure of the profits he expects to derive from his ownership. True, these profits are often not in the form of money. However, regardless of their form, they must be expressed in terms of money in order to state their commercial value.

Value for Rate Setting. One exception, where value defined as a measure of future profits cannot be used, is in the determination of value for setting utility rates. These rates are usually set by a governmental agency so they will yield a fair profit upon the value of the property. If the value of the property were measured by the present value of the future profits a vicious circle would be established. The higher the rates were set the greater would be the profits. In turn, the greater the profits the higher the rates would have to be in order to yield a reasonable return upon the value of the property. For rate setting some other method of determining value must be utilized. This problem will be discussed at length later in this chapter.

Purposes of Depreciation. Since property decreases in value, it is desirable to consider the effect that this depreciation has on engineering projects. Primarily, it is necessary to consider depreciation for two reasons:

1. To provide for the recovery of capital which has been invested in physical property.

2. To enable the expense of depreciation to be charged to the cost of producing products which are turned out by the property.

To understand these purposes, consider the case of a man who invested $3,000 in a machine for making a special type of concrete building tile. He found that with his own labor in operating the machine he could produce 500 tiles per day. Working 300 days per year he could make 150,000 tiles. He was able to sell the tiles for $40 per thousand. The necessary materials and power cost $20 per thousand tiles.

At the end of the first year he had sold 150,000 tiles and computed his total profit, at the rate of $20 per M, to be $3,000. This continued for two more years, at which time the machine was worn out and would not operate longer. To continue in business he would have to purchase a new machine.

During the three-year period, believing he was actually making a profit of $3,000 per year, he had spent the entire amount for his annual living expenses. He suddenly found that he no longer had his original $3,000 of capital, his machine was worn out, and he had no money with which to purchase a new one.

Analysis of the situation reveals that no provision had been made for recovering the capital invested in the tile machine. The machine, which was valued at $3,000 when purchased, had decreased in value until it was worthless. Through this depreciation $3,000 of capital had been lost.

The obvious error was the failure to recognize that depreciation would take place and make adequate provision to recover the capital which had been invested in the tile machine. *Thus it is essential that depreciation be considered so that capital may be recovered or maintained.* Failure to do this will always result ultimately in depletion of capital.

Since capital must be maintained, it is necessary that the recovery be made by charging the depreciation which has taken place to the cost of producing whatever products have been produced. Thus, in the case of the tile machine, production of 450,000 tiles "consumed" the machine. One might say that each thousand tiles produced decreased the value of the machine $\frac{\$3,000}{450} = \$6.67$.

Therefore $6.67 should be charged as the cost of depreciation for making each thousand tiles. Adding this cost of depreciation to $20, the cost of materials and power, gives the true cost of producing a thousand tiles. With the true cost known, the actual profit can then be determined. At the same time, with depreciation charged as an expense, a means is provided for recovery of capital.

It is apparent that depreciation is just as real a cost as rent, power, taxes, labor or materials. It differs from these expenses in that it is more difficult to forecast. Depreciation is an element of cost which must always be paid ahead of use.

Types of Depreciation. Depreciation is the shrinkage in value with the passage of time. This decrease in value may or may not be due to age. Usually depreciation can be divided into two types — *physical* and *functional*. Physical depreciation is nearly always due to the passage of time. Functional depreciation may be the result of age, but the greater portion is usually due to other factors.

Physical depreciation is due to the lessening of the physical ability of a property to produce results. Its common causes are wear and deterioration. These cause operation and maintenance costs to increase and output to decrease. As a result the profits decrease. Physical depreciation is mainly a function of time and use. It will be affected greatly by the maintenance policy of the owner. Some people contend that it is possible to maintain a property so that it is "good as new." This subject is open to discussion, but it is doubtful if anything that is subject to depreciation can ever be as good as new regardless of maintenance. A property might be improved so that it is more valuable than when it was new, but it is then not the same as it was originally. Improvement has been confused with maintenance.

Functional depreciation is more difficult to determine than physical depreciation. It is the decrease in value due to the lessening in the demand for the function of the property. This may be brought about in many ways. Styles change, population centers shift, more efficient machines are designed, markets are saturated. The result of such changes is to lessen the need for the output of a particular machine or property. This directly affects the profits and thus the value. While physical depreciation may be reasonably anticipated and estimated, functional depreciation is more elusive. Yet it is very real and its importance is increasing. Modern industry is characterized by rapid improvement and change. Indeed, in many businesses the greater portion of the total depreciation cost is due to functional factors. While it is difficult to determine, it cannot be ignored.

Reference was previously made to the idea that property might be maintained "good as new." This idea has been held to a considerable extent regarding railroad rights of way. It is probably true that a well-maintained right of way may be in as good physical condition when it is 10 years old as it was when new. But what about the functional depreciation? The truck and bus competition had a very great effect upon the functional depreciation of railroad rights of way. It appears that neglect of the functional depreciation factor during years of large profits may have contributed to the present financial condition of many railroads.

Since depreciation is measured by loss in value, and value is determined by future profits, those factors which affect the future profits must also affect depreciation. Any attempt to determine depreciation should consider these factors. Among such factors are the life of the property; future expenses for maintenance, operation and taxes; and future depreciation charges. This complex situation cannot be solved exactly. Future conditions cannot be determined exactly. However, it is necessary that depreciation be determined as closely as is reasonably possible. Not only must provision be made for replacement of equipment as it wears, but the correct depreciation charge must be made before the true net profit can be found. In addition, depreciation must be considered in establishing value for rate setting.

From the standpoint of accounting and management planning it is desirable that the method of determining depreciation be relatively simple and give uniform annual depreciation costs. In order to preserve the invested capital at all times, the accumulated amount of the depreciation charges should equal the actual decrease in value which has taken place. Considerable difficulty is encountered in attempting to fulfill all of these requirements. The only practical solution seems to be some simple method which approximates the actual depreciation as closely as possible. The Department of Internal Revenue has the following to say in their instructions for the filing of corporate income tax returns:

The amount deductible on account of depreciation . . . is an amount reasonably measuring the portion of the investment in depreciable property used in the trade or business by reason of exhaustion, wear and tear, including a reasonable allowance for obsolescence, which is properly chargeable for the year. . . . The capital sum to be recovered should be charged off ratably over the useful life of the property. Whatever plan or method of apportionment is adopted must be reasonable and must have due regard to operating conditions during the taxable year and should be described in the return.

Standing against these instructions are the decisions of the United States Supreme Court, which has held that there can be no set method of determining depreciation and value. This court has consistently held that each case must be decided in the light of testimony of competent experts.

Economic Life. Since obsolescence is a prime factor in depreciation, it is apparent that the physical life of a property is often not the life which must be considered in establishing depreciation rates. What is often called the *economic life* is more applicable. By this is meant the length of time during which the property will probably be operated upon an economic basis. The entire amount of depreciation should be written off during this economic life. In this manner, equipment which is unsatisfactory from the viewpoint of economy may be replaced without causing a capital loss, even though it may be in fair physical condition.

Quite a few data are available regarding the probable life of various types of structures and equipment. These have been prepared by various engineers, industrial authorities and the United States Bureau of Internal Revenue.[5] It should be remembered, however, that such data are based, for the most part, on averages and past performance. There is no guarantee that the future will bring the same results. However, they do give much useful data.

The Straight-Line Formula. This method of computing depreciation assumes that the loss in value is directly proportional to the age of the structure. This straight-line relationship gives rise to the name of the method. Thus with this formula if

L = useful life of the structure in years
C = the original cost
d = the annual cost of depreciation
C_A = the value at the end of A years

[5] Some of these are given in the *Cost and Production Handbook* by L. P. Alford; *Engineering Valuation* by A. Marston and T. R. Agg; and *Depreciation Principles and Applications* by E. A. Saliers.

C_L = the value at the end of the life of the structure, the scrap value (including gain or loss due to removal)

D_A = depreciation up to age A years

then

$$d = \frac{C - C_L}{L} \tag{23}$$

$$D_A = \frac{A(C - C_L)}{L} \tag{24}$$

$$C_A = C - \frac{A(C - C_L)}{L} \tag{25}$$

Example: Determine the yearly cost of depreciation, salvage value at the end of the sixth year, and total depreciation up to the end of the sixth year on a structure which cost $120 new and has an estimated scrap value of $20 at the end of 10 years.

$$d = \frac{\$120 - \$20}{10} = \$10 \text{ per year}$$

$$D_6 = \frac{6(\$120 - \$20)}{10} = \$60$$

$$C_6 = \$120 - \frac{6(\$120 - \$20)}{10} = \$60$$

This method of computing depreciation is more widely used than any other. It is simple and gives a uniform annual charge. In addition, it has the approval of the Internal Revenue Department. It does not take into account interest, operation and maintenance costs, or profits. Its proponents hold that these factors tend to balance each other and that since operation and maintenance, as well as the useful life, must be estimated there is little reason for attempting to use a more complex formula.

The Matheson Formula. This method assumes that the annual cost of depreciation is a fixed percentage of the salvage value at the beginning of the year. The ratio of the depreciation in any one year to the salvage value at the beginning of that year is constant throughout the life of the structure and is designated by k. Thus, depreciation during the first year

$$d_1 = Ck \tag{26}$$

Depreciation during the Ath year

$$d_A = (C_{A-1})k \tag{27}$$

Salvage value at age L years

$$C_L = C(1 - k)^L \tag{28}$$

Salvage value at age A years

$$C_A = C(1 - k)^A = C\left(\frac{C_L}{C}\right)^{\frac{A}{L}} \tag{29}$$

Rate of depreciation

$$k = 1 - \sqrt[A]{\frac{C_A}{C}} = 1 - \sqrt[L]{\frac{C_L}{C}} \tag{30}$$

The Matheson formula, like the straight-line method, is simple to apply. However, it has two serious defects. The annual cost of depreciation is different each year. More serious is the fact that with this formula a structure can never depreciate to zero value. It is used to quite an extent and is often called the *constant percentage method*.

Example: Determine the rate of depreciation and salvage value at the end of the sixth year for a structure that cost $120 when new and has an estimated life of 10 years. Scrap value at the end of its life is $20.

$$k = 1 - \sqrt[10]{\frac{\$20}{\$120}} = 0.1641$$
$$C_6 = \$120(1 - 0.1641)^6 = \$40.94$$

It will be noted that this method of determining salvage value gives a figure approximately $20 less than that found by the straight-line method. The heaviest depreciation costs occur during the first years of a structure's life. Proponents of this formula assert that the results more nearly parallel the actual second-hand sales value than do those obtained by other methods. This is undoubtedly true in the case of such things as automobiles, where new models and style changes are large factors in establishing the salvage value. However, it is not true of most industrial structures and equipment. The important thing is to obtain a measure of the future profits which can be expected.

The Sinking Fund Formula. This formula assumes that a sinking fund is established in which funds will accumulate for replacement purposes. The total depreciation which has taken place up to any given time is assumed to be equal to the accumulated value of the sinking fund at that time. In this manner the invested capital is preserved.

With this formula, if the estimated life, scrap value and interest rate upon the sinking fund are known, a uniform yearly deposit can be computed. This deposit is the annual cost of depreciation. Thus,

$$d = (C - C_L) \frac{1}{s_{\overline{L}|}} \tag{31}$$

$$D_A = (C - C_L) \frac{s_{\overline{A}|}}{s_{\overline{L}|}} \tag{32}$$

$$C_A = C - (C - C_L) \frac{s_{\overline{A}|}}{s_{\overline{L}|}} \tag{33}$$

Example: Using the sinking fund formula, determine the annual cost of depreciation and the salvage value at the end of the sixth year for a structure which cost $120 when new and which has an estimated life of 10 years and scrap value of $20. Interest on all deposits at the rate of 3% per annum.

$$d = (\$120 - \$20) \frac{1}{11.4638793} = \$8.72$$

$$C_6 = \$120 - (\$120 - \$20) \frac{6.46840988}{11.4638793} = \$63.60$$

The sinking fund method is probably used to about the same extent as the Matheson. It has many valuable features. It is relatively simple. The annual cost for depreciation is uniform. Interest is taken into account. The greatest drawback lies in the fact that few businesses ever maintain an actual depreciation sinking fund. The interest rate which could be obtained upon such deposits would be small — probably not over 3%. An active business is constantly in need of working capital, and this capital will earn much more than 3%. It is therefore a reasonable rule that all funds should be kept invested in the business and not remain idle. As a result, a fictitious depreciation fund is used and the actual amounts which have been charged to depreciation are left in the business in the form of assets and a "Reserve for Depreciation" account is used to record these funds. (This is fully explained in the chapter on accounting.)

Using the sinking fund method in the customary procedure, where a "depreciation reserve" is utilized, the business is actually borrowing its own depreciation funds. Therefore, there is no place from which interest on these funds could be obtained except from the business itself. There would be the situation of a business paying itself interest for the use of its own money. To accomplish this the cost of depreciation, equal to the sinking fund deposit, would have to be charged as an operating expense and then interest on the accumulated sinking funds would have to be charged as a financial expense. Such a procedure would accurately account for all expenses but might require considerable explanation to the income tax authorities.

When the funds which have been charged to depreciation are kept invested in the business, it is well to consider whether the net effect from the use of the sinking fund formula differs from that obtained by the use of the more simple straight-line method. All the funds that are accumulated for replacement come from the business. At the end of the life of the structure the total amount accumulated will be the same, being equal to the depreciable value. The actual difference of the amounts in the sinking fund at any time, by the two methods, will be small. It therefore

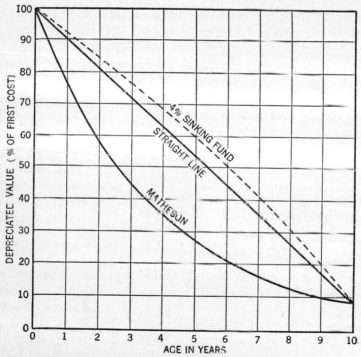

FIGURE 13. Comparison of depreciation formulas.

appears doubtful whether there is any advantage in using the sinking fund method for accounting purposes in most businesses. This fact will be demonstrated later. Where a separate and actual sinking fund is maintained, as in certain public enterprises, the sinking fund method is justified. The relative results obtained by the straight-line, Matheson, and sinking fund methods are illustrated in Figure 13.

The Gillette Formula. Numerous formulas have been derived to give the salvage value of a structure at any age. These are each based upon some hypothesis stating the factors the originator of the formula thought should be considered in determining value. None of these is widely used and many are of doubtful value. Two, however, do have some merit. The first was originated by H. P. Gillette.

This formula is based upon the principle that the owner of a structure is entitled to such a resale price as will enable the buyer to produce each unit at as low a cost as the average unit cost of production during the entire life of the structure.[6] This assumes annual service cost to be on the basis of:

$$
\text{Annual service cost} = w = \begin{cases} \text{Depreciation} \left[(C - C_L) \dfrac{1}{s_{\overline{L}|}} \right] \\ + \\ \text{Fixed charges [Cost } (C) \times \text{ rate } (r)] \\ + \\ \text{Operation cost } [O] \\ + \\ \text{Maintenance cost } [M] \end{cases}
$$

From the above, the unit cost over the L years of life, where U units are produced annually, would be

$$
w_L = \frac{1}{U} \left[\frac{(C - C_L)}{s_{\overline{L}|}} + Cr + O + M \right] \tag{34}
$$

For the buyer at age A, producing U'' units annually, and with fixed charges at the rate r'', operation costs O'' and maintenance M'',

$$
w_{L-A} = \frac{1}{U''} \left[\frac{(C_A - C_L)}{s_{\overline{L-A}|}} + C_A r'' + O'' + M'' \right] \tag{35}
$$

[6] H. P. Gillette, "Handbook of Cost Data."

By the principle of the Gillette formula, $w_L = w_{L-A}$. Thus,

$$\frac{1}{U}\left[\frac{(C-C_L)}{s_{\overline{L}|}} + Cr + O + M\right]$$
$$= \frac{1}{U''}\left[\frac{(C_A - C_L)}{s_{\overline{L-A}|}} + C_A r'' + O'' + M''\right] \quad (36)$$

Solving for C_A, the salvage value at age A years is

$$C_A = \frac{\dfrac{U''}{U}\left[\dfrac{(C-C_L)}{s_{\overline{L}|}} + Cr + O + M\right]s_{\overline{L-A}|} + C_L - (O'' + M'')s_{\overline{L-A}|}}{1 + r''s_{\overline{L-A}|}} \quad (37)$$

This formula makes a correct interpretation of unit costs. However, there is room for argument as to whether the buyer is entitled to the same unit costs as would be obtained throughout the entire life of the structure. The additional difficulty in applying this formula is in the many items which can be obtained only through estimate. It is doubtful if the future charges can be estimated with enough accuracy to justify such a complicated formula. The same difficulty exists in the case of future output.

Present Worth Depreciation Formula. This formula is essentially the same as that given by Marston and Agg in their excellent book on "Engineering Valuation." [7] Several changes have been made in order to give a somewhat more simple formula. It is based upon the principle that value is the present worth of all the future profits to be expected from the structure. Thus,

$$C_A = \binom{\text{Present worth of future}}{\text{operations' returns}} + \binom{\text{Present worth of}}{\text{scrap value}} \quad (38)$$
$$C_A = g''s_{\overline{L-A}|}v^{L-A} + C_L v^{L-A} \quad (39)$$
$$C_A = g''a_{\overline{L-A}|} + C_L v^{L-A} \quad (40)$$

where g'' = Equivalent equal annual profit plus annual depreciation cost for the $L - A$ years,

g'' = An equivalent, equal annual sum, having the same present value as the present value of [all future gross profits] − [all charges except depreciation] for the $L - A$ years.

Equation (40) may be used where it is possible to determine the factor g'' with some degree of certainty. This necessitates know-

[7] A. Marston and T. R. Agg, "Engineering Valuation."

ing pretty well what future income and expenses will be. These can seldom be known with any degree of exactness. About the best that can be done is to make an estimate of how future returns and expenses will compare with the past, basing this estimate upon expert opinion and careful study of all the factors involved. This estimate is expressed in the form of a ratio, being

$$R = \frac{g''}{g}$$

where g corresponds to g'', but for the entire L years of life.
At age zero

$$C = ga_{\overline{L}|} + C_L v^L \tag{41}$$

and

$$g = \frac{C - C_L v^L}{a_{\overline{L}|}} \tag{42}$$

also

$$g'' = Rg = R \frac{(C - C_L v^L)}{a_{\overline{L}|}} \tag{43}$$

Substituting this value of g'' in Equation (40),

$$C_A = R(C - C_L v^L) \frac{a_{\overline{L-A}|}}{a_{\overline{L}|}} + C_L v^{L-A} \tag{44}$$

Equation (44) may be used to obtain the value of C_A when R is estimated.

In using Equation (44), it must be remembered that C is not necessarily the first cost of the structure. If i is the *actual* rate of profit upon the initial investment, then C is the actual first cost. As a rule, however, one desires to determine what price, C_A, should be paid for a structure in order for it to earn a certain rate of return which corresponds to the i used in the calculations. In this case, in order to use Equation (44), one must first determine the value of C corresponding to the desired rate of return i. This is done by solving for C in Equation (44). This computed value of C is then used in the solution of Equation (41).

While the present worth equation is theoretically correct, one can easily see that it is somewhat difficult to apply. It also involves a number of factors that are not usually known with any degree of certainty. The vital factor R must be based upon estimate. As a consequence, it is doubtful if the results obtained by the use of this formula are ordinarily superior to those which may be had through the use of the simple straight-line method. Thus it appears that the more complex depreciation formulas have little actual value except in a few situations. It is not difficult to understand the widespread use of the straight-line method.

Service Output Method. Some companies have attempted to compute the depreciation of equipment upon the basis of its output. When equipment is purchased an estimate is made of the amount of service it will render during its economic life. Depreciation for any period is then charged upon the basis of the service that has been rendered during that period. This method has the advantages of making the unit cost of depreciation constant and giving low depreciation expense during periods of low production. That it is difficult to apply may be understood by realizing that not only the economic life, but also the total amount of service which the equipment will render during this period, must be estimated.

The so-called *machine-hour method* of depreciation is a modification of this method.

What Depreciation Method Should Be Used? With a number of methods of computing depreciation available, one needs to know which to use. Two of the more simple methods will suffice for nearly all cases. But these two are not interchangeable and are by no means sufficient unless used with discretion.

It should be emphasized that no depreciation formula should be used unless modifications are made in the established rates whenever the facts show that the theoretical salvage values are at variance with actual values. Book values of all properties should be examined periodically and adjusted when necessary so as to prevent their being greater than actual value. As the Supreme Court has stated, there can be no substitute for expert opinion which is guided by all the facts. Failure to apply good judgment to depreciation methods can result in only one end — loss of capital. It should be remembered that the prime purpose of considering depreciation is to preserve capital. When adopted methods of depreciation are failing to accomplish this purpose, they should be changed.

When it is necessary to alter depreciation rates or write off capital losses which have occurred because the rates have been in error, the Bureau of Internal Revenue requires a complete explanation of the adjustments. However, if they are founded on fact such claims of loss usually will be allowed.

The necessity for using two methods, the straight-line and the sinking fund, is best shown by an illustration. Consider the case where $100 is invested in a project which will last 10 years and will be worthless at the end of that time. The annual net profit before depreciation charges are deducted (gross profit less all expenses except depreciation) will be $15. The average rate of earning of all capital invested in the business is 7%. It is desired to determine the prospective rate of return and compare this with the actual results, first by the sinking fund method, and second, by straight-line depreciation.

With the conditions as stated the annual depreciation charge by the sinking fund method would be:

$$d = \frac{\$100}{s_{\overline{n}|}}$$

where $n = 10$ years and i, the rate of interest, would be 7% since the depreciation funds could be invested in the business and earn the same return as other capital. Thus,

$$d = \frac{\$100}{13.8} = \$7.24$$

The indicated rate of return on the investment would therefore be

$$\text{Rate of return} = \frac{\$15 - \$7.24}{\$100} \times 100 = 7.76\%$$

The actual resulting profits by use of the sinking fund method are shown in Table 8. Column 2 shows the annual profit before the depreciation charge is deducted. The uniform annual depreciation charge of $7.24 is shown in Column 3. Column 4 shows the annual profit from operation of the investment to be $7.76.

Since funds invested in the company earn an average return of 7% per annum, the amounts deposited in the sinking fund are invested in the business and therefore earn a profit at the rate of 7%. The amount in the sinking fund at the beginning of each

TABLE 8. EFFECT OF USING THE SINKING FUND METHOD
OF COMPUTING DEPRECIATION

(1)	(2)	(3)	(4)	(5)	(6)	(7)	(8)
Year	Profit before deduction for depreciation	Depr. charge	Operating profit, (2) − (3)	Depr. funds at beginning of year	Profit earned by and paid to depr. fund	Total profit, (4)	Worth at end of tenth year, (7) × (1+i)^n
1	$15	$7.24	$7.76	——	——	$ 7.76	$ 14.27
2	15	7.24	7.76	$ 7.24	$0.51	7.76	13.33
3	15	7.24	7.76	14.99	1.05	7.76	12.46
4	15	7.24	7.76	23.28	1.63	7.76	11.65
5	15	7.24	7.76	32.15	2.25	7.76	10.88
6	15	7.24	7.76	41.64	2.91	7.76	10.17
7	15	7.24	7.76	51.79	3.63	7.76	9.51
8	15	7.24	7.76	62.66	4.39	7.76	8.88
9	15	7.24	7.76	74.29	5.20	7.76	8.30
10	15	7.24	7.76	86.73	6.07	7.76	7.76
				100.04		$77.60	$107.21

year will earn profit during that year. The profit earned by the
sinking fund must be paid into the sinking fund since it belongs
to the fund and helps toward the accumulation of the amount
needed for replacement at the end of the life of the investment.
This profit corresponds to the interest earned by an ordinary
sinking fund. Only by this process is the capital maintained.

Column 5 shows the amount in the depreciation fund at the
beginning of each year. This, for the beginning of any year, is
equal to the amount available at the beginning of the previous
year, plus the deposit made at the end of that year, plus the
interest earned during that year. Column 6 indicates the interest
earned by the invested amounts in the sinking fund. These earnings are paid into the sinking fund. Column 7 shows the total
profit available to the owners of the business, being the same as
Column 4. At the end of 10 years these profits have amounted to
$77.76 or an average return of 7.76% on the $100 capital which
has been invested. It is thus noted that the actual return agrees
with the estimated value.

Now consider the same example, this time using the straight-
line depreciation method. The annual charge for depreciation
would be

$$d = \frac{\$100}{10} = \$10$$

The estimated profit would be

$$\text{Rate of return} = \frac{\$15 - \$10}{\$100} \times 100 = 5\%$$

Next examine Table 9 which shows the actual amounts which would be involved after the investment had been made. Column 2 gives the annual profit before deduction of depreciation charges. The annual depreciation charge is shown in Column 3. Column 4 shows the operating profit which remains after depreciation is deducted.

TABLE 9. EFFECT OF USING THE STRAIGHT–LINE METHOD
OF COMPUTING DEPRECIATION

(1) Year	(2) Profit before deduction for depreciation	(3) Depr. charge	(4) Operating profit, (2)−(3)	(5) Depr. fund at beginning of year	(6) Profit from depr. fund paid to owners	(7) Total profit, (4)+(6)	(8) Worth at end of 10 years, (7)×(1+i)^n
1	$15	$10	$5	—	—	$ 5.00	$ 9.19
2	15	10	5	$ 10	$0.70	5.70	9.79
3	15	10	5	20	1.40	6.40	10.28
4	15	10	5	30	2.10	7.10	10.66
5	15	10	5	40	2.80	7.80	10.94
6	15	10	5	50	3.50	8.50	11.14
7	15	10	5	60	4.20	9.20	11.27
8	15	10	5	70	4.90	9.90	11.33
9	15	10	5	80	5.60	10.60	11.34
10	15	10	5	90	6.30	11.30	11.30
				100		$81.50	$107.24

In the ordinary use of straight-line depreciation in a business, the amounts charged for depreciation are not put aside into a fund but are left in the company in the form of working capital or other assets.[8] A Reserve account is established to indicate the claim of this depreciation reserve upon some of the assets. With the depreciation funds left in the business in this manner, they act like any other capital funds and earn annual returns at the same rate. When a Reserve for Depreciation of this type is used in connection with straight-line depreciation methods, the earnings of the funds which have been charged for depreciation are available and paid to the owners as a portion of the profits of the

[8] See chapter on accounting for a more complete explanation of this procedure.

business. Thus Column 6 indicates the profits which are earned by the depreciation funds. Column 7 then shows the total profits which the owner receives from the business, being the summation of Columns 4 and 6. During the 10-year period, these would amount to $81.50.

A comparison of the totals of the "Total Profit" columns in the two tables indicates that there is some apparent discrepancy between the two methods of depreciation. This is clarified by examining Column 8 in each table. In this column the profits of the various years have been reduced to a common time — the end of the tenth year — by multiplying by the proper interest factor, $(1 + i)^n$. The totals of these two columns are seen to be identical within the accuracy of slide rule computations. Thus one may conclude that from the accounting viewpoint the two methods of depreciation are equivalent. The only possibility of difference occurs when the total accumulated profits are compared at some intermediate point between the beginning and end of the life of the investment. This difference at any time is so small that it may be neglected. One may then say that either method is satisfactory for accounting purposes. Since the straight-line method is the simpler, it is natural that it should be used for accounting purposes.

When one compares the predicted rates of return obtained by the two methods he concludes that they are far from equivalent. The totals of Column 8 in each table were the same. Therefore, the average earnings in Table 9, where straight-line depreciation was used, must have been the same as in Table 8. This indicates that the predicted rate of return based upon straight-line depreciation was wrong. The straight-line method fails to account for the earnings of the accumulated depreciation funds. Therefore, it always gives a predicted rate of return that is lower than the actual rate will be. Thus one may conclude that for accounting purposes either straight-line or sinking fund methods may be used without appreciable error. *For engineering estimates, however, the sinking fund method should be used in order to obtain a true answer.*

Depletion. When limited natural resources are being consumed, the term "depletion" is often used to indicate the decrease in value which has occurred. The term is commonly used in connection with mining properties. In any given parcel of mining property there is a definite quantity of ore available. As some of the ore is mined and sold, the reserve of ore shrinks and the value of the property normally diminishes. Thus a portion of the property is sold with each ton of ore that is mined and sold. When the entire deposit of ore has been mined, the property will be of little or no value. Unless provision is made to recover the invested capital as the property is sold, the net result will be loss of capital. This is prevented by charging each ton of product with the depletion which it has caused.

Valuation. The engineer is frequently called upon to decide upon the value of engineering properties. An adequate discussion of the methods used to arrive at the correct value of any property would require at least a good sized volume. It is obviously beyond the scope of this book. However, a few of the principles involved will be considered since they are so intimately connected with the subject of depreciation.

The reasons for determining the value of property vary. Similarly, a valuation that is correct for one need may not be correct for another. The need for determining the value of property often occurs when a private buyer is purchasing the property from a private owner. Again, the value of property may need to be known to serve as a tax base. When a municipality wishes to purchase a privately owned utility plant the value must be decided upon. In establishing utility rates the regulating bodies must arrive at a fair value of the property which is used to render the service. If a company examines the book value of its property at periodic intervals in order to determine whether the established depreciation rates are adequate, it must have some method of estimating the correct value of the property.

It would often be desirable to determine the present worth of the future profits which will accrue from ownership and use this figure as the value of the property. Such a determination, however, usually presents many difficulties. The future is usually most uncertain. In addition some rate of interest must be used in the calculations, and the choice of this interest rate will affect the final value.

In actual practice the valuation process often attempts to

determine how much would have to be spent to acquire a plant or property which under similar conditions would render the same future service as the property under consideration. In other words, value is often taken as the amount that would have to be spent to acquire a plant which would in the future render an equal amount of service at no greater unit cost. Some of the methods which are used to determine value in this manner are natural results of the various means by which such a fictitious equivalent plant might be obtained.

Historical Cost Less Depreciation. The first method which might be used is sometimes called *historical cost less depreciation*. In arriving at value by this method one considers the actual expenses which have been incurred in obtaining the property being valued. This historical cost is then reduced by the amount of depreciation that appears to have occurred. This depreciation must be considered in terms of the ability of the remaining property to render service. The depreciated historical cost is then taken as the true value.

It is apparent that the historical cost method neglects many factors. For example, no consideration is given to advance in technological methods which have occurred since the property was acquired. It is obvious that if an equivalent plant could be built, using modern methods and equipment, which would render the future service at much less unit cost, the existing plant could never be worth more than the more modern plant, regardless of how much might have been expended in acquiring the old plant.

The historical cost method also gives no consideration to changes in price levels which have taken place since the time of original construction. Drastic changes in price have sometimes made it possible to build a new plant at much less cost than was required for the old plant. It is apparent that such a factor should not be neglected in determining value.

Another serious objection to the historical cost method is that no consideration is given to the fact that the owners may have made unwise decisions and investments in the old property. Such a condition means that unwise expenditure in acquiring the property adds to its second-hand value. Such a condition, of course, is absurd.

Reproduction Cost New Less Depreciation. In order to overcome the weaknesses of the historical cost method, the fictitious equivalent plant or property is usually assumed to be obtained by building it by the most modern methods, according to most efficient design. This theoretical plant is then depreciated until it would be capable of rendering only the same amount of future service as the existing plant. This method is often called *reproduction cost new less depreciation*. In this manner technological progress and changes in price level are given consideration.

The results of this method are of obvious advantage to the seller of industrial property when price levels have risen; consequently it gained considerable favor during the period of 1900–1930. The method, however, does not consider whether the existing property is of correct size for actual future demand or whether it is the result of unwise investment policy. The question also remains of whether or not the owners should be given full advantage of increases in price levels which may have occurred.

The Prudent Investment Theory. Numerous persons believe that all one should be entitled to receive for any industrial property is the total that was "prudently" invested in the property, less the depreciation which has taken place. It is apparent that prospective profits do not enter into value determinations when this theory is applied. The Constitution and the Supreme Court of the United States have protected property *value* rather than actual *investment*. However, some regulating bodies appear to be swinging toward the prudent investment principle when establishing value for rate bases. The general argument behind such a trend is that the public should not pay more for a service than a fair return upon what has been prudently invested to provide this service. Where an enterprise is dependent upon the favor of the public for its existence and profits, the prudent investment theory has considerable merit. It will not be surprising if this theory gains wider favor among regulating bodies, and even the courts.[9]

---

[9] It is interesting to note that most advocates of the prudent investment principle do not discuss the application of this theory to a situation where despite the most prudent investment property values have declined. Thus the owner is apparently expected to stand any decline in value which may have occurred, despite his greatest care and honesty, but is not allowed to profit by increases in value.

It is apparent that regardless of which theory of valuation is applied a great amount of judgment must be exercised in determining what depreciation has taken place, or just what the ability of the property to render service may be. It is thus easy to understand why the Supreme Court has held that all the factors and the testimony of competent experts must be considered.

Supreme Court Decisions. Since valuation figures are often involved in legal litigation, it is well to examine briefly some of the decisions of the Supreme Court regarding these matters.

Smyth vs. Ames, 1898, 18 Sup. Ct. Rep. 418. In this early case involving valuation, the Supreme Court established a number of principles which have stood as the basis for many later decisions. These were:

1. "What a company is entitled to ask is a fair return upon the value of that which it employs for the public convenience."
2. "The public is entitled to demand . . . that no more be exacted from it . . . than the services rendered . . . are reasonably worth."
3. "In order to ascertain the fair value [all factors] are . . . matters for consideration, and are to be given such weight as may be just and right in each case."

These principles have been referred to in many cases where the court has decided what value should be assigned to property which is involved in rate cases.

City of Knoxville vs. Knoxville Water Co., 1909, 29 Sup. Ct. Rep. 148. In this case the court held that accrued depreciation must be subtracted in determining value and that the owners have a right to fair prices which will allow a fair net return after the cost of depreciation has been deducted.

Minnesota Rate Cases, 1913, 230 U. S. 352. The court denied the use of fixed formulas for determining value in the following statement: "The ascertainment of . . . value is not controlled by artificial rules. It is not a matter of formulas, but there must be a reasonable judgment having its basis in a proper consideration of all relevant facts."

McCardle et al. vs. Indianapolis Water Co., 1926, 47 Sup. Ct. Rep. 144. "It is well established that values of utility's properties fluctuate, and that the owners must bear the decline and are entitled to the increase. . . . But this does not mean that the original cost or the present cost or some figure arbitrarily chosen between these two is to be taken as the measure. The weight to be given to such cost figures and other items or classes of business is to be determined by the facts of the case involved."

Los Angeles Gas and Electric Corp. vs. Railroad Commission of California et al., 1933, 53 Sup. Ct. Rep. 637. "This court has further declared that, in order to determine present value, the cost of reproducing the property is a relevant fact which should have appropriate consideration."

All of these decisions may be summed up in two conclusions:

1. There is no fixed method of determining depreciation and value.

2. In determining value all factors must be considered. Among these are:

    a. First cost.

    b. Condition of the structure.

    c. Actual depreciation.

    d. Increase or decrease of price levels.

Intangible Values. In determining the value of industrial property or equipment four intangible items are often encountered. The first of these is *good will*. This item arises out of the public or trade favor which an enterprise may have earned through the service it has rendered. This may be of very real value to the business. In the sale of a structure good will is a legitimate item and is of value to the buyer. In establishing value for rate setting, however, little, if any, consideration is given to this item. In this case good will must have come through the business done with the consumers. The courts do not allow good will to be included so that the consumers must pay the utility a profit upon something which they have bestowed upon the business.

The second intangible item is value of *franchises*. This is also granted to the utility by the consumers. Therefore it cannot be considered in rate cases. Where value is being determined for sale purposes franchises have a real value to the buyer and may be considered.

The fact that an enterprise which is actually doing business is worth more than a similar one which possesses the same physical assets but is not operating is recognized in *going value*. Money must be spent in getting the business in an operating condition. The courts recognize this fact and allow this item to be included in all valuation work. As a rule, from 8 to 15% of the value of the assets is allowed for going value.

The fourth intangible is *organization cost*. Some money must be spent in organizing almost any business and arranging for its financing and building. These are legitimate expenses and are recognized as such by the courts.

Conclusion. The primary purpose of depreciation is to provide for recovery of capital that has been invested in physical property. It is a cost of production wherever this production causes the property to decline in value. Indirectly it provides a method of providing capital for replacement of depreciated equipment.

Since most businesses are not directly affected by Supreme Court decisions as to their methods of determining depreciation, a simple formula, which gives results that are as accurate as the estimated values used, is desirable. The straight-line formula meets this need in so far as accounting is concerned and is favored by the income tax authorities. The usefulness and need of more complicated methods is questionable except in making estimates of future profits. For this type of work it is desirable that the sinking fund method be used in order to give satisfactory results. If only two or three years are involved in the estimate, however, the error will be so small that the straight-line method may be used.

The functional element is so great in modern industrial depreciation that it would seem advisable to devote considerable attention to making certain that depreciation methods provide adequately for this factor. Adequate, yet reasonable, depreciation charges are of more importance than refined methods based upon debatable hypotheses. Regardless of what method is used, it is important that the results be examined periodically so that the computed values will not be at variance with obvious facts. When the theoretical values are found to be different from actual values, the theoretical figures should be adjusted. Failure to do this can result only in trouble.

The process of valuation is usually an attempt either to make an estimate of the present value of the future profits which will be obtained through ownership of a property or to determine what would have to be spent to obtain a property capable of rendering at least as efficiently the same future service as the property being valued. While the former is probably the correct process from a theoretical viewpoint, the latter is the process which is encountered in most valuation work.

While all factors should be considered in arriving at a correct value, the weight to be given to each cannot be arbitrarily established. What is just and proper in one case may be unjust and improper in another. All must be decided in the light of the circumstances and in accordance with good judgment.

REFERENCES

Gillette, H. P.: "Handbook of Construction Cost," Gillette Publishing Company, Chicago, 1922.

Kurtz, E. B.: "The Science of Valuation and Depreciation," The Ronald Press Company, New York, 1937.

Marston, A., and T. R. Agg: "Engineering Valuation," McGraw-Hill Book Company, Inc., New York, 1936.

Rautenstrauch, Walter: "The Economics of Business Enterprise," John Wiley & Sons, Inc., New York, 1939.

PROBLEMS

74. Define value.
75. What factors make it difficult to determine the exact value of a structure?
76. Is the cost of construction always a good measure of the real value of a new structure?
77. Name three articles for which the Matheson method of determining salvage values might give results which would be closer to the actual second-hand value than would be obtained by the sinking fund method.
78. A machine is purchased for $400. It is estimated that its useful life will be six years. The scrap value at the end of its life will be $40. (a) What will be the annual cost of depreciation, computed by the straight-line method? (b) What will be the salvage value at the end of four years?
79. A structure cost $22,000 and has been in existence for three years. Its estimated life at the time of erection was 12 years. What is the book value of the structure if a 4% sinking fund has been used for depreciation and the scrap value is estimated to be zero?
80. (a) Calculate the salvage value of an automobile which costs $1,000 when new and will have a scrap value of $240 at the end of its seventh year. Use the Matheson formula.
    (b) Compare the computed values with those given in Line A of Table 18.

81. What will be the depreciation cost for the first year if a $5,000 investment is to be depreciated in eight years by use of the Matheson formula? Assume the scrap value to be $500.

82. The Johnston Company requires that all investments in new equipment must be written off in four years. If a new machine costing $2,000 is estimated to have a life of six years, what would be this company's annual charge for depreciation on this piece of equipment? Use straight-line depreciation.

83. How much could one afford to pay for an oil well which would yield a return of $20,000 the first year, and $5,000 less each succeeding year until exhausted, if he wished an 8% return on his invested capital?

84. Twelve years ago the Coast Power Company purchased a synchronous condenser for $50,000. At the time of purchase it was estimated that the life of the machine would be 20 years and a straight-line depreciation reserve has been provided on that basis. The company now wishes to replace the old machine with a hydrogen-cooled condenser of modern design. It can sell the old condenser for $5,000. The new machine will cost $60,000. How much new capital will be required to make the purchase?

Chapter VIII

THE RELATIONSHIP OF ACCOUNTING TO ECONOMY STUDIES

Economy studies are ordinarily made before capital is invested. These studies are made so that capital will be used effectively. After money has been invested in an enterprise some method has to be used to determine how productive the investment has been. Accounting is the process which records the results of expenditure of capital so that the effectiveness of the investment can be determined. It is thus apparent that economy studies and accounting have quite different purposes. The former has a forward-looking viewpoint while the latter is, in the main, concerned with past events.

It may appear at first thought that because of the apparent difference in the viewpoints of economy studies and accounting the engineer does not need to concern himself with accounting. This is not, however, the case. It is true that the engineer does not need to concern himself with much of the detail of accounting in order to make satisfactory economy studies. However, a knowledge and understanding of the important fundamentals upon which accounting practice is based, together with an acquaintance with a few of those accounting details which are closely related to economy studies, will be found to be a real help to the engineer.[1]

The very fact that economy studies and accounting are concerned with the same factor, capital, prevents their being entirely divorced. Each has a definite place in the ordinary course of business. If an economy study brings about the investment of

---

[1] It is doubtful if the engineer who is making many economy studies could gain a thorough mastery of any other subject that would be of more value to him than accounting.

capital, accounting will be used to reveal to the owners of that capital the history and efficiency of the investment. Ultimately the owners of the capital will judge the effectiveness of an invest- ment by reference to accounting figures and statements. Since economy studies attempt to bring about the best utilization of capital, which accounting is to record, the two have considerable in common.

Many of the detailed figures of accounting practice will not be used, or even usable, in economy studies. Some figures and items, however, will be used directly or indirectly when economy studies are made. When this is the case it is desirable that the items be handled correctly by both the accountant and the engineer in the manner that is generally understood by the entire business world. In this way understanding and harmony will be pro- moted. When this is done the final accounting of an investment will tend to be a reflection of the results of the economy study that brought about the investment.

The Purpose of Accounting. Accounting has as its purpose the recording of all transactions that affect any investment of capital so that at any time the results of the investment may be deter- mined. To accomplish this it is necessary to utilize various kinds of books and printed forms in which all of the transactions may be recorded. Thus whenever any financial transaction occurs it is recorded in one or more of the accounting books. If all of the events that affect an investment are recorded, a summarizing of these makes it possible to determine what has resulted. Fairly well-standardized procedure has resulted from years of account- ing practice by which the recording and summarizing of financial transactions is done.

The Fundamental Terms of Accounting. Since accounting deals with monetary values which are owned or used by a person or business, the equation

$$\text{Assets} = \text{Equities} \qquad (45)$$

is a simple expression of the fundamental relationship of account- ing. *Assets* are defined as things of value. This definition is extremely broad — as it must be since it must include everything of commercial worth. *Equity* is the claim of anyone to ownership.

If one buys a $1,000 automobile but pays the dealer only $500, leaving a balance of $500 due, both the buyer and the dealer have an equity in the car. Equity, then, may be distributed among numerous persons. The equity of the person who normally possesses the asset is commonly known as *ownership*. The claims of others than the owners upon the assets are designated as *liabilities*. These liabilities would have to be paid by the owners in order for them to have complete title to all of the assets. Because the equities are usually divided in the manner which has just been mentioned, Equation (45) is often written in the following form:

$$\text{Assets} = \text{Liabilities} + \text{Ownership} \qquad (46)$$

This is often considered to be the fundamental equation of accounting. The item "Ownership" is sometimes referred to as "*Proprietorship*."

Liabilities may take many forms but usually are grouped into two classes. If the person who purchased the car mentioned in the preceding paragraph had agreed to pay the dealer the remaining $500 in 30 days, this claim upon the automobile would be said to be a *current liability*. This class of liabilities represents claims against the owners which must be paid in the near future. There is no exact rule as to how immediate the claim must be to be classed as a current liability. In general practice those claims which must be paid during the next accounting period (usually one year) are classed as current liabilities. The exact classification will vary from one business to another.

Liabilities that are not due for payment until sometime more than one year distant are usually listed as *fixed liabilities*. These are usually in the form of bonds or long-term notes, for which some refunding provision is being made.

A third type of liability is *prepaid income*. This type of liability arises when a business receives payment for a service before it actually renders the service. In this case the assets of the company have been increased through receipt of money. The person who paid this money is entitled to receive future services and therefore has a claim against the company until these services are fully rendered.

Assets may also be divided into several different classes. A business will possess cash and numerous other items which will be converted into cash or salable goods in the normal process of business during the next accounting period. Such items of value are classed as *current assets*. These will include cash, accounts receivable during the next period, raw materials and inventories of finished goods which will be sold.

Those assets which will not be converted into cash, or sold or be converted into salable form during the coming accounting period are *fixed assets*. These include the buildings, land, machinery, furniture and fixtures which are utilized in producing the goods or services that are to be offered for sale. The term "fixed" does not, however, necessarily mean fixed as to position or location. A railroad locomotive is a fixed asset but is not stationary.

A third type of asset corresponds to the third type of liability which was mentioned and is *deferred charges*. In this case a charge, or expense, has been paid before any benefit has been received therefrom. An example is prepaid insurance. It is customary to pay insurance premiums in advance. Thus, when a year's premium is paid at the beginning of the year the purchaser is entitled to receive protection during the year to follow. Until he has received all of this protection the unused portion is of value to him and is therefore an asset.

Proprietorship may also exist in several forms. In the case of a single owner it is in the capital account of Mr. X. For a partnership, X and Y will each have capital accounts. In a corporation the shares of common and preferred stock represent ownership. If the business has earned profits these are shown as *Undeclared Dividends* or as *Surplus* until they are distributed to the owners or transferred to their capital accounts as additions to their investment in the business.

The Balance Sheet. One of the most important things to any business is the relationship between its assets, liabilities and ownership at a particular time. This is the principal reason for accounting. If Equation (46) is rewritten in the following form:

$$\text{Assets} - \text{Liabilities} = \text{Ownership} \qquad (47)$$

a convenient method is indicated for determining the amount of ownership.

For example, if Henry Smith wishes to determine just what his ownership or *net worth* is, he might do it in the following manner. On one sheet of paper he makes a list of all his possessions of value as shown in Figure 14. On another piece of paper

POSSESSIONS OF HENRY SMITH

1.	Cash	$ 78.00
2.	Government bond	100.00
3.	Automobile	900.00
4.	Furniture	600.00
	Total	$1,678.00

FIGURE 14. Assets of Henry Smith.

he lists all the amounts he owes to other people. This list, shown in Figure 15, constitutes his liabilities. He now can perform the

WHAT HENRY SMITH OWES

5.	Borrowed from John Jones	$ 2.00
6.	Grocery bill	6.00
7.	Balance due on car	250.00
	Total	$258.00

Excess of Possessions over Debts

8.	Ownership (net worth)	$1,420.00

FIGURE 15. Liabilities and ownership of Henry Smith.

operation which was indicated in Equation (47) and determine his net worth. This he does as follows:

Assets	$1,678.00
Less Liabilities	258.00
Ownership	$1,420.00

The excess of assets over liabilities is the claim Henry Smith has on the assets he possesses, or is his net worth or ownership. He records this amount on the second sheet of paper as shown in Figure 15.

These two sheets of figures show the relationship between Henry Smith's assets, liabilities and ownership at one particular time. It is customary to list all of these items on one page, placing the assets on the left-hand half of the page and the liabilities and ownership on the right half. In this form it is known as a *balance sheet*, probably deriving this name from the fact that the totals of the items listed on each half of the sheet are the same. This form of balance sheet for Henry Smith is shown in Figure 16.

BALANCE SHEET

Henry Smith

March 10, 1939

Assets			Liabilities		
Cash		$ 78.00	Borrowed from		
Government bond		100.00	John Jones	$ 2.00	
Automobile		900.00	Grocery bill	6.00	
Furniture		600.00	Due on car	250.00	
			Total liabilities		$ 258.00
			Ownership		1,420.00
		$1,678.00			$1,678.00

FIGURE 16. Balance sheet for Henry Smith.

BALANCE SHEET

Jameson Manufacturing Co.

December 31, 1939

Current Assets			Current Liabilities		
Cash	$ 68,352.12		Accounts		
Government Bonds	10,000.00		Payable	$ 15,287.52	
Accounts Receivable	21,550.00		Notes Payable	1,200.00	
Inventory	37,250.00		Total		$ 16,487.52
Total		$137,152.12	Fixed Liabilities		
Fixed Assets			7% Bonds	$ 15,000.00	15,000.00
Factory			Ownership		
Buildings	$100,000.00		Preferred Stock	$ 25,000.00	
Trucks	3,852.00		Common Stock	150,000.00	
Machinery	87,350.00		Total		$175,000.00
	$191,202.00		Surplus	$ 90,000.00	90,000.00
Less Reserve for Depreciation	32,400.00				
Total		$158,802.00			
Prepaid Charges					
Insurance	$ 462.40				
Taxes	71.00				
Total		533.40			
		$296,487.52			$296,487.52

FIGURE 17. Balance sheet for a moderate sized business.

Henry Smith's balance sheet showed the relationship between his assets, liabilities and ownership at one time, in this case March 10, 1939. If he should spend 50 cents for a movie the relationship would be changed, and a new balance sheet would be required to show the new condition of his finances. This is one of the fundamental facts about a balance sheet — it shows the relationship between the assets, liabilities and ownership at one specified time. Any additional transaction renders the balance sheet obsolete.

Since the balance sheet for Henry Smith included only a few items, the statement was very simple. In a large business there are a great number of assets and liabilities, and the balance sheet must be more complicated. A balance sheet of a medium-sized

CONDENSED STATEMENT OF CONDITION, JUNE 30, 1938

Bank of America National Trust and Savings Association

Resources		
Cash in Vault and in Federal Reserve Bank		$ 143,690,185.82
Due from Banks		82,101,490.50
Securities of the United States Government and Federal Agencies		440,200,387.05
State, County and Municipal Bonds		92,807,218.51
Other Bonds and Securities		42,361,927.91
Stock in Federal Reserve Bank		2,580,000.00
Loans and Discounts		629,125,363.97
Accrued Interest and Accounts Receivable		2,413,156.22
Bank Premises, Furniture, Fixtures and Safe Deposit Vaults		35,816,479.84
Other Real Estate Owned		2,734,226.05
Customers' Liability on Account of Letters of Credit, Acceptances and Endorsed Bills		23,723,128.20
Other Resources		974,161.64
Total Resources		$1,498,527,625.71
Liabilities		
Capital		$ 50,000,000.00
Surplus		40,000,000.00
Undivided Profits		22,231,747.90
Reserves		4,605,784.53
Liability for Letters of Credit and as Acceptor, Endorser or Maker on Acceptances and Foreign Bills		23,911,383.35
Deposits:		
Commercial	$565,301,767.71	
Savings	792,476,942.22	
Total Deposits		1,357,778,709.93
Total Liabilities		$1,498,527,625.71

FIGURE 18. Balance sheet for a large bank, with assets and liabilities listed in a single column.

business is shown in Figure 17. This balance sheet is in the most common form. Assets and liabilities are divided into several groups to give greater clarity. The totals of each group are given so that comparisons of the different groups may be readily made.

Balance sheets are sometimes arranged in other forms than that shown in Figure 17. One of these is illustrated in Figure 18. In Figure 19 the balance sheet of the Mammoth Holding Company is shown. Here the figures for two dates are given so that a comparison between values for the two dates may be made with facility. Such a statement is known as a "comparative balance sheet."

Since a balance sheet is designed to state information about the financial condition of a business, it is important that the information it contains shall be accurate and present a true picture. It is just as important that the information be presented in a simple, concise form that may be understood by the persons who are going to make use of the statement. Preparation of a balance sheet in such a form that it will mislead the user as to the financial condition of the business is little different from the use of false figures in the statement. The present trend is toward simplified financial statements. Such a trend should be encouraged by everyone who has any responsibility for the making of such statements.

Recording Transactions Which Change the Balance Sheet. The balance sheet shows the relationship between Assets, Liabilities and Ownership. It thus enables one to determine the exact status of his investment of capital at a particular time. It does not, however, provide a means of recording the events which have brought about the relationship it shows.

It would obviously be impracticable, if not impossible, to make a new balance sheet for a large enterprise each time any transaction took place. Fortunately, such a procedure is not necessary. A business is interested in having a record of all of its transactions and keeping these records in such a form that information for a balance sheet may be obtained whenever desired. In order to do this the various items which appear on the balance sheet, such as Cash, Accounts Receivable, Accounts Payable,

MAMMOTH HOLDING COMPANY
Comparative Balance Sheet

	December 31, 1937	December 31, 1936
Assets		
Current Assets:		
Cash in Banks — On Demand	$ 11,768,103	$ 9,372,897
United States Gov't Securities (1)	2,920,083	2,275,000
Misc. Short Term Securities	3,301,163	2,292,764
Accounts Receivable	100	101
Accrued Interest Receivable	672,248	670,140
Total Current Assets	$ 18,661,697	$ 14,610,902
Investments:		
Notes Receivable from:		
A & B Power Co., Inc. (2)	$ 5,700,000	$ 6,700,000
A & B Power Co., Inc. (3)	35,000,000	35,000,000
Big Gas Corp.	28,925,000	28,925,000
Bonds:		
South Country Utility Co. 6%	1,040,000	1,160,000
Middle Power & Light Co. 4¾%	5,037,120	5,037,120
Miscellaneous (4)	4,206,325	4,494,470
Red Gas Service Co. 6% Debentures due July 1, 1953 (5)	25,000,000	25,000,000
Island Electric Co. 6% Debentures due May 1, 1948 (6)	20,000,000	20,000,000
Stocks and Option Warrants (7)	408,809,052	408,809,012
Stocks of Wholly Owned Subsidiaries	2,600,000	2,610,000
Total Investments	$536,317,497	$537,735,602
Deferred Charges	810,530	847,976
Total Assets	$555,789,724	$553,194,480
Liabilities		
Current Liabilities:		
Accounts Payable	$ 42,494	$ 16,349
Dividends Declared on Preferred Stocks	2,108,482	2,108,482
Taxes Accrued	2,202,577	1,967,373
Total Current Liabilities	$ 4,353,553	$ 4,092,204
Capital Stock (8)	171,901,234	171,901,234
Reserves (Appropriated from Capital Surplus)	4,901,740	4,803,301
Surplus:		
Capital Surplus	$314,165,749	$314,134,939
Earned Surplus	60,467,448	58,262,802
Total Surplus	374,633,197	372,397,741
Total Liabilities	$555,789,724	$553,194,480

NOTES:

1. Valuation at Market Quotations of United States Government Securities owned at December 31, 1937, was at that date $2,951,600 and of those owned at December 31, 1936, was at that date $2,329,000.
2. By agreement payable simultaneously with the bank loans of A and B Power Company, Inc., in amount of $22,800,000, which have been extended to October 26, 1939.
3. Presently subordinated to other indebtedness of A and B Power Company, Inc., consisting of bank loans of $22,800,000, the $5,700,000 similar debt due this Company and Debentures of $50,000,000 until the bank loans are paid.
4. Valuation at Market Quotations of Miscellaneous Bonds owned at December 31, 1937, was at that date $5,212,700 and of those owned at December 31, 1936, was at that date $6,120,000.
5. Payment of principal and interest assumed by United Gas Corporation.
6. The interest rate on Island Electric Company 6% Debentures was reduced, by agreement, for the period from May 1, 1935, to October 31, 1937, to a rate of 4% per annum and for the period from November 1, 1937, to October 31, 1939, to a rate of 4½% per annum.
7. Valuation at Market Quotations of Stocks and Option Warrants owned at December 31, 1937, was at that date $109,693,700 and of those owned at December 31, 1936, was at that date $218,396,000.
8. Represented by:

	Shares Authorized	Shares Outstanding	
	Dec. 31, 1937	Dec. 31, 1937	Dec. 31, 1936
$5 Preferred Stock	1,000,000	300,000	300,000
$6 Preferred Stock	2,500,000	1,155,655	1,155,655
Common Stock and Scrip ($5 Par Value)	20,000,000	5,267,147	5,267,147

(All Preferred Stock has no par value — stated value $100 a share; entitled upon Liquidation to $100 a share and Accumulated Dividends.)

FIGURE 19. Comparative balance sheet for Mammoth Holding Company.

Inventory, etc., are recorded as separate accounts. These are known as *Ledger Accounts*. With the records of the transactions kept in these ledger accounts, the balance sheet then represents a summation of these ledger accounts at any stated time. A common form of ledger sheet, with a few entries, is shown in Figure 20.

Effect of Business Transactions upon Ledger Accounts. In order to keep a satisfactory record of business transactions it is necessary to know how these transactions affect the various ledger accounts. The normal transactions of a business, which must be recorded, are essentially of three types:

1. Those involving a relationship with persons outside the business. These would involve purchases, sales, payments and collections.

MANUFACTURING EXPENSE

A	B	C	D		E		F	G	H	I		J	
1940							1940						
Jan.	1	Balance	J	2	20,000	00	Apr.	5		J	14	600	00
Mar.	14		J	10	1,200	00							

Column A: Month for debit entries.
"   B: Date for debit entries.
"   C: Description of debit entries, if necessary.
"   D: Source of entry.
"   E: Amount of debit entries.
"   F: Month for credit entries.
"   G: Date for credit entries.
"   H: Description of credit entries, if necessary.
"   I: Source of entry.
"   J: Amount of credit entry.

FIGURE 20.   Typical ledger sheet arrangement.

2. Those which represent internal changes within the business. These would result from ordinary business operations and the passage of time. Use of materials and depreciation are such transactions.

3. *Book* transactions, which are transfers within the account books in order to summarize or draw conclusions from the accounts.

Since all ledger accounts are essentially of three types: assets, liabilities or ownership, the effect of business transactions will be a change in assets, liabilities or ownership. Considering the fundamental accounting equation

$$\text{Assets} - \text{Liabilities} = \text{Ownership}$$

it is apparent that if only one factor in this equation is changed equality no longer exists, and one side becomes greater than the other. If an entry recording a transaction tends to make the left-hand side of this equation greater than the right-hand side, such an entry is called a *debit* entry. If an entry tends to make the right-hand side of the equation become greater it is called a *credit* entry.[2]

---

[2] The terms "*debit* entry" and "*credit* entry" should never be connected with "debt" and "credit," where credit is used in connection with the credit rating of an individual or firm. There is no connection between the terms. Unfortunately, students often allow the similarity of sound and spelling to cause confusion in determining whether an entry should be a debit or credit.

A little reflection leads to the conclusion that debit entries (tending to make the left-hand side of the equation greater than the right-hand side) could arise in three ways: increases of assets, decreases in liabilities or decreases in ownership. Similarly, credit entries (making the right-hand side of the equation larger) would arise through: decreases in assets, increases in liabilities or increases in ownership. The general rule for determining debit and credit entries is shown in Table 10.

TABLE 10. TRANSACTIONS RECORDED AS DEBIT AND
CREDIT ENTRIES

Debit entries	*Credit entries*
Increases in assets	Decreases in assets
Decreases in liabilities	Increases in liabilities
Decreases in ownership	Increases in ownership

It is customary accounting practice to make all debit entries on the left-hand half of the ordinary ledger page and credit entries on the right-hand half, as shown in Figure 20.

Double Entry Bookkeeping. If the fundamental relationship, Assets − Liabilities = Ownership, is to be maintained at all times, it is apparent that every business transaction must result in at least two entries in the ledger accounts. Since a debit entry tends to unbalance the equation in favor of the left-hand side, a credit entry would be required to restore the balance.

For example, suppose a business bought some equipment by the payment of cash. The acquisition of the equipment would mean an increase in the assets of the business and would therefore be recorded by a debit entry. However, in order to bring about this increase in assets, cash was paid out. This resulted in a decrease in the amount of cash which the business had and would be recorded by a credit entry since it represents a decrease in assets. Similarly, for all transactions it is necessary to make at least one debit and one credit entry to record completely the changes which have occurred in the assets, liabilities or owner-ship. This circumstance gives rise to the term "*double entry bookkeeping*."

It should be recognized that two or more credit entries may be required to balance one debit entry, or vice versa. The basic rule remains, that the sum of the debit entries for any transaction must equal the sum of the credit entries in order to preserve the balance of the fundamental equation.

The Journal. One of the primary purposes of accounting is to provide a record of business transactions. Since at least two ledger accounts are affected by each transaction, it is inconvenient to make the original record of transactions directly in the ledgers. Therefore, the original record of a transaction is customarily made in a book, called a *journal*, or in some other convenient substitute for a journal.

If an ordinary journal is used, the entries are made in a manner similar to that shown in Figure 21. In the first two columns the date is recorded. In the next column the ledger accounts that are affected by the transaction are listed. The account to be debited is listed first. The account to be credited is listed

JOURNAL

Brown Manufacturing Co.

Date		Items	Debits	Credits
Jan.	1	Cash 　James Brown, Capital To record investment of James Brown to begin business.	5000 00	5000 00
	2	Burden (Rent) 　Cash Rental of building for month of January.	250 00	250 00
	2	Equipment 　Cash 　Notes Payable Equipment for plant. Estimated life 5 yrs. 6%, 90 day note given to A Company.	2000 00	1000 00 1000 00
	15	Memo: Employed 3 workmen. Salaries to be $150 per month.		
	16	Prepaid Expense (Insurance) 　Cash Insurance premium for one year.	240 00	240 00
	18	Purchases 　B Company Raw materials on open account. Terms — 90 days.	230 00	230 00

FIGURE 21. Typical journal page.

below and offset to the right to indicate that it is to be credited. Below the names of the two (or more) ledger accounts a brief description of the transaction is given if necessary to show what was involved.

In the fifth column the amounts of the debit entries are given, opposite the account in which they are to be made. The amounts to be credited to ledger accounts are indicated in the sixth column.

After the record of a transaction is complete in the journal, it is necessary to debit and credit the ledger accounts that are indicated in the journal entries. This process is called *posting*. As each item in the journal is posted to a ledger, the page number of the ledger is recorded in column 3 of the journal, known as the *ledger folio* column.

In many businesses it is impracticable to make the original record in a journal. For example, each salesgirl in a large department store could not go to a single book and record each sale as it is made. Thus it is often necessary to utilize cash register records, sales book duplicates, multi-columnar journals or other types of records as the original record of business transactions. These tend to lessen the manual labor required to record the multitudinous transactions of a large business and to decrease the possibility of error. At the close of the day's business the summation of these records is transferred to some type of journal.

The entries in the journal are posted in the ledgers at convenient intervals. Care must be exercised in making journal entries, since it is the book of original record. The ledger accounts become secondary records, and in case of disagreement between the ledgers and the journal the latter is considered to be the final authority.

Making the Balance Sheet. As has been pointed out, the journal and the various ledger accounts provide a convenient and systematic means for recording and segregating various financial transactions. The figures contained in the ledger accounts provide information from which the net worth of an investment can be determined at any time.

The entries which are made in the journal, and which are transferred to the proper ledger accounts, record transactions that have added to, or subtracted from, the worth of an investment. In order to determine the net effect upon the worth of the invested capital it is only necessary to balance the positive entries against those which have a negative effect. This is done in ordinary accounting practice by closing and balancing the various ledger accounts. This process consists of adding the debit and credit entries and determining the excess of one over the other. The excess is said to be the "balance" of the account and will have a positive or negative effect on the worth of the investment depending on whether the debit or credit entries,

CASH									L 2	
1941 Jan.	1	Balance Forward		$	768 00	1941 Jan.	3	Purchases	J–7	$ 87 00
	6	Sales	J–7		69 00		8	Taxes	J–8	102 00
	8	Sales	J–8		103 00		11	Insurance	J–8	42 00
	10	J. H. Clark Co.	J–8		39 00		17	Purchases	J–9	137 00
	14	Sales	J–8		86 00		22	Purchases	J–9	79 00
	16	Sales	J–9		238 00		28	Office supplies	J–9	22 00
	20	Sales	J–9		92 00		31	Salaries	J–9	427 00
	24	Sales	J–9		168 00			Balance		817 00
	27	J. Doe Company	J–9		47 00					
	30	Sales	J–9		103 00					
					$1,713 00					$1,713 00
		Balance forward		$	817 00					

FIGURE 22. Typical ledger sheet.

respectively, are greater. Figure 22 shows a ledger account which has been closed and balanced.

When all of the ledger accounts are closed and balanced properly the balances represent the worth of the account as an asset, liability or claim of ownership. If these balances are listed in the proper form they become a balance sheet, showing the relationship between assets, liabilities and ownership which has resulted from the various transactions which have taken place and have been recorded. Thus the process of accounting starts with a given investment of capital, represented by various types of assets which are claimed by persons outside or within the business. All events that affect the investment are recorded and handled so that their net effect can be determined at any time. This net effect may be shown on a new balance sheet which sets forth the new relationship that exists between the assets, liabilities and ownership as the result of the various trans-actions. This accounting

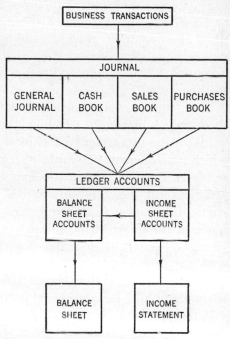

FIGURE 23. Diagram of accounting procedure.

process is represented graphically in Figure 23. This is, of course, a simplification of most accounting procedure.

The Income Sheet Accounts. It will be noted in Figure 23 that some of the ledger accounts are grouped under the heading "Income Sheet Accounts." These accounts are used so that the accounting system may have greater flexibility and facility and furnish information which is useful to management in controlling a business. While an accounting system could handle all details by using only balance sheet accounts, such a system would be inconvenient, and essential information would be difficult to obtain. The income sheet accounts are used to record the transactions which bring about many of the changes in the balances of the balance sheet accounts.

If one analyzes the changes that occur in the balances of balance sheet accounts, he will find that most of them are due to revenue which is received from the sale of goods or services or to the expenses which are incurred in the production of the goods or services. These items of income and expense, such as sales, purchases, salaries, wages, sales expense, taxes, insurance and depreciation expense, are recorded in appropriate income sheet accounts. The changes in balance sheet account balances are due to these items of expense or revenue.

The transactions recorded in the income sheet accounts are those which normally produce the increase or decrease in the value of an investment of capital. Therefore it is these items which management attempts to control so as to obtain favorable results. They represent the expenses and revenues that occur after capital has been invested. For this reason they are of particular interest to the engineer. They record the actual occurrence of things which he predicts and estimates in making economy studies. It is desirable for the engineer to be acquainted with the terms and methods which the accountant uses in handling these items so that he may treat them in the proper manner when they must be considered in an economy study.

A few words are in order regarding some of these terms. When the accountant speaks of *gross revenue* he refers to all of the proceeds which are received by the business as the result of the sale of goods or services. *Net revenue* or *net income* is defined as the amount by which the equities of the proprietors or owners are increased because of successful conduct of the business. One hopes that a portion of gross revenue will be net income.

Accountants define *expense* as the cost of producing revenue. Obviously many different expenses arise. These include the usual items such as expense for materials, labor, taxes, insurance, sales and shipping. An additional expense which is of great importance to the engineer is that due to depreciation.

The Income Statement. The information contained in income sheet accounts is summarized in the *income statement*. This financial statement shows in a brief, concise form the pertinent facts regarding the source and extent of the revenue and the extent and distribution of the expenses so as to show whether the business has been operated at a profit or a loss during the period covered by the statement. These statements are sometimes called *profit and loss statements*.

Income statements may vary in form to an even greater extent than do balance sheets. The very different natures of the many types of business make it necessary to adapt the income statement to the particular enterprise in order to show the information to the best advantage. The only requisite is that the statement should show the information in a clear, concise and complete manner. Figure 24 shows the income statement for The Brown Manufacturing Co. for the period January 1 through February 28, 1939. This statement is much less complicated than the form shown in Figure 25, which is one required by the Internal Revenue Department for filing corporate income tax returns.

Though the statement shown for The Brown Manufacturing Co. is relatively simple, it is entirely adequate for this particular

THE BROWN MANUFACTURING CO.
STATEMENT OF INCOME
January 1, 1939, to February 28, 1939

Income from Sales			$1,755.00
Less Cost of Goods Sold			
Materials			
Inventory Jan. 1	$ ——		
Purchases	480.00		
	$480.00		
Inventory Feb. 28	250.00		
Total Materials		$ 230.00	
Burden		1,354.55	
Cost of Goods Sold			1,584.55
Gross Profit			$ 170.45
Other Expenses			
Interest			8.17
Net Profit			$ 162.28

FIGURE 24. Income statement for The Brown Manufacturing Co.

ADJUSTED NET INCOME COMPUTATION

GROSS INCOME

Item No.

1. Gross sales (where inventories are an income-determining factor)_____ $_____ Less returns and allowances_____ $_____

2. Less cost of goods sold (from Schedule C)_____

3. Gross profit from sales (item 1 minus item 2)_____

4. Gross receipts (where inventories are not an income-determining factor)_____ $_____

5. Less cost of operations (from Schedule D)_____

6. Gross profit where inventories are not an income-determining factor (item 4 minus item 5)_____

7. Interest on loans, notes, mortgages, bonds, bank deposits, etc. (See Instruction 18–(1))_____

8. Interest on obligations of the United States (from Schedule P, line 19 (a) (4)). (See Instruction 18–(2))_____

9. Rents. (See Instruction 19)_____

10. Royalties. (See Instruction 20)_____

11. (a) Capital gain (or loss) (from Schedule E). (If a net loss, do not enter over $2,000)_____

    (b) Gain or loss from sale or exchange of property other than capital assets (from Schedule F)_____

12. Dividends (from Schedule G)_____

13. Other income (state nature of income)_____

14.   Total income in items 3, and 6 to 13, inclusive_____ $_____

130

DEDUCTIONS

15. Compensation of officers (from Schedule F) .... $ ....

16. Salaries and wages (not deducted elsewhere) ....

17. Rent. (See Instruction 23) ....

18. Repairs. (See Instruction 24) ....

19. Bad debts (from Schedule I) ....

20. Interest. (See Instruction 26) ....

21. Taxes (from Schedule J). (Do not include Federal excess-profits tax) ....

22. Contributions or gifts paid (from Schedule K) ....

23. Losses by fire, storm, shipwreck, or other casualty, or theft. (Submit schedule, see Instruction 29) ....

24. Depreciation (from Schedule L) ....

25. Depletion of mines, oil and gas wells, timber, etc. (Submit schedule, see Instruction 31) ....

26. Other deductions authorized by law (from Schedule M) ....

27. Total deductions in items 15 to 26, inclusive .... $ ....

28. Net income for excess-profits tax computation (item 14 minus item 27) ....

29. Less: Federal excess-profits tax. (See Instruction 33) .... $ ....

30. Net income (item 28 minus item 29) .... $ ....

31. Less: Interest on obligations of the United States (item 8, above) ....

32. Adjusted net income (item 30 minus item 31) .... $ ....

Schedule C.—COST OF GOODS SOLD. (See Instruction 17)

(When inventories are an income-determining factor)

1. Inventory at beginning of year .... $ ....

2. Material or merchandise bought for manufacture or sale ....

3. Salaries and wages ....

4. Other costs per books. (Attach itemized schedule) ....

5. Total (lines 1 to 4) .... $ ....

6. Less inventory at end of year ....

7. Cost of goods. (Enter as item 2, page 1) .... $ ....

FIGURE 25. Income statement as required by the Internal Revenue Department from corporations.

131

company, whose business is small and whose operations are not extensive. An examination will show that the statement is divided into four sections. The first section shows the revenue from the major operations of the business — from the sale of goods.

The second section determines the cost of producing these goods. The cost of the materials used in the goods produced must be determined in this section. Obviously, the total material available for use during a period is the sum of the materials on hand at the beginning of the period plus those purchased during the same time. If the inventory of materials remaining on hand at the close of the period is then subtracted from this total, the difference is the amount used in production during the period. To the cost of materials must be added the productive labor costs and items of manufacturing overhead or burden. By subtracting the cost of the goods or services produced from the income from sales the gross profit from sales is obtained.

In the third section of the income statement the costs of selling the goods and management expenses are listed. These are expenses which are the result of administration and are subtracted from the gross profit to obtain the net profit. In the case of The Brown Manufacturing Co. selling and administrative salaries were negligible and were included in the overhead. The item "interest" is a management expense since it arose through a particular method of financing the purchase of equipment. It is therefore included in this section of the statement.

The fourth section shows the net profit or loss and indicates whether there has been any distribution of these funds. Thus it would show if the profits had been used to pay dividends or had been set aside as surplus.

From an income statement in this form one may determine whether the expenses of one phase of the business, such as sales expenses, are out of line with other items. The statement shows the effect of any unusual financial methods which may have been used. Not only are the sources of income revealed, but the extent and distribution of this income may be determined. If one wishes to make a detailed study of the financial structure of an enterprise a comparative income statement, showing the values for two or more periods, is very useful.

Reserve for Depreciation. Previous mention has been made of the fact that in ordinary business practice the amounts charged to depreciation are not put into an actual fund to provide for replacement of depreciated equipment, and that the customary account, "Reserve for Depreciation," is not an actual, separate fund. If a piece of equipment costing $1,000 is expected to have a useful life of five years, the annual depreciation, upon a straight-line basis, would be $200. At the end of the first year the value of the equipment would be $800.

The decline in value of the asset might be recorded as shown in Figure 26. At the end of the first year a credit entry would be

EQUIPMENT

| Jan. 1, 1938 | $1,000 | Dec. 31, 1938 Depreciation | $200 |

FIGURE 26. Method of charging depreciation directly to the Equipment account.

made in the equipment ledger showing the depreciation that had taken place. (The debit entry for this same amount would be charged to production expense or overhead.) The debit balance of the Equipment account would then be $800, the depreciated value of the equipment.

The same result could be obtained by using the method indicated in Figure 27. In this case a separate account, "Allowance

EQUIPMENT

| Jan. 1, 1938 | $1,000 | |

ALLOWANCE FOR DEPRECIATION

| | Dec. 31, 1938   Equipment | $200 |

FIGURE 27. Method of recording depreciation in a separate account.

for Depreciation," is used to record the depreciation which has accrued. This account is in reality a *contra account* against the Equipment account. Such an account is usually called *Reserve for Depreciation* instead of "Allowance for Depreciation." It is sometimes called *Accrued Depreciation*. This is probably the most satisfactory name and could well be used to a greater extent.

The effect of handling this Reserve account in various ways is shown by the simple balance sheets of Figure 28. It is assumed

BALANCE SHEET 1

Equipment	$1,000	Ownership	$1,000
Total	$1,000	Total	$1,000

BALANCE SHEET 2

Equipment	$1,000	Ownership	$1,000
Other Assets	200	Res. for Deprec.	200
Total	$1,200	Total	$1,200

BALANCE SHEET 3

Equipment Cost	$1,000		Ownership	$1,000
Less Res. for Deprec.	200			
		$ 800		
Other Assets		200		
Total		$1,000	Total	$1,000

FIGURE 28. Simplified balance sheets showing the effect of using the ordinary Reserve for Depreciation.

that the only asset is the equipment which cost $1,000, and this is balanced by $1,000 in Ownership. This is indicated in Balance Sheet 1 of Figure 28.

Balance Sheet 2 shows the effect of keeping in the business the amounts that have been charged for depreciation during the year. They would be invested in other assets of some type. If the credit balance of the Reserve for Depreciation account is shown as a liability on the balance sheet, the totals of both sides of the sheet are $1,200. This practice is likely to give a wrong impression since the equipment is no longer worth $1,000, but only $800. Thus the totals of both sides of the balance sheet are too large by $200. This has resulted from handling the Reserve account as a liability instead of as a contra account against an asset account.

Balance Sheet 3 shows a preferable method of handling such reserve accounts. The original cost of the equipment is shown, but the amount of accrued depreciation, as indicated by the Re serve account, is subtracted from the cost so that only the depreciated value is included in the total of the balance sheet. The total assets and ownership remain the same as in Balance Shcet 1.

It can be seen from Figure 28 that the sums charged as the expense of depreciation were not paid into a sinking fund to accumulate. If this had been done the fund would earn from zero to 3 or 4% interest, depending on whether it was put into a safe deposit box or invested conservatively. Instead, being invested in the business in the form of other needed assets or working capital, it earns the same rate of return as other capital funds that are invested in the enterprise. This rate of return, in a well-managed business, will greatly exceed the rate of interest that would be obtained from outside investment of the funds. In this manner the money set aside for depreciation is diverted into the most useful channels.

In modern business a depreciated asset is very seldom replaced by an exact duplicate. The needs of business are constantly changing, and by the time a plant or equipment is worn out it has been replaced by assets of a different type and its utility has ceased to exist. Thus, since the type of assets needed by a business is constantly changing, it is essential that any method of handling depreciation reserves fulfill the following conditions:

1. Proper amounts must be charged for depreciation and set aside in some manner.

2. The total assets must be maintained to preserve the invested capital.

3. Depreciation funds should be kept actively invested in the business.

4. Depreciated assets should show on financial statements at their depreciated value.

It is true that, through the use of the customary depreciation reserve, it is possible for equipment to become worn out and no funds be available for replacement although the correct depreciation has been charged at all times. This merely means that the management has not maintained the proper ratio between cash and other assets. No one would expect all the invested capital of a business to be kept in the form of cash. It is no more reasonable to expect that depreciation reserves should all be in the form of cash. Management must look forward and provide funds for replacement. However, this is no greater responsibility than is placed on management for the conduct of the other affairs of a business. No one would question giving management the responsibility of keeping enough of the assets in the form of cash so that the payroll could be met. If the executives are capable of managing a business, they should also be capable of having the necessary cash available when fixed assets must be replaced.

It has not been the intention of this brief chapter to attempt to teach accounting procedure. Instead, an attempt has been made to point out the purpose and use of accounting so that its relationship to engineering economy may be understood. For details of accounting technique the student is referred to the references listed below.

REFERENCES

Paton, W. A.: "Essentials of Accounting," The Macmillan Company, New York, 1938.

Eggleston, D. C.: "Modern Accounting Theory and Practice," John Wiley & Sons, Inc., New York, 1930.

Greer, H. C.: "How to Understand Accounting," The Ronald Press Company, New York, 1928.

Harding, C. F., and D. T. Canfield: "Business Administration for Engineers," McGraw-Hill Book Company, Inc., New York, 1937.

Howard, S. E.: "The A.B.C. of Accounting," Princeton University Press, 1929.

PROBLEMS

85. Explain the difference in the viewpoints of economy studies and accounting.
86. What is the function of ordinary accounting?
87. Explain the relation between the fundamental equation of accounting, Assets — Liabilities = Ownership, and the rule for determining whether an item is a debit or a credit entry.

    Designate which accounts are debited and credited to record the following items:

    a. Rent payments.
    b. Interest payment on an outstanding note.
    c. Sale of goods for cash.
    d. Receipt of cash in payment of goods which were sold on open account.
    e. Receipt of money received from the sale of stock.
    f. Payment for fire insurance.

88. Distinguish between current assets and fixed assets.
89. What is the purpose of the journal?
90. From the following items, determine the ownership and draw up a balance sheet.

a.	Notes payable	$ 1,000
b.	Accounts receivable	12,120
c.	Prepaid insurance	860
d.	Furniture and fixtures	21,250
e.	Accounts payable	4,600
f.	Accrued taxes	1,180
g.	Cash	16,405
h.	Reserve for depreciation	8,400

91. Differentiate between revenue and income.
92. What are two purposes of an income statement?
93. Explain what is meant by a "Reserve" account.

Chapter IX

COST ACCOUNTING

Definition and Purpose. Cost accounting, in simple terms, is the determination of the cost of producing a product or rendering a service. In order to accomplish this, one must first determine what expenses are incurred in a business undertaking. An accounting system must then be established so that these expenses may be recorded in such a manner that the various costs of production may be found.

The engineer is probably as much responsible for the high degree of development of cost accounting as is the accountant. Since the engineer has had a voice in management he has constantly demanded improvements in the method of determining the costs of utilizing the processes and equipment which he has originated. This demand, together with many practical suggestions, has been a stimulus to the accounting profession in working out improved methods of cost keeping.

Some idea of the tremendous scope of the subject may be had from the large number of books that have been written about it. To gain a thorough knowledge of cost accounting would require a great amount of study and practice. Obviously, one chapter can do no more than give a view of its possibilities and uses and point out that the problems it presents are solved in an analytical manner, as are most of the engineer's problems. In fact, one might say that cost accounting is "accounting engineering."

Three Types of Cost Accounting. Cost accounting had developed very naturally into three types. After an article has been produced, one wishes to know how much it has cost. Cost accounting originated in this manner. By carefully accounting for all of the expenses of every type during the period of production, the

138

actual cost of manufacture may be determined. However, with this method the cost is not known until production of the goods or service is finished. This method of obtaining cost figures is often called *post-mortem* cost accounting. Costs are determined after they occur. Accounting of this type is used to a considerable extent and fills a very real need. It is essential that costs be known. Even if they are not determined until after they have taken place, this is better than never knowing what they were. In small industries which produce only small lots of goods of the same kind, it is often not feasible to use more advanced methods of cost analysis than are found in post-mortem cost determinations.

The second type of cost accounting attempts to make it possible to know what costs will be before production takes place. The advantage of knowing what future costs will be is very evident. Such costs must, of course, be based upon experience, careful specification of materials and processes, and detailed analysis and distribution of overhead expenses. These costs are estimates, but with intelligent preparation they can be given a high degree of accuracy and thus made to approximate actual values very closely. Because of this they are sometimes called *predicted costs*.

Well-prepared predicted costs are ideal figures. The realization of this fact, and the desire to make actual costs match the ideal, gave rise to the third type of cost accounting. This is, in reality, not a distinctly different type of cost accounting. It is a broader and extra use of the second type of cost figures. Costs are predetermined as before with as great accuracy as possible. These are set up as *standard costs*. All operations are then performed in the manner which was specified for these standard costs. Thus the cost accounting system becomes not only a means of determining costs but also an aid to control. This use of cost accounting as an instrument of control is peculiarly adapted to the needs of the large scale, standardized production that characterizes modern industry. With such production the standard costs can be more accurately determined, and at the same time the need for a means of controlling costs becomes more essential. The importance of the cost accounting system becomes apparent.

The Elements of Cost. One of the first problems in cost accounting is to determine the elements of cost which arise in producing an article or rendering a service. A study of how these costs occur then gives an indication of the accounting procedure which must be established in order to give satisfactory cost information.

As stated by the economist, the three factors that contribute to production are land, labor and capital. From an engineering and managerial viewpoint it is suitable to consider the elements of cost of production to be *materials, labor* and *overhead*. It may readily be seen that the latter grouping includes the factors as given by the economist. Cost accounting, then, must provide a method of determining or predicting the cost of utilizing materials, labor and capital.

Materials Cost. It is probably easier to determine the cost of the materials used in manufacturing an article than either of the other two cost elements. Materials are tangible things, and their extent can usually be found by weighing, measuring or counting. If their amount can be found by these methods it is not difficult to determine their value. Some materials, however, are difficult to measure. The exact amount of glue used in making a chair would be difficult to determine. Still more difficult would be the measurement of the exact amount of coal which was used to produce the steam which generated the electricity which was used to heat the glue. Some reasonable line must be drawn, beyond which no attempt is made to measure directly the material which is used for each unit of production.

Most materials are measured and charged directly to the cost of producing a product. This is done as long as the value of the material can be determined without the cost of the determination becoming an appreciable amount, relative to the cost of the material itself. Such materials are classed as *direct materials*. The other materials, whose value cannot be readily determined with economy or exactness, are classed as *indirect materials* and handled as a part of the overhead expense. As the extent of a business increases, the importance of determining the exact cost of as many of the materials as possible increases proportionately. It is not uncommon for large companies to compute material costs to four or five decimal places. It should always be remembered, however, that there is little advantage in knowing that the cost of a certain material is $0.04562 per pound when it is impossible to determine whether one-sixteenth or one-quarter of a pound is used in each unit produced.

A record of the direct materials used is ordinarily obtained through the use of inventory cards and requisition blanks. The

INVENTORY CARD						
Article 3/4" brass collar				Stock Number 786A		
Date	Received	Cost	Balance on Hand	Average Cost	Delivered	Requisition Number
9/2	5,000	$0.0400	5,000	$0.0400		
9/4			2,000		3,000	B 475
9/20	3,000	$0.0420	5,000	$0.0412		

FIGURE 29. Stockroom inventory card.

inventory cards are maintained in connection with the perpetual inventory of materials in the storeroom. There are many kinds of these cards, but the main purpose is to record the amount and cost of material brought into the storeroom, the amount and value of the material taken from the storeroom on requisition, and the amount of the material remaining in the storeroom. One of these cards is kept for each type and size of material in the raw materials stores. A sample card is shown in Figure 29. On this particular type of card the average cost of the material on hand is kept, so the value of any material sent from the storeroom may be computed.

Other types of stock cards may carry less or more information than the one illustrated in Figure 29. Some of the more elaborate cards show the department to which the material was issued, the maximum and minimum quantity to be kept on hand, the name of the supplier, and any other information which may be thought necessary. The more elaborate the card is, the more the amount of labor required to maintain the card system. As simple a form as possible helps to prevent neglect and carelessness in recording essential information.

The pricing of materials raises one of the troublesome problems encountered in cost accounting. As mentioned, using the average cost of material on hand is one method. Another is to assume that the oldest material is always used first. Thus in this "first

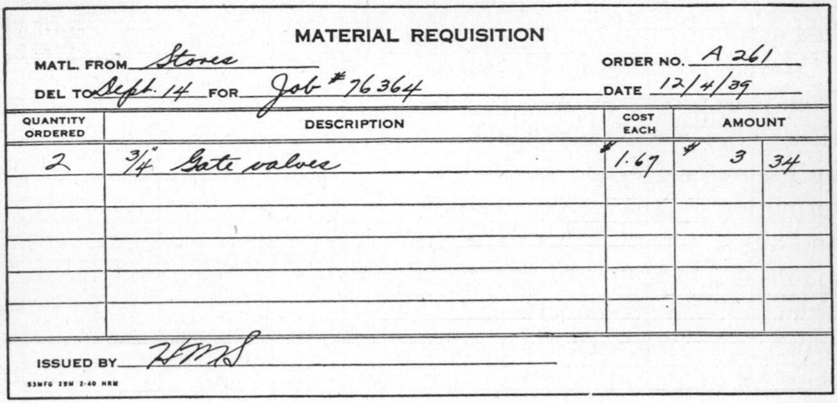

MATERIAL REQUISITION

MATL. FROM Stores ORDER NO. A 261

DEL TO Dept. 14 FOR Job # 76364 DATE 12/4/39

QUANTITY ORDERED	DESCRIPTION	COST EACH	AMOUNT	
2	3/4" Gate valves	$ 1.67	$ 3	34

ISSUED BY HMS

53MFG 2M 2-40 HRM

FIGURE 30. Material requisition blank.

in-first out" method, each lot of a particular material is carried at its actual cost. The oldest lot is assumed to be used first, and the operation is charged with the cost of the material assumed to be used. In this manner the value of the inventory tends to reflect latest market value. However, the cost of production figures are not indicative of the cost of future operations since out-of-date materials costs are included.

The "first in-first out" or the "average cost" methods do not cause serious difficulty when materials do not fluctuate appreciably in value. However, in times of rapid price change there is great advantage in having cost figures reflect existing conditions. This can be brought about by pricing existing inventories at existing market values. This is admittedly contrary to the old accounting practice of listing assets at "cost or market — whichever is lower." However, the method does recognize fact, which is what business should be guided by. This method is not widely used, but there are indications that it may be in the future.

With this method it would be necessary to revalue inventories whenever market values changed appreciably. This extra work is offset by having cost figures in line with existing conditions and thus more usable for control work. Increases or decreases in the value of inventories would be charged directly to the profit and loss account.

Materials are usually ordered from the storeroom by a requisition blank. Such a blank is shown in Figure 30. The essential information is the name, amount and stock number (if any) of the material required, and the work order number or department to which the material is to be charged. The value of the issued material is computed from the cost figures shown on the stock card and entered on a copy of the requisition. This copy is then sent to the accounting department. In this manner the cost of materials which are placed in production is obtained.

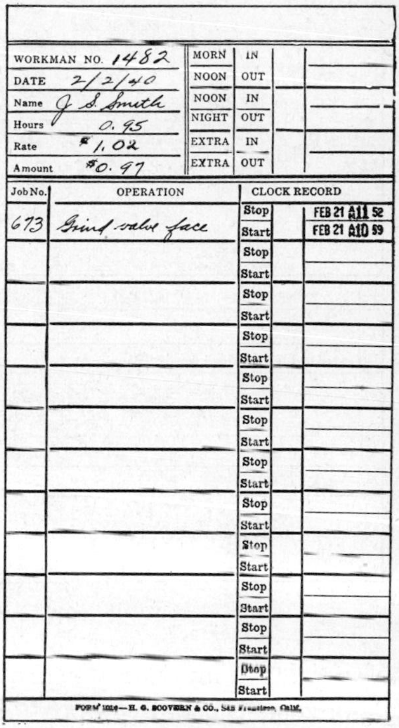

WORKMAN NO. *1482*	MORN	IN	
DATE *2/2/40*	NOON	OUT	
Name *J. S. Smith*	NOON	IN	
Hours *0.95*	NIGHT	OUT	
Rate *$1.02*	EXTRA	IN	
Amount *$0.97*	EXTRA	OUT	

Job No.	OPERATION		CLOCK RECORD	
673	*Grind valve face*	Stop	FEB 21 A11 52	
		Start	FEB 21 A10 59	
		Stop		
		Start		
		Stop		
		Start		
		Stop		
		Start		
		Stop		
		Start		
		Stop		
		Start		
		Stop		
		Start		
		Stop		
		Start		
		Stop		
		Start		
		Stop		
		Start		
		Stop		
		Start		
		Stop		
		Start		

FORM 1016 — H. S. SCOTTEN & CO., San Francisco, Calif.

FIGURE 31. Ordinary job clock time card.

Numerous other methods of handling cost of materials are used. The references at the end of this chapter give many of these, together with the forms used by specific companies.

Labor Costs. The labor that is used in producing goods or rendering services must be paid for. In order to do this one must know how much labor is utilized in the production of one unit or in one operation. In this task the procedure is dependent upon the method of wage payment.

Where the workers are paid a fixed weekly or monthly salary, determination of post-mortem unit cost is simple. An effort to predetermine unit labor costs presents a much more difficult task. After the work is completed the unit cost may be found by dividing the total salaries of the production period by the number of units produced during that period. However, there is seldom any guarantee that the same workers will produce the same number

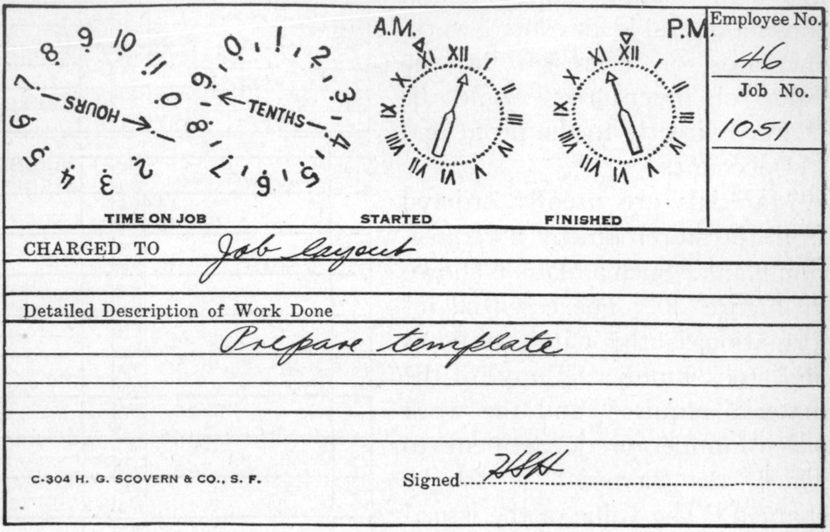

FIGURE 32. Calculagraph time card.

of articles in an equal, future period. Precise predetermination of labor costs is usually impossible with this system of wage payment.

Where wages are based on an hourly rate, approximately the same difficulties are encountered as with payment of fixed salaries. The exact amount of time consumed by an operation may be found after the task is completed if suitable means are provided. This is usually accomplished through the use of some kind of time clock and job card. Samples of two types of records, obtainable by the use of two types of time clocks, are shown in Figures 31 and 32. From these records and the known hourly rates of pay the labor cost is determined. With this method of wage payment, accurate predetermination of labor costs is still difficult even though each task is given an *allowed time*.

The piece rate system of wage payment was originated not only to provide a method that would pay the worker in proportion to the work accomplished but also to ensure constant labor costs for the performance of a given operation. In this system the wage paid for the performance of a set task is based upon a scientific study of the actual labor required. Whenever the same task is performed, the wage paid is the same amount. With piece rates established, the labor cost for a given operation is known before or after the operation is performed. This method of wage payment is widely used by progressive companies, and its use is increasing rapidly. A more detailed discussion of the various wage payment methods is given in a later chapter.

Where labor adds directly to the manufacture of an article, or the rendering of a service, the cost of this labor may usually be charged to the production process without particular difficulty. However, like indirect materials, labor is often expended so that it benefits the production process only in an indirect manner. For example, the accounting department of a business usually does not add directly to the value of the products produced. Yet it is essential to have an accounting department to keep the cost and payroll records. Thus the expense of maintaining the accounting department is one of the costs of production just as truly as is the wage of the worker who performs actual operations on the article produced. In order to know the entire cost of production it is necessary to charge the expense for labor in the accounting department to the articles produced.

Obviously, the accounting department adds to the value of the goods produced only in an indirect manner. Thus the expense of labor in the accounting department is said to be an indirect labor expense of production. Like indirect material expense, indirect labor expense is charged to production in an indirect method, usually by assigning it to burden or overhead. The final assignment to production expense is made by distributing the items of overhead or burden in some equitable manner.

Other indirect labor expenses are those due to supervision and the maintenance, personnel and stores departments.

The Elements of Overhead Expense. In order to produce an article or render a service, a business must pay for services and supplies that do not add directly to the value of the product. For example, it is necessary to have janitor service. Taxes must be paid. Office supplies are required. The indirect labor and materials previously mentioned must be paid for. Thus any expense that cannot readily be charged to fundamental production operations is ordinarily charged to the overhead or burden account.

One should never consider that these expenses are nonproductive, meaning that they add nothing to the utility or value of the product. In a well-managed business there is no such thing as a nonproductive department or expense. While the term "nonproductive" is often used, what is actually meant is that nonproductive departments or expenses add to the total value of products in an *indirect* manner.

Included under overhead will be indirect labor, indirect materials, rent, depreciation, taxes, insurance, supervision, maintenance and many other such items.

Interest as an Element of Cost. There has been considerable discussion among accountants and engineers as to the handling of interest (profit) on owned capital as an element of cost. As has been pointed out in earlier chapters, this form of interest must be considered in nearly all economy problems. It is apparent, however, that cost figures which include interest on owned capital will be considerably different from similar figures wherein interest has not been included.

The manner in which the minimum profit on owned capital is considered is not of prime importance. It is important that the method used be correct and that the figures which result are understood.

In most cost determinations for economy studies it appears to be good practice to omit minimum profit as a cost item and consider it as a separate factor. However, in numerous instances including minimum profit as a cost item makes comparisons somewhat easier. In such cases minimum profit may be included as a cost element, but should be clearly indicated so there will be no doubt as to what the item is.

When minimum profit is included as a cost, one should keep in mind the fact that the resulting cost is affected by the rate of profit used. Thus total costs may be made abnormally high by using a high rate of profit. Similarly, costs will be low if low rates of profit are used. Since there is no exact method of determining what rate of return should be used, it is evident that one should exercise considerable care in selecting the rate which is to be used in a particular problem.

When one wishes to compare the production costs of one company with those of another, it is clear that some method of considering the amount of capital required, and the cost of obtaining it, is desirable. The obvious method is to consider interest upon invested capital as an element of cost.

One finds that many of the uniform accounting systems recommended by various trade associations consider interest on owned capital as a cost of production. In this way the association can make a valid comparison of the costs of the various members.[1] With all the member companies figuring their costs in the same manner, the cost figures of the various producers yield much more significant information. If such figures are used only for legitimate control purposes there is no harm and much good in considering interest as a cost in computing them.

It is apparent that the handling of profit on owned capital as a cost is a debatable subject. In most ordinary business transactions it is not considered to be a cost.

Handling Overhead Expenses. As pointed out in the preceding paragraphs, the determination of the first two cost elements of production, materials and labor, may be made almost a routine matter by employing the proper systems. Likewise, they may be predetermined without much difficulty. Accounting for the various indirect expenses is quite a different matter. If the actual total cost of production is to be known, the correct amount of overhead expense due to each element of production must be added to the direct labor and material expenses. Therefore some reasonably accurate and feasible method of distributing overhead expense must be used. At the end of an accounting period the total of the overhead expenses which have been incurred may be

---

[1] There is evidence that one reason trade associations recommend inclusion of interest on capital as a cost is to influence small marginal producers not to cut selling prices. Such producers tend not to consider the cost of obtaining capital and thus sell their output at prices which may yield less than a reasonable return upon their actual investment.

found. Determining what portion of this total is attributable to any one operation or product is a very real and difficult problem. Yet it is of vital importance to be able to make this distribution of overhead expense.

If only one product is being produced, or one operation being performed, the unit overhead cost would be simple to compute. Division of the total of the indirect expenses by the number of units produced would distribute the overhead very accurately. Unfortunately, this condition almost never exists. Modern industry is exceedingly complex. The problem is well illustrated by considering a company which manufactures two products. Product A is produced by a series of large machines which cost over $100,000 and are operated entirely by 5 men. Product B is manufactured by handwork and requires the labor of 100 men who work at inexpensive benches. The total number of each article produced, and their total value, are approximately the same. How are some of the overhead expenses to be distributed between the two products?

Obviously, the 100 men who produce product B require much more supervision, heat, light and floor space than do the 5 men who operate the machines for product A. The depreciation, taxes and insurance on the machinery required for the manufacture of product A are far greater than for the cheap benches used by the other group. The difficulty of making an equitable distribution of the overhead expenses between these two products becomes evident at once. When there are many products the problem becomes extremely involved. The same is true when an attempt is made to distribute overhead to each machine or operation. This, however, is the type of distribution that is ultimately desired. The correct distribution of overhead expense becomes the major problem in cost accounting.

Bases of Overhead Distribution. It is usually necessary to use some arbitrary basis for distributing the various items of expense. A method that is correct for one case may be incorrect for another. The test of the correctness lies in whether the results fit the existing conditions.

Some of the methods that are used for distributing overhead expense are:

1. Direct materials.
2. Direct labor.
3. Man-hours.
4. Machine rate.

Distribution According to Direct Materials. The theory of this method is that products or processes cause overhead expense to be incurred in direct proportion to the value of the direct materials which are consumed. Thus if $1 worth of direct materials is involved in one job and $2 worth in a second job, the latter is charged with twice as much overhead expense as the former. It is apparent that this method is very simple to use. It is equally apparent that it fails to coincide with the facts in many, if not most, cases.

For example, assume that one job requires only the hand labor of one workman for an hour. A second job, using the same value of materials, may require several large and expensive machines with their operators, floor space, power, depreciation and maintenance. No such simple method will handle this situation satisfactorily.

Distribution According to Direct Labor. By this method the overhead expense assigned to a job or operation is assumed to be in direct proportion to the value of the direct labor expended. This method is simple and used to quite an extent. Undoubtedly it usually gives a better distribution than does the direct materials method. However, in most cases it is not sufficiently accurate.

It is apparent that where machines of greatly different cost and size are operated, the overhead cost of each will be different. The overhead expense of operating a half-ton truck would not be the same as that of a four-ton truck trailer job. Yet the drivers of each might receive the same wage. With the direct labor method of overhead distribution the overhead expense of operating each truck the same length of time would be identical, since the same amount of wages would be paid. The same situation exists in plants where machines of greatly differing sizes and costs are operated. In such circumstances the direct labor method of distributing overhead expense is far from accurate or satisfactory.

Distribution According to Man-Hours. The assumption in this method is that overhead accrues in direct proportion to the number of man-hours consumed. It obviously fails to consider the variations in cost of machines, the amount of floor space needed, maintenance costs, or differences in wage rates. While it is used to some extent, it is not accurate in most cases.

Distribution by Machine Rates. In most modern operations machinery is an important factor in the production process. A large part of overhead expense is due to the fact that machinery is employed.

The fundamental reason that overhead expenses are incurred is the fact that certain tasks or operations are performed. Thus each operation necessitates a certain amount of overhead expense. Since most operations are performed with the aid of machines or equipment, overhead can conveniently be attributed to the operation of machines. If a machine is operated for one hour, one can determine the amount of overhead expense which resulted from such operation. Knowing the overhead expense which results from each hour's operation of a machine, one can establish this amount as the *machine rate* for the equipment involved. Determining the overhead for the production of any particular product is then merely a matter of multiplying the operation time on each machine by the machine rate of each piece of equipment.

For example, a certain product is made on a screw machine. It requires 2 minutes time. The cost of the material is $0.02. The machine operator receives $1.20 per hour. The machine rate is $2.40. The total unit cost would be:

$$
\begin{array}{lr}
\text{Direct materials} & = \$0.02 \\
\text{Direct labor} \quad \$1.20 \times \tfrac{2}{60} = & 0.04 \\
\text{Overhead expense } \$2.40 \times \tfrac{2}{60} = & \underline{0.08} \\
\text{Total unit cost} & = \$0.14
\end{array}
$$

Once machine rates have been determined, their use is simple and accurate. The big problem, of course, is determining the correct rates. However, although the process usually involves quite a bit of work, machine rates can be determined without too much work or expense.

An additional advantage of machine rates is the fact that a single machine rate may apply to a number of different products. For example, an ordinary engine lathe may be used for producing hundreds of different products. But the overhead expenses involved in operating that particular lathe would be the same regardless of what product it was producing. The same machine rate can be used in computing the cost of any article on which this lathe is used.

Determination of Machine Rates. In computing machine rates it is necessary to consider each element of overhead expense and determine what portion of it is due to the operation of each machine. Each item of overhead must be allocated according to some reasonable plan.

A consideration of overhead expense elements makes it apparent that all cannot be distributed upon the same basis. The depreciation charge in the machine rate will be directly proportional to the depreciable value of the machine. Thus depreciation charges are based upon the cost and service life of the equipment. Rent, on the other hand, will have no connection with the cost of the equipment. It will, instead, be a function of the floor space which the machine utilizes.

Each element of overhead cost should be analyzed to determine a reasonable basis for distribution. Some of the commonly used methods are:

1. Building expense (rent, depreciation, taxes, insurance, etc.); proportional to floor area used.

2. Heat; proportional to floor area or volume of space.

3. Light; proportional to connected lighting load.

4. Power; proportional to connected power load.

5. Depreciation on equipment; proportional to value of equipment used.

6. Personnel department expense; proportional to number of employees.

7. Supervision expense; proportional to number of employees. Other expenses, such as stores and accounting, must be distributed by special arbitrary methods that fit the existing conditions.

In order to distribute the various overhead expenses to the individual machines, each item of expense must be handled separately. For example, the total personnel department expense would be distributed to the various machines, probably upon the basis of the number of workers taking part in the operation of the machine. The other overhead expense items, taxes, depreciation, rent, power and light, etc., would then be handled individually, each upon the correct basis of distribution. When all the overhead expense items have been distributed, addition of all the expenses assigned to a particular machine gives the total overhead due to the operation of the machine. This total is then adjusted to an hourly basis to obtain the machine rate.

It is sometimes more convenient to distribute the overhead expenses to the productive departments, preliminary to distribution to the machines. The advantage of this can be seen by considering the case of the personnel department. This "nonproductive" department renders some service to other "nonproductive" departments, such as the accounting department, as well as to the productive departments. In order to get an accurate distribution, the personnel department expense would be distributed to all departments to which it renders service. Other "nonproductive" department expenses are in turn distributed in a similar manner. By this process, all the "nonproductive" expenses are distributed to the productive departments. The final distribution to machines is made within the productive departments.

Regardless of what method is used, the principle is one of assigning "nonproductive" expenses to the individual machines in proportion to the service which the machine receives.

Standard Costs. When a satisfactory method of distributing overhead expense to the various unit operations of production has been established, it is then possible to determine standard costs. Each unit produced is the result of definite operations being performed upon certain materials. From a managerial viewpoint it is most desirable to know in advance what material, labor and operational expenses will be involved in producing any article. This is necessary in order to establish a selling price that will result in a reasonable profit. In addition, if an accurate theoretical production cost is known, the actual cost figures can then be compared with the theoretical values to determine how efficiently the production process has been carried out.

A standard cost is merely a theoretical cost, accounting for materials, labor and overhead, and computed for some arbitrary volume of output. Certain conditions are required in order that standard costs may be established accurately. First, the quantity and quality of materials which are to be used must be specified exactly so their cost can be computed. Second, the amount and kind of labor must be known. This is usually accomplished by the use of piece work wage payment so that the amount that will be paid for each operation is specified. Third, the volume of output must be known so that the attending overhead expense can be established. With a reasonable amount of experience the amount of overhead expense which should exist for a given volume of production can be determined with a good degree of accuracy. The established amount of overhead can then be used to compute the machine rates.

By combining the computed material, labor and machine rates a theoretical production cost can be obtained. This theoretical production cost is established as the *standard cost* of production. It thus becomes an ideal value which should be attained in actual practice if all the operations are carried out in the manner which was assumed. Obviously, if the operations are not carried out in exactly the prescribed manner, the actual cost figures will differ from the standard costs. This fact makes standard costs very useful as means of control. It is only necessary to compare the actual and standard costs to determine how efficiently a business is operating. A careful analysis of those expenses which have exceeded the standards will reveal the phases of the production process that require additional attention. In practice, department foremen are held accountable for deviations of actual costs from the established standards. In this manner a closer control over production costs is obtained. Standard costs are more important as aids to control than as a help in establishing selling prices.

In setting up standard costs it is important that they be practical as well as theoretical standards. For example, in nearly all cases there will be some unavoidable waste in material and labor. Certain excess overhead expenses will occur which can never be anticipated. These items should be considered carefully and a reasonable allowance provided when a standard cost is computed. Unless they are included, after careful consideration, much grief is likely to result.

In using standard costs for control purposes the department foreman and managers should be held accountable only for those items of expense over which they can exercise some control. For example, depreciation rates, wage rates and other such items are usually established by persons outside the operating departments. It is obviously unfair to expect a foreman to be concerned over variations in these expenses over which he has absolutely no control.

Relation of Production Control to Cost Accounting. If cost standards are to be established, they must be based upon a well-controlled and carefully specified process. Obviously, if an operation is never done twice in the same manner, or with the same materials, it is useless to attempt to establish standard costs. The term itself implies a standard method of operation.

It is the duty of the production control department to specify exactly the materials that are to be used in each product. This will enable costs for materials to be determined before processing takes place. In the same manner the operations to be performed by manual labor or by machines must be determined and specified in detail. This will fix the amount of the labor cost. With these first two elements of manufacturing cost known through specification of material and procedure, the third element, overhead expense, may be determined.

Another important function of the production control department is the constant checking which is necessary to assure that the standards of material and performance are being met at all times. This department usually originates the orders for production. This may be done by merely issuing an order number calling for the manufacture of a certain number of given articles. In other cases they may issue complete instructions for all of the operations which must be performed, accompanying these with all necessary requisitions for materials and a schedule of all tools and machines to be used. Regardless of the particular manner in which the details are carried out, the responsibility for the origination of work orders and the checking to assure that these orders are carried out in the manner specified must be assumed by some department. This is the important task of the production control organization. Without it, standard costs would be impossible.

Over- and Underabsorbed Accounts. Standard costs must be established for a particular set of conditions. If actual conditions, under which production is actually carried out, vary from those assumed, it is only logical that the actual costs will differ from the standards. Such differences may occur in material cost, labor cost or overhead expense. It is natural to expect certain variations under ordinary operating conditions. Provision for such variations is made in the standard costs by including reasonable allowances, as was mentioned previously. These common deviations are charged to *Variance* accounts. A Variance account is usually provided for each cost element, material, labor and overhead. Under normal conditions the deviations should, over a period of time, be in line with the allowances which have been provided in the standard costs. The balances of the Variance accounts are periodically charged to Profit and Loss.

The greatest problem in handling the variations from the standards arises when the volume of production is different than that assumed in establishing the standard. The problem may be clarified by a simple illustration. Assume that a man has driven his car, *on the average*, 6,000 miles per year. He pays $2.50 per month ($30 per year) as rent on a garage for storing his car. He thus figures that it costs him ½ cent per mile for garage rent. He considers this to be his "standard cost" for garage rent. During the following year he drives his car only 1,000 miles. According to his cost standard he should only pay $0.005 × 1,000, or $5, for garage rent. Obviously the results are in error because his operating "volume" was different from the standard. His standard costs failed to absorb $25 of his actual expense. Similarly, if he should drive the car more than 6,000 miles per year, the actual cost of garage rental would be more than absorbed by the standard costs.

In connection with industrial production, under- and overabsorbed costs present serious difficulties. If a plant is forced to operate at less than normal capacity the total unit cost will nearly always exceed the standard cost. This would indicate that the products would have to be sold at a higher price to obtain a reasonable profit. Yet at such times higher selling prices are usually out of the question. It is more likely that the goods would have to be sold at lower prices. If the inventory value of finished goods were based upon the actual unit cost, inventories would tend to have higher values, although from the standpoint of profit possibilities they would actually be worth less.

From the viewpoint of control, further difficulties are encountered. Actual costs would exceed the standards. Pressure would be put upon the operating personnel to reduce costs. Yet most of the increased costs would be due to increased overhead over which the operating staff would have little or no control. Similarly, when production is greater than normal the actual costs would be less than the standards. This would make it appear that the operating departments were more efficient than usual when such would not be the case.

It is apparent that such variations in unit costs are due, not to production methods, but to the extent to which the production facilities are utilized. Before a comparison of standard and actual costs can be significant, the actual costs must be adjusted to account for the difference between actual output and the assumed normal.

For control work, a satisfactory result is obtained either by using an output factor or allowance which is applied to actual costs before they are compared with the standard costs or by supplying new standards each month, these being adjusted for the scheduled output for the period. In this manner the production departments are held accountable for those production costs which they can control.

For accounting and managerial purposes it is customary to base inventories and production costs upon the standards, regardless of volume. The over- or underabsorbed costs are charged to Profit and Loss accounts. They are considered the costs resulting from managerial policy and efficiency. Thus, since they can be controlled by the management, it is up to the management to adjust policies so as to keep the over- or underabsorbed costs at a minimum.

Obviously, over- or underabsorbed costs will, to a great extent, depend on the volume assumed for computing the standard costs. By assuming a small enough volume, underabsorbed costs would be eliminated. However, this would result in high standard costs, making higher selling prices probable and increased operating efficiency unlikely. On the other hand, if too large volume is assumed, too low selling prices may result, and the operating departments may lose all respect for standards which can never be attained. Thus, as in all cases where standards are being established, great care must be taken that they will be reasonable, workable figures which will be useful for both accounting and control purposes.

The field of cost accounting has only been scratched in this chapter. Fundamental purposes and principles have been stressed. There are numerous books on the subject; many are very good. It is necessary that the methods used by different businesses vary considerably. The principles, however, will be much alike. Each system should accomplish the purpose for which it was intended. In no case should the cost of the method or the system exceed reasonable amounts. Neither should cost figures ever be used for purposes and conditions for which they are not intended.

Many examples of the systems used by various companies, together with the necessary forms, may be found in the references listed below.

REFERENCES

Atkins, P. M.: "Textbook of Industrial Cost Accounting," McGraw-Hill Book Company, Inc., New York, 1924.

Eggleston, D. C., and F. B. Robinson: "Business Costs," D. Appleton-Century Company, Inc., New York, 1921.

Gillespie, C. M.: "Accounting Procedure for Standard Costs," The Ronald Press Company, New York, 1935.

Reitell, C., and C. Van Sickle: "Cost Finding for Engineers," McGraw-Hill Book Company, Inc., New York, 1930.

Alford, L. P.: "Cost and Production Handbook," The Ronald Press Company, New York, 1934.

Bangs, John R., Jr.: "Industrial Accounting for Executives," McGraw-Hill Book Company, Inc., New York, 1930.

Bangs, J. R., and G. R. Hanselman: "Accounting for Engineers," International Textbook Company, Scranton, Pa., 1941.

PROBLEMS

94. What use has the engineer for cost accounting?
95. What should determine the amount of money that should be spent on a cost accounting system?

96. Name the three types of expenses that are ordinarily considered to be incurred in production.
97. Of what value are "post-mortem" costs?
98. Explain the difference between predetermined costs and standard costs.
99. Explain how standard costs may be used as a means of controlling production expense.
100. Why is it difficult to predict unit labor costs when workers are paid day wages?
101. What is the difference between a productive and a nonproductive department?
102. What is the fundamental factor in deciding to which department an overhead expense item should be assigned?
103. In producing wood plyboard, sheet glue is often used. Should the cost of the glue in this product be considered as a direct material expense or an indirect expense?
104. Give a logical basis for the distribution of the following overhead expenses:
    a. Workmen's compensation insurance.
    b. Telephone bills.
    c. Fire insurance.
    d. Night watchman's salary.
    e. Maintenance and repair.
    f. Depreciation on buildings.

Chapter X

INVESTMENTS

The purpose of business enterprise is to obtain profit. Profit may be defined as the difference between income and expense. This is a very simple definition, but it does give an indication of the factors that must be studied in order to determine whether or not a particular investment should be made. The detailed investigation and analysis of all the factors involved usually requires considerable time, knowledge and experience.

While profit may be determined by subtracting expenses from income, it is also necessary to know the amount of capital which is required to accomplish the desired purpose. In fact, when the amount of available capital is limited, as it often is, this one factor may be the determining element. In any case the profit must be related to the required capital so that the rate of return upon the investment may be determined.

In the determination of income, one must consider several items. First, income usually is obtained from the sale of goods or services. Thus it is necessary to decide what goods or services are to be offered for sale. Not only must the nature of the goods or services be determined, but the revenue which can be expected from their sale must likewise be estimated. This amount is usually related closely to the selling price. It may also be determined in whole or part by the available market or by competitive conditions. The selling price may be affected by the market and competition, but also may be determined by the cost of production.

In many economy studies the investment is to be made in order to bring about a decrease in production costs. In such cases the return from the investment is not affected ordinarily by the fac-

159

tors mentioned in the previous paragraph. Thus the problem becomes somewhat more simple but is handled in the same manner.

As has been mentioned in previous chapters, production cost is made up of a number of items. These are ordinarily classified as material, labor and overhead expense. It is usually not difficult to predict material and labor expenses with a fair degree of accuracy. Overhead expenses, however, are more troublesome. Fortunately some of the elements of overhead expense are subject to control and therefore may be held close to estimated values. Such items as maintenance and depreciation are very difficult to predict with a high degree of accuracy. Depreciation expense, for example, is dependent upon the economic life, and this can seldom be controlled. Yet depreciation expense must be estimated with such accuracy that the investor is able to recover his capital through accounting for depreciation. *It should always be remembered that until invested capital has been recovered there is actually no profit.*

In nearly all industrial investment, there is no guarantee that the owner will be able to recover his capital. Since the investment is being made for future periods of time, many of the factors which are considered in predicting income and expense are only estimates. At their best, estimates are not 100% accurate. Thus if income and expense are predicted and expected profit determined from these figures, the result is not entirely accurate. Naturally one should use all the information and knowledge which are available so that the predicted profit figures will be as reliable as possible. But it must be remembered that in spite of all caution the results still are not absolutely reliable. Thus when an economy study is made to determine the profit which can be expected from investment of capital funds, there is an element of risk which is present although it is not indicated entirely in the numerical answer. Thus the final step in analyzing the results shown in an economy study is to decide whether or not the expected rate of profit is sufficient. To do this, one must consider this profit in the light of the risk involved, other investment possibilities and any other pertinent data which are available.

Determination of Income. Since the amount of profit which may be obtained from an industrial investment is dependent directly upon the income that results, this factor should receive careful consideration. In a great many cases less attention has been given to this factor than it deserves. It is, of course, difficult to determine exactly what income can be obtained from the sale of goods or services. This is particularly true when an entirely new enterprise is being developed. However, this difficulty does not lessen the importance of knowing what the income will be.

Naturally the first step in determining income is to decide exactly what goods or services are to be offered for sale. This is usually the easiest part of the task. However, this is often passed over with too little consideration. Since under present market conditions most businesses are subject to severe competition, it is essential that one keep the ultimate user closely in mind when designing a new product. If one could sell electric refrigerators to the Eskimos, one could probably make a nice profit. Unfortunately the word "if" in the previous statement is the controlling word. Similarly before being carried away by a predicted profit figure one should determine whether there is a very large "if" in the idea. It is very easy to make an economy study and determine the profit that can be obtained from the sale of goods or services if one assumes that they can be sold. Selling the same goods or services may be a different matter. Thus it becomes essential in an economy study regarding the advisability of investment to know that there is a market for the product or service which is to be presented. It is usually much cheaper to make changes which will increase the salability of a product while it is in the design stages than after it has been placed on the market.

Modern use of market research is a distinct step toward eliminating useless effort in attempting to market products for which the public has no need or desire. If the doubt concerning the marketability of a product is considerable, it is entirely proper to determine whether a thorough market survey should be made in order to reduce this uncertainty. Such procedure is entirely in line with the purpose of economy studies.

Connected very closely with the problem of marketability is the selling price. The selling price often can be adjusted only slightly because of competition and production costs. However, in many cases the producer is able to vary the selling price through a considerable range. As was shown in previous chapters, this may have a pronounced effect upon the amount of income received. Of course it will also affect production costs. Adequate market surveys are often helpful in arriving at the most satisfactory selling price.[1] If factual information is not available one should be careful about increasing the selling price of a product in order to show greater income. A slight increase in selling price, without a consideration of the results on volume of sales, may make a radical change in profit. This factor should be handled with caution.

Required Investment. After a decision has been made regarding the type of goods or services which are to be offered for sale and the amount which can probably be sold, it is necessary to determine how much capital will be required to bring about the desired results. This element in an economy study can usually be determined with good accuracy. If the exact amount of output is decided upon, the productive facilities can be estimated with little difficulty. Of course, if the product is something entirely new and involves equipment of a new type, there may be some uncertainty regarding the output which can be expected. However, a reasonable amount of study should yield a satisfactory answer in nearly all instances.

Once the type and amount of physical equipment have been determined, the cost of acquisition may be determined by a straightforward method of estimation. Prices for buildings may be obtained from experienced construction engineers and contracting firms. Similarly, the cost of various types of equipment may be obtained from the producers of the equipment or, in the case of new types of equipment, by obtaining bids for its construction. Thus so far as the physical plant is concerned, little difficulty is usually found in determining the amount of capital necessary.

The amount of capital that will be required for certain intangibles is more difficult to determine. Usually many expenses besides those for a physical plant must be incurred before any prod-

---

[1] One should always be careful in establishing a selling price greater than that which is necessary to produce a reasonable profit. The long-range effect on sales may more than offset any immediate profit which may be obtained.

uct may be sold. A certain amount is necessary as working capital to provide for the purchase of raw materials, to pay salaries and to permit the organization of all the necessary factors of production. It is just as necessary to have capital for these items as it is to provide funds for the physical plants. In many cases the capital for these items is neglected, and an attempt is made to start an enterprise with insufficient capital. The result is usually disaster.

Obviously it is not easy to determine the amount of capital which should be on hand for these intangible factors of production. In most cases the amount is underestimated. This is especially true in cases of small concerns or entirely new enterprises. This phase of a study concerning the advisability of investment should receive very careful consideration and application of all the experience which is available.

The impracticability of an enterprise sometimes becomes apparent as soon as the amount of required capital is determined. If the amount is far above that which is available through any legitimate method of finance, there is little need to make further investigation. Many persons and companies would have been much better off financially if they had determined carefully the entire amount of capital which was required before they embarked upon rather risky enterprises. One might as well admit that what may be a good investment for persons possessing adequate capital may be an extremely poor investment for those without it.

It must be recognized that a particular investment possibility may be entirely sound and advisable in spite of the fact that the person considering it does not have sufficient capital. In other words, the situation may be one in which the required amount of capital would earn a very satisfactory return. The only difficulty is the fact that the persons considering the enterprise do not have adequate capital. A detailed economy study may show the soundness of the proposed investment and enable the facts to be presented so that the required capital may be obtained by legitimate borrowing or through the sale of stock. Such methods of obtaining capital are entirely legitimate provided the possibilities of profit are sufficiently large to balance the additional liabilities which such financing may involve.

Determination of Production Costs. After the capital requirements have been determined, one may make an estimate of the cost of production. Material and labor costs may be determined without much difficulty. If the details of the product are known, the amount of material required can be determined and its value computed. As mentioned previously, an accurate estimate of labor cost is more difficult to make. If a product is to be manufactured, or some process is involved where labor is paid on the basis of units produced, the problem is quite simple. On the other hand, where fixed salaries are involved, one may have to rely on past experience or upon estimate. The accuracy of such estimates will of course depend upon the conditions and the experience and judgment of the person doing the estimating. If labor costs are estimated in this manner, the final cost figures will in turn contain an element of doubt.

Overhead expenses other than maintenance and depreciation may be estimated with a fair degree of accuracy for any proposed amount of output. Of course this requires experience in such matters. However, such expenses are subject to a considerable degree of control, and once the estimates have been made operations may often be regulated to keep within the estimated figures. Thus it is usually possible to assume that the estimate of these expenses is quite accurate *if it has been made by competent persons in a scientific manner*.

In determining depreciation and maintenance expense, one must estimate what the economic life of the physical plant and equipment will be. It is usually impossible to know exactly how long any property can be operated upon an economic basis. There are two possible ways of handling this situation. One is to make every effort and use all the available information and experience to determine what the probable economic life will be. In most cases such a determination, in spite of all effort, will still be subject to great error. It is impossible to predict what new developments in the future may affect the economic life of any property. Therefore it is often the practice in economy studies to assume a write-off period which is considerably less than what one might reasonably expect the actual economic life to be. In other words, the depreciation is based upon a relatively short period, considerably less than the physical life might be expected to be and somewhat less than a reasonable expectation of economic life. The result of this procedure is that production cost estimates will tend to be high, but the amount of time which must pass before the invested capital will be recovered under the proposed setup will be shortened. Both of these results tend to make the study more conservative. Any error resulting from this practice tends to make production costs high and predicted profit correspondingly less, and there is the probability that the actual economic life will be greater than the one which has been used in the study. Thus the error tends to prevent investment in doubtful enterprises.

The use of such shortened write-off periods is of course an entirely arbitrary matter. Most large companies have established arbitrary write-off periods for various classes of plants and equipment. Surveys have shown that the tendency of these companies is toward the use of shorter write-off periods, especially when considering new equipment. Most plants now are written off within five or ten years and equipment in much shorter times. A very common write-off period for equipment in economy studies is two years.[2] However, one should use care in arbitrarily establishing a fixed write-off period which must be used in all economy studies. Such a practice is not in accordance with sound engineering. Each case should be considered in the light of the facts by giving due consideration to the past experience of the persons or companies involved. Undue shortening of the write-off period, when such is not justified by the facts, is just about as bad as using too long periods. It may be just as bad not to make an investment that is economically justifiable as it is to make one that is unsound.

In attempting to predict maintenance costs one usually must be guided by past experience and judgment. It is nearly impossible to anticipate just what the maintenance expense for any particular piece of equipment will be. However, one may usually obtain worth-while information by comparing the equipment

---

[2] Quite often the write-off period used for an economy study will be different from that which may be used for accounting purposes. This is due to the fact that the income tax authorities will not allow certain types of equipment to be written off in less than a definite period of time.

and the anticipated operating conditions with similar equipment with which he has had experience. The usual tendency is to underestimate maintenance costs.

The determination of fuel and power costs must also be based to a considerable extent upon comparison and past experience. There are considerable data available regarding power consumption for various types of plants and equipment. These may be consulted whenever necessary and will be found very helpful. Most of these data appear to give values on the high side, so their use will give conservative results. Such data may be found in various handbooks.

The Determination of the Rate of Return. After the income, operating costs and required investment have been determined as accurately as is practicable, one may compute the rate of return which may be expected from the investment of the capital. Profit is determined in the usual manner by subtracting costs from income. Obviously this profit figure has no particular significance except in the light of the amount of capital which is required to produce it. Thus the estimated profit should be divided by the required capital so as to determine the annual rate of return on the investment. This is the figure which is ordinarily used to determine the advisability of business investments. With the rate of return determined, one must then decide whether it is sufficiently great to justify making the investment.

Determination of the Sufficiency of an Anticipated Rate of Return. In order to determine whether the predicted rate of return is sufficiently great to justify the investment of capital, one must consider a number of factors. It is perhaps helpful to review briefly just what is involved when money is invested in an ordinary industrial enterprise. First, the capital is used to buy certain properties which are to be utilized to produce goods or services. One expects to obtain income from the sale of such goods or services. If the income so derived is greater than the cost of producing and selling, a profit will remain.

In this whole process of obtaining a profit in an industrial enterprise one usually has no guarantee that he will be able to sell the products. Neither is there any *absolute* knowledge of what the cost of production will be. In addition there is no assurance that the original capital will be recovered. Thus there is usually a considerable element of uncertainty as to whether the expected profit and recovery of capital will occur. This is true in most cases regardless of what care has been used in making the study. In some cases this uncertainty will be very great while in others it may be rather small. But in practically all cases, risk is involved. In the end one must decide whether the anticipated rate of profit is sufficient to offset whatever risk may exist and whether the proposed investment is the most satisfactory possible for the capital involved.

Since it is not possible to obtain an absolute measure of the risk element in any enterprise, the most logical method of solution is to compare the possible profit with that which could be obtained from other investment possibilities where risk factors are known or are comparable. The basis for such comparison is usually taken to be the return which is obtained if capital is invested in some very conservative manner such as in savings banks, government bonds or the bonds of some well-established corporation. In such investments the element of risk still exists but is extremely small. As long as the economic structure of the nation is at all sound, the risk might be said to be the minimum which is possible for any type of investment.

If capital is invested in a very conservative investment, such as those which have been mentioned, the rate of return is rather small, usually varying anywhere from 1½ to 4%. This rate of return will change with time. During the years prior to 1928 it was possible to obtain 5 or 6% return on conservative and sound investments. At the present time one is fortunate if he can obtain 2 or 3%. Thus the rate of return which may be obtained with a minimum of risk will vary from time to time.

Next in line would be the rate which could be obtained from a high grade bond. This rate is usually about 1 to 1½% higher than going rates of interest. Thus when bank interest rates are 2%, highest grade bonds yield 3 to 3½%. The risk involved in such investments is definitely greater than is associated with insured bank deposits, but is still very small. Such investments would fail to pay their interest and become insecure only in case of a national disaster.

As the next example one might consider high grade preferred stocks which yield a return of 1 to 2% more than highest grade bonds. Thus at this time such stocks pay about 4 to 5½%. The risk is greater, especially the possibility of the capital value of the investment being lessened or wiped out in time of severe business depression.

Common stocks of well-established companies may be purchased at the present time which yield returns 1½ to 2% above those of preferred stocks. Thus a return of 5 to 7% *may* be realized. The word "may" is emphasized advisedly. These stocks yield such a return only when business conditions are good. Their market value fluctuates from day to day, so there is no assurance of receiving the purchase price if the stock is sold. Of course they *may* increase in value. Obviously, there is quite a bit of risk involved in investing in such stocks. However, many such stocks are those of large and well-established corporations whose histories are well known. They would not be considered more than slightly speculative.

When one reviews the risks attending the types of investments which have just been mentioned, it is apparent that few investments in business ventures are as little risky as these. Therefore one would expect that projected ventures should offer considerably greater profit possibilities before investment in them is justified. Thus money should seldom be invested in an industrial undertaking unless an adequate economy study indicates the possibility of receiving a profit greater than 8%. And this low a profit figure would correspond only to an enterprise about which there was a great amount of accurate information. In the average business a prospective return in the neighborhood of 10 to 15% is required to justify the uncertainties which exist in the facts revealed by well-prepared economy studies. A little cold consideration of the risks actually attendant on many proposed investments makes required returns of 20 and 25% seem well justified.

Thus the only satisfactory answer to the question, "How great a return is enough?" is that the return should be commensurate with that which can be obtained from other investments in which there is the same amount of risk. The answer is best obtained by the method of comparison which has been discussed. It is a common rule in business that money should not be invested in ordinary business enterprises unless the prospective return is at least two or three times the rate which can be obtained from conservative investments such as high grade bonds. Thus at present from 7 to 10% would be considered a minimum required return. These figures would hold only when the enterprise was considered to involve only moderate risk.

It should be mentioned that whether or not one should invest in very risky enterprises, even when they offer the prospect of very high rates of profit, is an entirely different question.

Factors Affecting Risk. The factors that may affect the risk involved in any investment are many and varied. It would be almost impossible to list and discuss them all. There are four factors, however, which are nearly always present.

The first factor, which is always present, is the possible inaccuracy of the figures used in the study. If exact information is available regarding the items of income and expense, the resulting accuracy should be good. If, on the other hand, little factual information is available and nearly all the values have to be estimated, the accuracy may be high or low, depending upon the manner in which the estimated values are obtained. Are they sound, scientific estimates or merely guesses?

The accuracy of the income figures is difficult to determine. One can usually be guided only by the method by which they were obtained. If they are based upon a considerable amount of past experience or have been determined by adequate market surveys, a fair degree of reliance may be placed on them. On the other hand, if they are merely the result of guesswork, with a considerable element of hope thrown in, they must of course be considered to contain a sizable element of uncertainty. Thus to a great degree the amount of risk resulting from uncertainty in the income figures must be determined by exercising good judgment. Evaluation of this risk requires mature judgment and experience.

If the income is in the nature of a saving in existing operating costs, there should be less risk involved. It is usually easier to determine what the exact saving will be since one has considerable experience and past history on which to base the estimates.

In most cases the income figures will contain more error than any other portion of a study, with the possible exception of depreciation costs. If short write-off periods are used for computing depreciation, the element of uncertainty in the depreciation figure is reduced and the income figure would probably be the most uncertain of all those in the economy study.

There should be no large error in estimates of capital required except perhaps in the amount allowed above the actual cost of plant and equipment. If one can feel confident that the amount allowed for this purpose is on the high side, the resulting study is apt to be conservative. This element again requires careful study and experience to be certain that one is not underestimating the amount of required capital.

Among the cost figures depreciation is undoubtedly the element which should be considered most carefully. It is seldom that the actual physical life of the plant or equipment can be used in determining depreciation. It must always be remembered that only through providing for depreciation is the capital recovered. Obviously it is better to err on the side of too short a depreciation period than to make the period too long. Of course this process can be carried to an extreme. In determining the amount of risk which results from depreciation estimates one should be guided by past experience of the company involved as well as that of other companies which have operated similar properties. The important thing is to be certain that the period selected is short enough to assure that the invested capital will be recovered.

The accuracy of the other cost elements will depend to a great degree upon how carefully the estimates have been prepared. If thorough investigations have been made and all of the items considered in detail, it is reasonable to assume that they will not be in great error.

Another element of risk is the type of business involved. Some lines of business are notoriously less stable than others. For example, most mining enterprises are more risky than large retail food stores. However, one cannot arbitrarily say that an investment in any retail food store always involves less risk than investment in mining property. Whenever capital is to be invested in an enterprise, the nature and past history of the business should be considered in deciding what risk is present. In this connection it becomes apparent that investment in an enterprise which is just being organized, and thus has no past history, is usually rather uncertain.

A third factor affecting risk is the type of physical plant and equipment involved. Some types of structures have rather definite economic lives and second-hand values. Others are such that little is known of their physical or economic lives and they have almost no resale value. A good engine lathe can always be used for many purposes in nearly any shop. Depreciation on such a lathe can be estimated fairly accurately. Quite different would be a special type of lathe which was built to do only one unusual job. Its value would be dependent almost entirely upon the demand for the special task which it can perform. Thus the type of physical property involved will have a direct bearing upon the accuracy of the depreciation figures and thereby affect the risk. Where money is to be invested in specialized plant and equipment, this factor should be considered carefully.

The fourth, and very important, factor which must always be considered in evaluating risk is the length of time that must pass before all the conditions of the study become fulfilled. The conditions which have been assumed in regard to income and expense must exist throughout the write-off period in order to obtain the predicted profit. In other words, not only must the plant or equipment have an economic life equal to that of the write-off period, but all of the other items, such as income, material and labor costs, must remain relatively the same or the resulting profit will change. A particular piece of equipment might operate satisfactorily and be able to produce at as low a unit cost as is indicated in the economy study, but market conditions might have changed so that the product can no longer be sold. Similarly material costs might have increased to such an extent that profit would be eliminated. In other words, one must remember that *all of the factors involved in the study must continue throughout the write-off period as predicted or the predicted profit will not be obtained.* A long write-off period naturally decreases the probability of all of the factors remaining as estimated. Therefore a long write-off period, even though justified by the probable life of the equipment involved, always increases the risk in an investment. One simply cannot prophesy exactly what the future will bring.

Example of a Study for a New Enterprise. In order to study an application of the principles which have been discussed, the following typical case of a proposed new enterprise is presented.

TABLE 11. INVESTMENT REQUIRED FOR A 2,000–KW. POWER PLANT

Item	Estimated cost
Land	$ 4,000
Building and chimney	92,000
Boilers and condensers	55,000
Turbines and generators	60,000
Piping	40,000
Switchboard and wiring	25,000
Fuel burning equipment	4,000
Water supply	10,000
Fuel storage	6,000
Crane	2,000
Miscellaneous	8,000
Distribution lines	47,000
Total investment	$353,000

A group of men are considering building a power plant to develop electric energy for a mine and the surrounding village. The maximum load is estimated to be 1,500 kw. and the average output 950 kw. The group contemplates installing four 500-kw. turboelectric generators with the necessary boilers, auxiliary

TABLE 12. ESTIMATED ANNUAL OPERATING EXPENSES FOR A PROPOSED 2,000–KW. POWER PLANT

Item	Cost
Fuel oil	$ 52,000
Labor	16,300
Lubrication	400
Repairs and maintenance	18,500
Taxes and insurance, 4%	14,100
Depreciation (estimated life 15 years, 8% sinking fund)	12,850
Miscellaneous overhead	3,000
Total	$117,150

equipment and distribution lines. The estimated cost of the installation is shown in Table 11. The estimated annual operating expense is given in Table 12. It is estimated that the generated power could be sold at an average price of $0.0209 per kw.-hr. The question is to decide whether they should invest their money in the proposed power plant.

The estimated costs, shown in Table 11, were assembled after careful study and consultation with competent authorities and are felt to be accurate. In the preparation of the figures shown in Table 12 it was necessary to estimate many of the values by gathering as much information as possible and making use of the past experience of similar plants. Thus, while the costs of building the plant can be determined with a good degree of accuracy, the various operating expenses, such as "Repairs" and "Depreciation," are only estimates or "enlightened guesses." Similarly, the revenue to be obtained from the sale of the power cannot be known exactly. Yet, upon such figures the decision regarding the investment of a large sum of money has to be based. Some adequate method of determining the wisdom of investment is required in such cases. Once money is invested in a power plant it is relatively unavailable for a considerable period of time. The solution, therefore, must deal with the investment over a period of years.

The amount of the required investment for the proposed electric power plant is shown in Table 11 to be $353,000. The estimated expenses, as shown in Table 12, are $117,150. Capital maintenance is provided for through the "Depreciation" entry. An 8% sinking fund formula was used since the usual "Depreciation Reserve" would be utilized in the normal accounting. A rate of 8% is justified since it is known that the investment will not be made unless the expected rate of profit is in excess of this figure. With the annual charge for depreciation included, the items shown in Table 12 represent all the expenses that will be encountered after the power plant is placed in operation.

The estimated annual income from the sale of the average 950 kw. of power at $0.0209 per kw.-hr. throughout the year is $174,000.[3] Subtraction of the estimated expenses of $117,150 from the estimated annual income leaves a prospective annual profit of $56,850. This would be an annual rate of return of 16.1% upon the invested capital. If the actual income and expense after the investment has been made turn out to be as estimated, the

---

[3] Slide rule results are used throughout this problem. The error introduced by this instrument is considerably less than that due to the impossibility of predicting future results exactly. Its use is therefore justified in such computations.

actual rate of return on the investment will be 16.1% as predicted. The probability of the actual results coinciding with the estimated values must be considered in making the decision as to the wisdom of investment.

In estimating the amount of risk involved in the proposed investment the first factor to consider is the cost of the power plant. All of the items of cost were obtained from actual contractors' estimates except the "Miscellaneous" item and the cost of the distribution lines. The cost of the distribution lines is estimated after rather careful analysis and is considered to be accurate. The miscellaneous expense of $8,000 is felt to be adequate, although it might be several thousand dollars too low.

The income figures are considered to be quite accurate. The major portion of the output from the power plant would be sold to the mine. A number of the men who are going to invest in the power plant are also large stockholders in the mine. Thus the sale of power is assured. The assumed load factor is unusually high, but this is felt to be justified since the consumption of power at the mine could be controlled to quite an extent so as to give a high factor. Thus the men concerned feel there would be no difficulty in disposing of the power at a favorable price.

It is thought that the estimated operating expenses probably are less accurate than any other items in the study. However, these are the result of sound study and comparison with other similar power plants. The amounts for "Repairs and Maintenance" and "Taxes and Insurance" have arbitrarily been set higher than it is expected they will actually be. Thus it is believed the actual operating expense will not exceed the estimates.

Undoubtedly the factor which contributes most to risk is the length of time over which the plant is to be written off. From the viewpoint of physical life, a 15-year write-off period is not at all excessive for a power plant of this type. From an economic viewpoint, however, a 15-year period is a rather long time, especially where the major source of revenue is dependent upon the operation of a mine. It is very difficult to predict what will happen for 15 years in the future. In this case the mine has been in operation for several years on a small scale. Extensive surveys have been made to determine the quantity and quality of the ore which remains. Unless an extremely severe and long national depression occurs, or some entirely unforeseen development should take place, the mine should continue to be profitable for many years beyond the selected amortization period. However, these possibilities do exist and add to the risk involved in the proposed investment.

Considering all of the factors, it is apparent that the proposed investment is a much greater risk than investment in sound common stocks would be. For example, if the estimated income figures should be only 16% too high the profit would be cut in half. The capital recovery period is rather long. It is felt that such an investment should offer a prospective profit of at least twice that which could be obtained from good grade common stocks. This would make a prospective profit of about 12 to 14% necessary. Since the proposed power plant offers a prospective profit of over 16% it appears to be a good, though somewhat speculative, investment and the power plant should be built.

Minimum Pay-Out Period. Where rather long capital recovery periods are involved, and as a result considerable risk is usually present, a further check is often made to determine the advisability of investment. This consists of determining the minimum time which must pass before the investors will have recovered their invested capital in the form of earnings. Unfortunately, this minimum pay-out period is not always computed in the same manner. The two most commonly used methods differ only in that minimum interest is included in one and omitted in the other. Each is entirely satisfactory and useful if one knows what is included and what the results mean.

By the first method one determines the minimum time which will elapse before actual income will have exceeded actual out-of-pocket expenses by an amount equal to the capital investment. In other words, how long will it be before the owners could abandon the business without losing any of their capital, but also without receiving any interest on their funds?

To obtain this figure the estimated out-of-pocket[4] expenses are subtracted from the estimated earnings. This gives the amount

---

[4] Those expenses which are actually paid for in cash. In Table 12 this would include all but "Depreciation."

available annually to insure the investors against loss of capital. By dividing this amount into the total invested capital the minimum pay-out period is obtained. Thus for the power plant which was discussed previously the pay-out period would be determined as follows:

Estimated income	$174,000
Estimated out-of-pocket expense	104,300
Available for pay-out	69,700

$$\text{Minimum pay-out period} = \frac{\$353,000}{\$69,700} = 5.06 \text{ years}$$

Thus, in this case, while conditions would have to remain as anticipated for 15 years for the owners to recover their capital and receive a 16.1% profit, after five years they would be assured of no actual loss in capital.

The other method of determining the minimum pay-out period assumes that one wishes to know the minimum time which must pass before the invested capital would be available together with a low rate of profit. It is computed in the same manner as before except that profit on the invested capital is included as a cost. It is an entirely useful method except for the fact that the interest rate selected has a great effect on the result. Rates of profit about the same as ordinary bank interest rates are commonly used in such computations, although many advocates of this method use much higher rates. If a 4% interest rate were used, the pay-out period for the power plant would be:

Estimated income		$174,000
Estimated out-of-pocket expense	$104,300	
Profit on capital [5]	14,100	
		118,400
Available for pay-out		$ 55,600

$$\text{Minimum pay-out period with interest} = \frac{\$353,000}{\$55,600} = 6.35 \text{ years}$$

For low rates of profit the difference in the results obtained by the two methods is not great. If high rates are used the results vary considerably and the pay-out period determined by using the high profit rate loses most of its significance.

Example of a Proposed Investment to Reduce Expenses. A manufacturer of jewelry is contemplating the installation of a

---

[5] Note that profit upon the entire amount of capital invested is used. This is necessary, since the sinking fund method was used for computing depreciation.

system which will recover a large portion of the fine particles of gold which result from the various manufacturing operations. At the present time a little over $3,000 worth of gold per year is being lost. This figure has been determined accurately from the known weights of incoming and outgoing material. The proposed recovery system would involve a network of exhaust ducts and separators. The complete installation would cost $4,000. It is known from the history of other installations of equipment of this type that at least two-thirds of the gold lost at present could be recovered. The best estimates available are that it would cost $600 per year for operation expense and $200 per year for maintenance and repairs and that taxes and insurance would be approximately 2%. The company demands that all equipment be written off within five years. The average earnings of the company have been around 8% for several years. Should the gold recovery installation be made?

Such an investment is made to reduce some of the operating expenses; in this case the cost of material used. Thus the saving (income) to be obtained by making an investment is almost entirely within the control of the investors. The company knows exactly what expenses have been. If the efficiency of the proposed equipment is known, the only factors which should affect the saving are the variation of production, operation and maintenance expense of the proposed equipment, and depreciation expense. In most cases of this type these items are known or may be predicted quite accurately. The company would have a good idea of how its volume might vary. Operation and maintenance expenses can usually be estimated accurately, especially if historical data are available on the proposed equipment. Depreciation costs can be placed on the safe side by requiring the equipment to be written off in a period shorter than the actual physical life.

For the gold recovery system the total annual operating costs would be:

Operation	$ 600
Maintenance	200
Taxes and insurance	80
Depreciation (8%, S. F.)	682
Total	$1,562

Since the resulting saving in recovered gold would be two-thirds of $3,000 or $2,000, the actual net saving resulting from the investment of $4,000 would be $2,000 − $1,562 = $438. This is a return of almost 11% on the invested capital.

In deciding whether or not this possible return of 11% is sufficient to justify investment, each factor which might contribute to risk must be examined so that a measure of the total risk may be obtained. In this case it appears that the factors are quite well controlled or known. There is little reason to believe that much more risk would be involved than is present in all of the normal operations of the company. Thus the company has its own experience to use as a basis of comparison. If the company is sound and its business quite stable, certainly a return of 11% should be satisfactory since the average capital invested in the company is earning only 8%.

Thus it may be seen that when capital is being invested in a going concern in order to bring about reduction in expenses, or where company funds are used for the same purpose, the risk is usually easier to determine and is often much less than where entirely new enterprises are involved. As a result the rate of return required for such investments is often lower, being only a little more than the existing rate of earning of the company.

Investment Where Income Is Unknown. Decisions to invest or not to invest capital often must be made when it is impossible to know or evaluate the return. In some cases it is not particularly necessary to know what the income will be. This often occurs when public or governmental improvements are made. The returns are often in nonmonetary form, yielding convenience and satisfaction to the public. When companies spend large sums of money to create customer or employee good will, a precise measurement of the return is impossible. Yet such investments must often be made.

Probably the only rule that can be established for such cases is that no more should be invested than is required to give a satisfactory result. Obviously, this rule cannot be followed rigidly. In building public roads, for example, it may be advisable to spend more than a bare minimum in order to assure permanence and low maintenance cost. In such cases the rule of least annual cost becomes important. The income (or at least a large part of it) resulting from many projects that at first thought do not appear subject to the type of analysis under discussion can be measured if the undertakings are analyzed fully. Whenever this can be done it should not be neglected. Greater efficiency in the use of capital is bound to result. Some of these cases will be discussed in later chapters.

Rules for Investment Economy Studies. In making economy studies to determine the advisability of proposed investments the following rules should be remembered:

1. *The capital resources should be safeguarded and kept intact.* When capital is invested there is an expectation of a profit. This profit is based upon the amount of the investment. If the amount of the investment is not maintained, after some time has passed the investor finds that his capital has disappeared. While he may have been receiving some income from his investment, this income was not all profit but was in part his original capital. As a result a time is bound to be reached when his investment has been entirely consumed and the property in which his money was invested has become of no further use. He now finds that he has neither income nor capital. Such a condition can be avoided only by maintaining the investment through rigid deductions from income for depreciation. Adequate provision should be made to safeguard against obsolescence.

2. *The invested capital should earn a fair rate of return.* Our entire economic system is based upon the principle that capital should be productive. Capital is accumulated and invested in order that a profit may be earned. There may be considerable difference in opinion about what constitutes a fair rate of return, but there is not a doubt that modern business cannot exist without some profit. The engineer must see that his mechanisms are economically as well as physically productive and make allowance for this in his selection decisions. Investment decisions should be based upon the indicated rate of return.

3. *Adequacy of the expected profit should be decided in the light of the risks involved and other investment possibilities.* Since profit is the reward for risking capital in business ventures, the risk involved in any proposed investment should be analyzed, and the

profit should be commensurate with this risk. Other investment possibilities should be considered in deciding whether the proposed investment offers the most satisfactory use of the capital.

4. *Funds for capital maintenance should be provided from the earnings of the invested capital.* Invested capital is expected to earn a profit. In the same manner capital should be expected to pay its own operating expenses. A true profit is not realized until all operating expenses have been paid. The capital maintenance charges for any particular property should be paid from the earnings of that property and not from the earnings of some other investment. In other words, each investment should stand on its own feet. Any analysis of long-term costs is not complete until provision has been made for the investment to provide its own capital maintenance.

5. *All economic selection calculations should be made in accordance with the generally used methods of business in so far as possible.* Business has as its principal goal the production of goods, or the rendering of a service, for profit. In order to do this there is need for the services of accountants, lawyers, bankers and numerous other professional workers. All must do their work in a manner which can be readily understood by the others. Only in this way can each be most useful to the enterprise. In making economy studies, the engineer must use whatever data are necessary to make them as nearly factual as possible. However, whenever possible the figures for studies of estimated future results should be similar to those which will be used, after the investment is made, to record and check its performance. All persons, including the engineer, should utilize methods and terms that are accepted and used by the business as a whole. This will avoid confusion and do much to ensure better cooperation.

6. *Above all other rules, investment decisions should be based on the existing facts.* Many business procedures are carried out on an empirical basis. As long as conditions do not change, a standardized procedure gives satisfactory results. But no set of generalized principles can account for changing conditions. Thus in no case should any decision be based on other than the existing facts.

REFERENCES

Eidmann, F. L.: "Economic Control of Engineering and Manufacturing," McGraw-Hill Book Company, Inc., New York, 1931.

Grant, E. L.: "Principles of Engineering Economy," The Ronald Press Company, New York, 1938.

Kimball, D. S., and D. S. Kimball, Jr.: "Principles of Industrial Organization," McGraw-Hill Book Company, Inc., New York, 1939.

PROBLEMS

105. Name some of the factors which must be considered in determining whether a calculated prospective return is sufficient to justify investment.

106. The prospectus of an oil field development company states that "investors should obtain not less than a 25% return on their money." The nearest producing oil well to the proposed development is 40 miles away. There are no reputable oil men connected with the development company. Banks are paying $1\frac{3}{4}\%$ on time deposits at this time. What are some of the factors which you would consider before deciding whether you should invest any money in the proposed oil development?

107. Joe Poppsis has an opportunity to buy a peanut stand for $600. The present owner has not been able to make the business pay, but Joe feels that this is due to the owner's lack of business acumen. He estimates that an additional $100 will be required to put the stand in good condition. He believes that he can sell at least 1,500 bags of peanuts each week at 5 cents per bag. His raw peanuts will cost 2 cents per bag and his other operating expenses will be $10 per week. Joe wishes to recover his capital within five years. He is obtaining 3% on his money, which is invested in bonds. Joe has a steady job and earns $30 per week. Operating the peanut stand would require all of his time.
    a. What would be the return on Joe's investment?
    b. Would you advise Joe to buy the peanut stand?

108. The Esco Manufacturing Company is located outside a large city. All of their materials and finished products have to be hauled to and from the plant by truck. The average cost paid to a trucking company for this service is $1.20 per ton. It is estimated that if they acquired the necessary land and built a spur railroad track to their plant they could reduce the cost of transporting material to 22 cents per ton. The spur track would cost $40,000. It is estimated that a conservative life for this track would be 10 years. Annual maintenance charges would be $250, and taxes at the rate of 1%. It is thought that an average of 40 tons of freight per day would be affected by the proposed change. The plant operates an average of 300 days per year. The company has sufficient capital available for this investment if it is found to be advantageous. Average earnings of the company over a period of years have been a little over 7%. Should the spur track be built?

109. If it were necessary for the Esco Company to obtain the capital for the proposed spur track by selling a $40,000 issue of 7%, noncallable, 10-year bonds, should the construction be undertaken?

110. A hotel in the Sacramento Valley is contemplating the installation of an air conditioning system. The lowest satisfactory bid for the installation is $18,000. It is estimated that the system will have to be operated at full capacity during 14 weeks of the year and at reduced output for the equivalent of eight weeks each year. It will cost $18 per day to operate at full capacity and $12 per day at reduced output. Annual maintenance costs are estimated at $125. The life of the installation is estimated at 15 years. The hotel has 150 rooms. It is estimated that with the air conditioning system 90% of the rooms could be rented during the 20 weeks of the summer season at an average profit of $2 per day whereas without the air conditioning system only 80% of the rooms would be occupied. Other first-class hotels in the city have installed similar air conditioning systems. Assuming money to be worth 6%, would you recommend the installation?

111. To provide 3 inches of rock wool insulation on the ceilings of a five-room house will cost $80. It is estimated that this insulation will reduce the fuel bill by 20%. The annual fuel bill has averaged $78. The owner of the house is obtaining a return of 3% on his invested savings. How long would the rock wool insulation have to last in order to justify its installation?

112. A small chemical plant has its own power plant but requires "stand-by" service from a utility company so that continuous service will be available. The company is paying $100 a month for this stand-by service. In addition they pay an average of $700 a year for purchased power while their plant is being overhauled.

   A Diesel plant for stand-by is being considered. This installation would cost $42,000. Maintenance of this plant under these conditions is estimated at $200 per year. Taxes and insurance will be 1% of the first cost. It is estimated that the Diesel plant will last at least 20 years. The additional expense of operating the proposed stand-by plant during overhaul of the main plant is estimated to be $300. The average earnings of the company have been slightly over 6%. Would you advise the installation of the stand-by plant?

113. A certain dock is worth $620,000. The average value of the merchandise on the dock is $500,000. The insurance rate on the dock is 1.02% and on the goods stored on the dock 0.97%. A proposal for the installation of a fire sprinkler system is being considered. This system will cost $14,500 and effect a saving of 23% in both insurance premiums. Annual maintenance and inspection cost is estimated to be $100. Annual taxes would be $70. The owners of the dock demand that the investment in such equipment be written off within 10 years. Operation of the dock has given a return of over 7% on the invested capital. Sufficient funds are available for purchasing the sprinkler system. Would you advise installation of the sprinkler system? Give full reasons.

114. The manufacturer of an automatic coal stoker guarantees that a saving of at least 20% can be effected in the fuel bill when their stoker replaces hand firing. A department store is considering the installation of one of these stokers which will cost $4,300. The average annual fuel bill has been $1,420. A conservative estimate of the life of the stoker is 10 years,

with annual charges for operation and maintenance of $140. Taxes and insurance are estimated at $45 per year. The stoker will also effect a saving of $1,320 annually in labor. If the store's capital is worth 7%, would you advise the installation?

115. In the operation of a pot heater curing unit in a tire factory the tire molds are removed from the heaters by manual labor. One man is required for this task, which is a very tiring one. An employee has designed a machine that will automatically remove the molds from the heaters and couple them on the conveyor. The machine will cost $2,200 to build and should last for several years. It is estimated that it would cost $200 per year to operate and maintain the remover. Use of the machine would eliminate one man from the crew on each shift. The man could be employed elsewhere in the plant. Each man on the curing unit crew receives $1.08 per hour. The plant operates three 6-hour shifts per day for an average of 250 days per year. The company requires that all such equipment pay for itself within one year. Average earnings of the company have been 8%. Taxes and insurance on the machine would not exceed $8. Should the machine be built and used?

Chapter XI

ALTERNATIVE INVESTMENTS

It is a common experience to find that most business ventures may be carried out in different manners. While the physical results may be the same, or approximately the same, the required capital and the operating expenses of the various methods may vary considerably. With this situation existing, it is often necessary to decide not only whether an enterprise should be undertaken but also in what manner it should be conducted.

The decision regarding several investment alternatives, or levels, is made quite simple if one remembers that the purpose of investment is to obtain the greatest possible return from *each* dollar of capital. Theoretically, one should consider each unit of capital separately before investing it. In actual practice there are usually only a limited number of choices. The minimum amount of capital required by any of the possibilities represents the least, or basic, investment that can be made to obtain the desired results. The investment of an additional amount of capital will bring different revenue or cause different expense of operation, or both. Any change in profit which occurs is obviously the direct result of the additional capital which was invested. Thus one may measure the effectiveness of the investment of additional increments of capital beyond the minimum which would be required to obtain the desired results. If the additional return obtained by investing an additional amount of capital is better than could be obtained from investment of the same capital elsewhere, the investment should probably be made. If such is not the case one obviously would not invest more than the minimum amount required. Thus, in determining how much should be invested, each possible increment of investment must be considered as a separate investment possibility. Of course, along with this one must consider any possible effect of a change in the total amount invested on the investment as a whole.

Fixed Revenue or No Data Regarding Revenue. Many economy studies must be made where data regarding the revenue which will result from several possible levels of investment are not known. It is known in such cases that some one of several methods is to be used. In other words, there is no question as to whether or not the project is to be undertaken. One is only to determine the manner in which it shall be done.

In such studies it is ordinarily assumed that the physical output from each method will be the same and that the revenue will be the same for each and may thus be neglected. Different levels of investment will result only in different operating expenses. Thus the result of investment beyond the minimum will be an increase or decrease in operating expense. Obviously, if the operating expense increases with increased investment the additional amount of capital should not be invested. If increased investment, however, results in decreased operating expenses, one must decide whether the decrease in expenses is sufficient to justify the additional investment. Such a case may be illustrated by the following example.

A company is going to install a new molding press. Three different presses are available. The essential differences as to cost and operating expense are as follows:

	A	B	C
Cost (installed)	$3,000	$3,800	$6,200
Power, per year	340	340	800
Labor, per year	3,300	3,000	2,400
Maintenance, per year	200	250	350
Taxes and insurance	2%	2%	2%
Life (economic)	5 years	5 years	8 years

Each press will produce the same number of units. Other items of expense than those listed will not vary appreciably. Capital is worth 7% to this company. Which press should be chosen?

Since each press will produce the same output, the only justification there can be for investing more than $3,000 is the possibility that use of additional capital will bring about sufficient

saving in operating expenses to warrant the additional investment. To determine whether the resulting savings will justify
the additional investment, examine Table 13 where the operating
expenses of each press are tabulated. It will be noted that the
total operating expense of press B is $95 per year less than that
of press A. This saving can be brought about by the investment
of $800 more than would be required for the purchase of press A.
Thus the investment of $800 will produce a saving (return) of
$95. This would be a yield of approximately 11.9% upon the
required investment of $800. Since it was stated that capital is

TABLE 13. COMPARATIVE TOTAL ANNUAL COSTS OF
THREE MOLDING PRESSES

Item	A	B	C
Power	$ 340	$ 340	$ 800
Labor	3,300.	3,000	2,400
Maintenance	200	250	350
Taxes and insurance	60	76	124
Depreciation (7%, S. F.)	522	661	605
Total operating expense	$4,422	$4,327	$4,279

worth 7% to this company, if one assumes that this rate is all
the company can obtain from the use of idle capital elsewhere,
the investment of the additional $800 is justified.

Considering press C by comparing it to press B, one finds that
a *further* saving of $48 per year can be obtained by investing an
additional increment of $2,400. This saving would be a return
of only 2% upon the capital required to produce it. Obviously
this return does not justify the investment of the additional
$2,400.

From this example and the previous discussion it is seen that
where no revenue data are given each increment of capital above
the minimum must be considered as a separate investment possibility. By this method of analysis the same method and reasoning that are used for deciding whether an investment should be
made may be used to determine the amount that should be
invested. It should be recognized, however, that the risk factors,
and consequently the rate of return which should be demanded,
may be somewhat different for alternatives of investment than
they would be for deciding upon the original investment.

Other Factors Which May Affect the Decision. There are some factors which occasionally may alter the choice between alternative investments even though one has been found to yield a satisfactory return on the additional capital required. One of these factors is the amount of capital required. It may be found that the alternative having the minimum annual cost requires considerably more capital than another having slightly higher annual cost. If the amount of capital available is limited, or if capital is very difficult to obtain, it may be necessary or wise to select the alternative which may be slightly less efficient but requires only an amount of capital which is available. If capital is limited, such a choice is necessary in order to make an enterprise possible. It should be recognized, however, that the enterprise will not have as low unit costs as it would have if the most economic alternative could have been used. In making such a choice one must decide whether it is more desirable to operate somewhat uneconomically or not do business at all.

Another factor which might cause preference to be given to an alternative that does not give minimum annual cost is the economic state of business at the particular time. If times are difficult and the state of affairs uncertain, it may be advisable to operate with slightly increased costs rather than to tie up larger amounts of capital than are absolutely necessary. Such a decision must, of course, be made with all the facts and results in mind.

A third factor which may alter the choice among alternative investments is the greater economic life of some of the alternatives. One of the alternatives may have minimum annual cost but also a much longer physical and economic life. Even though the longer economic life seems well justified, the very fact that a longer capital recovery period is involved makes the risk greater than for the other possible choices. Thus, even though the annual cost may be somewhat less, such an alternative may not always be chosen. This is particularly true where the annual cost is only slightly less than some other alternative that involves a shorter economic life. A further fact which often influences such decisions is that alternatives having longer economic lives usually require the investment of greater amounts of capital. Of course there are situations where long economic life is desirable. In such cases a consideration of the facts will bring about the correct decision.

Alternative Investments Having Varying Revenues. Alternative levels of investment often offer different revenues. In some cases the results obtained by one method are considerably different from those which would be had from another. All but the main objective may be quite different. Where the magnitude of the results, as well as the operating expense, is changed by varying the method and the amount of the investment, the economy study must consider all of these facts. While such studies are usually somewhat more complex, the main purpose is still to determine whether the proposed investment offers the best use for the capital.

When a change in the method, or amount invested, causes a difference in output or revenue, several possibilities result. Among these are the following:

1. Additional investment above a required minimum may increase the rate of return on the total investment above that which can be obtained by minimum investment. This means that the added increment of invested capital will earn a higher rate of return than can be obtained from the minimum investment. Because of certain circumstances the added increment of capital is more productive than the basic investment. Where the return from the minimum amount of capital is not quite sufficient to justify investment, the investment of an added amount of capital may remove a proposition from the doubtful or undesirable class to the satisfactory or advisable level.

If the rate of return should continue to increase with added increments of capital one would like to invest as much capital as possible, assuming that unlimited funds are available and that the soundness of the investment does not decrease. These conditions, of course, seldom exist. Funds are usually somewhat limited, and increasing size, resulting from increased investment, usually results in greater risk. Moreover, it is very seldom that added increments of capital continue to earn rates of return equal to or greater than the preceding amounts which have been invested.

2. The second possible result from increased investment is that investment of an additional increment of capital will cause the rate of return on the total investment to decrease. This means that the rate of return resulting from the added increment of capital is less than that which can be obtained from the original amount. For example, assume that from the investment of A dollars, X dollars of profit will result. X/A is the rate of return resulting from the investment of A dollars. If $A + B$ dollars were invested, the profit would be $X + Y$ dollars. Since Y dollars of profit resulted from the investment of B dollars of additional capital, the rate of return upon the additional capital would be Y/B. If Y/B is less than X/A, the investment of the additional amount of B dollars was not as good a proposition as resulted from the investment of A dollars.

When such a situation exists, the decision as to the correct amount to invest is not always simple. For example, consider the following data regarding two investment alternatives A and B:

	A	B
Cost	$3,500	$5,000
Annual operating expense	1,400	1,240
Annual income	1,900	1,920
Annual profit	500	680

Alternative B shows an annual profit of $180 more than alternative A. However, it would be necessary to invest $1,500 of additional capital in order to obtain this additional profit. This means that the actual annual rate of return on this $1,500 of additional capital would be 12%. While this is a fairly good rate of return, one should consider that the investment of $3,500 in alternative A would produce a return of 14.3%. Considering the entire $5,000 which would be invested if alternative B were used, one finds that this choice would result in a return of 13.6% upon the total investment. Thus in a case of this type one has several factors to consider before arriving at a decision as to the method which should be used.

It is entirely logical and proper to want to accomplish any undertaking with the investment of as little capital as possible. There should be a good reason for utilizing any method which requires more than the minimum amount of capital. If the rate of the additional return that will result from the added investment is greater than the rate produced by the minimum investment, this may be a satisfactory reason for increasing the size of the investment. Such a condition results in the return on the entire amount invested being greater than the rate which would be earned by the investment of only the minimum amount.

If, however, the rate of return from the added increment of investment is less than that which would be obtained from the minimum amount of capital, the decision must be made by considering all the possibilities for investment of the increment of capital *and* the effect upon the minimum amount of capital. For example, in the illustration just discussed, the added increment of $1,500 which would be required for alternative B would earn a return at the rate of 12%. If this amount of capital were on hand and no other investment opportunity of a similar risk were available which offered this great a return, the use of this capital to employ alternative B would be the best available investment for this money. While the additional $1,500 would not be invested as effectively as the basic $3,500, it would be earning at a rate that would satisfy its owner and might thus be called a *contentment* rate. However, when such a decision is made one must keep in mind the fact that the entire amount which is invested becomes a single investment and thereafter earns a rate of return determined by the revenue produced by the entire investment. Thus in the previous problem, while from a theoretical view the basic $3,500 earns 14.3% and the incremental $1,500 earns 12%, actually the entire investment of $5,000 earns 13.6%. Therefore, not only must one determine what return the added investment will produce, but he must also consider the effect which the added investment will have upon the minimum investment which would secure the desired results.

3. A third possibility is that added investment would have no effect upon the rate of return which the total investment would earn. This means that the rate of return earned by the added increment of capital is the same as that earned by the basic investment. Under such circumstances the only limit to the amount that should be invested is the amount of capital that

the owners have available and wish to tie up in one enterprise. However, one should always keep in mind the hazards which result from investing too much capital in a single enterprise. Actually this third possibility is seldom encountered.

An Example of Increasing Investment Affecting the Rate of Return. An excellent example of the conditions which may arise

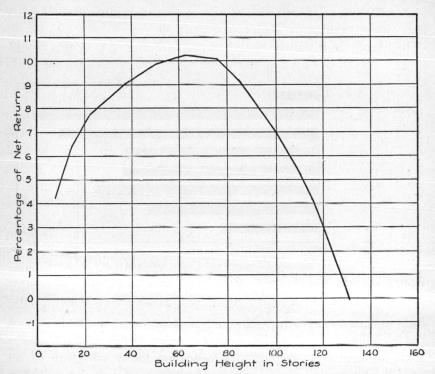

FIGURE 33. Return from the investment required for building skyscrapers of various heights.

when added increments of investment produce unequal rates of return is found in a study which was made several years ago by W. C. Clark and J. L. Kingston.[1]

The study was made for a theoretical office building of various heights which was to be built on a plot of ground in New York City where land was worth $200 per square foot. Data were

---

[1] Clark and Kingston, "The Skyscraper," American Institute of Steel Construction, Inc., New York.

compiled for the cost of erecting buildings of the heights indicated in the chart of Figure 33. Estimates were made of the
expected income and expenses of each structure. From these
data the expected return on the total investment was computed
and plotted as shown in Figure 33. In addition it was possible
to determine what return could be expected from the investment
necessary to add a certain increment to the height of the building. These results are shown in Figure 34.

In Figure 33 it will be noted that a building of 8 stories would
yield a return of only slightly over 4%. This would not be suffi-

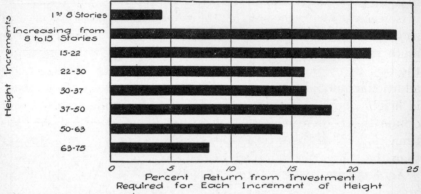

FIGURE 34. Return yielded by investments required to add various increments
to the height of proposed skyscrapers.

cient to justify investment in such a structure. As the height of
the building is increased the probable return is also increased
until a maximum of 10.2% is indicated for a structure of 63
stories. Increasing the height beyond 63 stories would result in
an actual decrease in the rate of return. The projected curve
indicates that for a building of 131 stories the rate of return
would be zero.

The bar chart of Figure 34 presents some significant points of
this situation. The bars represent the rate of return which would
result from the investment necessary to provide each additional
increment to the height of the building. Additional investment
used to increase the height from 8 to 15 stories would yield a
return at the rate of 23.69%. Each successive increment of
approximately 7 stories up to a total height of 50 stories yields a

decreasing rate of return. The increase from 37 to 50 stories would produce a larger rate of return, but this is due to the lessened effect of the set-back ordinance. Beyond 63 stories the increases in investment would yield a rate of return less than the maximum of 10.2% shown in Figure 33. As a result, the rate of return on the total investment is decreased with each additional increment of height beyond 63 stories. A point is reached, beyond 100 stories, where each additional amount invested has a negative rate of return.

This study points out how investment beyond the minimum may be necessary to make a project feasible. At the same time it is necessary to know how far the investing of additional capital should be carried. The number of stories that will bring a maximum rate of return upon the total investment is theoretically the best investment. If no better opportunity for investment of additional amounts of capital exists than is offered by the increase in height above this point, it is logical to build more stories and obtain this contentment rate of return. This process could continue as long as the return from each additional story is greater than the contentment return.

An Example of Alternative Investments. An example of the application of the principles which have just been discussed to a somewhat more complex problem is found in the following case.

In the example discussed in the preceding chapter, where investment in a proposed power plant was being considered, three types of plants were investigated. These were (a) steam, (b) Diesel and (c) hydroelectric. In each case the amount of the required investment was different and the operating costs varied. It was therefore necessary to make a study of the investment and operating costs for each type of plant. Since the output of each was identical, the income would be the same. With the income, expense and investment factors known, a comparison had to be made which would show the relative advantages of the several alternative plants.

The costs of building the various types of power plants are shown in Table 14. The Diesel plant was to consist of four 500-kw. engine and generator units which would be installed in a build-

TABLE 14.   CONSTRUCTION COSTS FOR THREE PROPOSED
TYPES OF 2,000-KW. POWER PLANTS

	Steam	Diesel	Hydroelectric
Land	$ 4,000	$ 4,000	$ 2,000
Chimney	12,000	—	—
Building	80,000	75,000	60,000
Dam site and dam	—	—	420,000
Boilers and condensers	55,000	—	—
Generating units	60,000	240,000	86,000
Piping	40,000	15,000	10,000
Switchboard and wiring	25,000	25,000	35,000
Fuel burning equipment	4,000	—	—
Water supply	10,000	10,000	—
Fuel storage	6,000	5,000	—
Crane	2,000	2,500	3,500
Distribution lines	47,000	47,000	47,000
Transmission lines and transformers	—	—	30,000
Miscellaneous	8,000	8,000	10,000
Total investment	$353,000	$431,500	$703,500

ing on the same site as for the proposed steam plant. For the
hydroelectric plant it was necessary to purchase a dam site several
miles back in the mountains and construct the necessary dam
and transmission lines. From the total investments required, as
shown in Table 14, it will be noted that the additional investment needed for a Diesel plant, over that required for the steam
plant, is $78,500. To construct a hydroelectric plant would
require $272,000 more than was necessary for the Diesel plant.

The operating costs of the three types of power plants are
shown in Table 15. The last item in the table, "Savings over

TABLE 15.   ANNUAL OPERATION COSTS OF THREE TYPES OF
2,000-KW. POWER PLANTS

	Steam	Diesel	Hydroelectric
Fuel oil	$ 52,000	$ 30,950	$ —
Labor	16,300	13,800	22,500
Lubrication	400	1,150	950
Repairs and maintenance	18,500	17,500	12,000
Taxes and insurance (4%)	14,100	17,260	28,150
Depreciation (8% S. F.)			
Steam plant, life 15 years	12,850		
Diesel plant, life 12 years		22,500	
Hydro plant, life 20 years			15,330
Miscellaneous overhead	3,000	3,000	3,000
Total	$117,150	$106,160	$81,930
Savings over next lower cost installation		$ 10,990	$24,230

next lower cost installation," shows the amount that would be saved in operating costs by investing in a more expensive type of plant. For example, it was estimated that it would cost $10,990 per year less to operate the Diesel plant than would be required for the steam installation. Similarly, the annual cost of operation of the hydroelectric plant would be $24,230 below that of the Diesel plant. These figures, with those obtained from Table 14, furnish the necessary information for determining the advisability of increasing the amount to be invested in the power plant.

The additional investment of $78,500 in a Diesel plant would bring about a saving of $10,990. The annual rate of return on this increment of capital would thus be 14%. Since the probable return on the capital required for a steam plant would be 16.1%, it is apparent that the investment of the additional $78,500 would not be as profitable as the minimum investment of $353,000. It would be advisable to invest the additional capital required for the Diesel plant only if this extra capital were available and no better investment possibility could be found.

The case of the hydroelectric plant is more easily decided. Investment of $272,000 more capital than would be required for the Diesel plant would produce an additional saving of $24,230. This saving is equal to only 8.9% on the required capital. This rate of return would be much too small to justify the investment of such a sum over a 20-year period.

Investigation of the effect of investing the additional amount required for a Diesel plant upon the total amount of capital shows that the net profit which would result would be $174,000 — $106,160 or $67,840. This would give a rate of return of 15.7% upon the total investment of $431,500, as compared to the return of 16.1% which could be obtained from the investment of the minimum of $353,000.

One factor in favor of the Diesel plant was the fact that the write-off period was three years shorter than for the steam plant.[2]

In this case the decision was actually made in favor of the

---

[2] The shorter write-off period was used because historical data for Diesel power plants are not as extensive or reliable as those for the other types of plants being considered.

Diesel plant. Extra capital was available, and no other use for these funds offered as satisfactory a rate of return. It was acknowledged that the rate of return which would be earned by the basic investment of $353,000 would be lowered slightly, but it was felt that the shorter write-off period offset this loss.

Minimum Annual Cost Method of Comparison. A method of comparing alternative investment possibilities that is used to some extent is that of "Minimum Annual Costs." This method consists of adding minimum required profit [3] on each investment to the other items of annual cost. Use of this method requires the user to decide upon a minimum rate of profit which will justify the investment of the required capital.

The minimum annual cost method would be applied to the problem of the three types of power plants as follows:

	Steam	Diesel	Hydroelectric
Fuel oil	$ 52,000	$ 30,950	$ —
Labor	16,300	13,800	22,500
Lubrication	400	1,150	950
Repairs and maintenance	18,500	17,500	12,000
Taxes and insurance (4%)	14,100	17,260	28,150
Depreciation (8% S. F.)			
Steam plant, life 15 years	12,850		
Diesel plant, life 12 years		22,500	
Hydro plant, life 20 years			15,330
Miscellaneous overhead	3,000	3,000	3,000
Minimum profit (8%)	28,240	34,520	56,280
Total annual cost	$145,390	$140,680	$138,210

From these figures, it is seen that the hydroelectric plant offers the minimum annual cost when 8% is the minimum required profit. It will be noted, however, that this method does not tell, without further computations and interpretation, what the actual return on the investment for each type of plant will be. Neither does it show the rate of return to be obtained from each increment of investment. Thus the use of this method is likely to lead to confusion, and even erroneous results, unless it is understood thoroughly and interpreted correctly. For example, as has been shown previously one would not wish to invest in the hydroelectric power plant unless capital was not limited and no better investment opportunity could be found for the extra capital that

---

[3] This minimum desired profit is often listed as "interest" by those who use this method.

would be required. The minimum annual cost method fails to bring out this very important information. The necessary information can be determined, but only by additional computation and interpretation.

The minimum annual cost method is useful for certain types of studies. Later chapters will show where this method can be used advantageously. No matter where it is used, one should appreciate exactly what the results mean. It is especially important that one realize the effect of the selected rate of minimum profit upon the results. Where the amounts of capital required by the various alternatives differ considerably, a small change in the selected rate of profit may swing the minimum annual cost from one alternative to another. Thus for general use there are a number of disadvantages which probably offset the simplicity of this method.

Actual Practice vs. Theoretical Policy. In some situations the decision indicated by a study of alternate proposals is different from that which would be made in actual business practice. For example, consider the case of two machines, A and B. Machine A will cost $1,000 and have a life of 20 years. Its annual operation and maintenance charges will be $300. Machine B would cost $1,200 and have a life of 30 years. Operation and maintenance costs for this machine would be only $275 per year. Taxes and insurance on the two machines would be at the rate of 5%. Which machine should be purchased?

Determining the rate of return on the increased investment would give:

	Machine A	Machine B
Depreciation (6% S. F.)	$ 27.20	$ 15.20
Operation and maintenance	300.00	275.00
Taxes and insurance (5%)	50.00	60.00
Total annual cost	$377.20	$350.20
Saving		$ 27.00

Rate of return on the additional investment — 13.5%.

This would indicate that machine B should be purchased since one could obtain a return of 13.5% on the additional investment of $200. In actual practice, however, it is very doubtful if the more expensive machine would be purchased.

This contradiction between the theoretical and actual practice is merely due to the fact that 30 years is entirely too long a period to try to account for in ordinary industrial practice. The scrap value of second-hand equipment is so little that there would probably be no appreciable difference in the amounts that could be obtained from the sale of the two machines at the end of their functional lives. In most businesses it is impossible to know what machines will be needed 10 years in advance. Therefore one would be willing to pay very little, if anything, to obtain a machine which would have a physical life much longer than this. A machine with a physical life of 20 years would undoubtedly serve any purpose one might wish it to fulfill. It would thus be doubtful practice to invest additional money to obtain longer life. If a more expensive machine has smaller operating expenses, two machines may be compared upon the basis of equivalent lives in order to determine which should be purchased, even though it is known that the more expensive one will outlast the other. This assumes, of course, that the cheaper machine would have a long enough life to satisfy all reasonable needs. All economy studies must be considered in the light of actual conditions in order to prevent erroneous results.

Conclusion. Any investment of an increment of capital greater than the minimum required to obtain satisfactory physical results may be considered as a separate investment possibility. Considered in this manner the rate of return may be determined and weighed against the risks and other investment possibilities.[4]

However, the effect upon the return earned by the minimum possible investment must also be examined. Once an increment of capital is invested it becomes a part of the whole and must be considered as such. Consideration should always be given to the possibility of attaining a satisfactory result with the investment of a minimum amount of capital.

If added increments of capital are invested although their

---

[4] One other method of comparing alternative investments is used to some extent. This is the "capitalized cost method." This will give satisfactory results if used correctly. However, results obtained by this method are easy to misinterpret, and this has been done to a considerable extent. It appears that the more simple and fundamental method described in this chapter is as easy, or easier, to use and is less likely to lead to erroneous conclusions. "Engineering Economy" by E. L. Grant contains a description of this method.

rate of return is less than that of the basic capital, the return is in the nature of a contentment return. Such investment may be justified when extra capital is available and no other investment possibility is as satisfactory.

REFERENCES

Eidmann, F. L.: "Economic Control of Engineering and Manufacture," McGraw-Hill Book Company, Inc., New York, 1931.

Grant, E. L.: "Principles of Engineering Economy," The Ronald Press Company, New York, 1938.

Kimball, D. S., and D. S. Kimball, Jr.: "Principles of Industrial Organization," McGraw-Hill Book Company, Inc., New York, 1939.

Raymond, F. E.: "Quantity and Economy in Manufacture," McGraw-Hill Book Company, Inc., New York, 1931.

Tyler, C.: "Chemical Engineering Economics," McGraw-Hill Book Company, Inc., New York, 1926.

PROBLEMS

116. Explain where the problem of alternative levels of investment is the same as any problem of investment.

117. Why must the effect upon the minimum amount of capital be considered when contemplating the investment of added increments?

118. A manufacturer offers a gasoline engined truck for $1,840. A Diesel truck with the same rated capacity can be purchased for $2,500. It is estimated that the Diesel truck will operate for $\frac{1}{2}$ cent per mile less for fuel and oil. All other operating expenses of the two trucks are estimated to be equal. The truck is to be operated 40,000 miles per year, and traded in on a new one at the end of three years. The trade-in value of each truck is estimated to be $300. Which truck should be purchased?

119. An auto supply chain store guarantees its "first line" tires for 20,000 miles. A 6.00–16 tire of this make sells for $10.60. A tire of the same size, produced by a nationally known manufacturer, retails for $14. This tire does not carry an all-inclusive guarantee but has the reputation of often giving over 30,000 miles of service Which tire is the better buy?

120. A consolidated school district is planning a new school building. A light and power company is attempting to induce the school supervisors to install an electric heating system for the building instead of a coal burning plant. The electric plant would consist of individual heating elements and a ventilating fan in each room. These would be thermostatically controlled. The coal burning plant would consist of a combination steam and forced air system, supplied by coal burning boilers.

The electric heating system will cost $3,500 to install and will consume 120,000 kw.-hr. of power annually at a cost of $0.015 per kw.-hr. It will require no attention of any kind. The coal burning plant will cost $4,700 to install and will burn 34 tons of coal per year. Coal is worth $8 per ton. In addition, this system will require an additional expenditure of $2,000 for building a boiler room and stack. It will also require the services of an extra caretaker at $1,500 per year.

Maintenance expense for the electric plant is estimated at $50 per year and for the coal plant at $150 per year. The school district will issue 10-year, 6% bonds to cover the cost of the building and equipment. Any equipment should be written off within this period. Which heating system should be installed?

121. An ordinary red cedar telephone pole costs $17.80 in place. The average life of such poles in a certain locality is 20 years. A wood preservative process claims to increase the life of such poles 30% and costs $6.50. Insurance and taxes are 1%. If money is worth 4%, should a company have all of its poles processed?

122. Copper transmission line costs 15 cents per pound and aluminum 21 cents per pound. The resistivity of these is 10.4 ohms per circular mil foot and 17.0 ohms per circular mil foot, respectively. The weight of copper per circular mil foot is 0.0000303 lb. and of aluminum 0.0000092 lb. If taxes and insurance are 1%, which material is cheaper for the same conductivity?

123. A factory is building 10 new machines to replace some old equipment which is out of date. It is necessary to have a type of drive that will enable the machines to operate at six different speeds. Two types of drives are available which will perform satisfactorily. The first consists of a standard $\frac{1}{2}$ horsepower, single-speed induction motor, which will be connected to a standard type of variable-speed driving mechanism. This motor costs $24 and the variable-speed mechanism $47. The efficiency of the motor is 88% and that of the variable-speed drive mechanism, 84%.

The alternative is to obtain a special six-speed motor which costs $105 and has an efficiency of 91%.

It is estimated that the maintenance costs of the special six-speed motor would not exceed $5 per year while that for the single-speed motor and variable-speed mechanism would be $15 per year. Taxes and insurance are $1\frac{1}{2}\%$. All such equipment is written off in two years. Money is worth 8% to this company. Electric power costs $1\frac{3}{4}$ cents per kw.-hr. The machines will operate an average of 2,800 hr. per year and require an output of 300 watts from the driving units. Which type of drive should be selected?

Chapter XII

FIXED, DIFFERENTIAL AND SUNK COSTS

Many economy studies are concerned with going enterprises, or with parts of going enterprises. Investments are considered which would affect directly only a small portion of a business. In other cases the general operations of a company are to be altered or added to only slightly, and perhaps temporarily. In order to make a correct economy study of such projects it is necessary to consider certain factors in a different manner than would be used when a new enterprise is being considered.

When additions are made to a going business, or when temporary changes are made, it is natural to expect that the operating costs will be affected. This, of course, is exactly what happens. Obviously, economy studies of such projects must deal correctly with the costs and the effect on them of the proposed change. In such studies one must consider costs which fall under one of the three following headings: *fixed costs*, *differential costs* and *sunk costs*. Actually these classifications are the natural result of a factual examination of their natures. If one considers the basic facts contained in such problems he will have little difficulty in handling these costs in the correct manner.

Fixed Costs. *Fixed costs are those which will exist unaltered whether or not a given change in operations or policy is adopted.* In other words, a proposed change will have no effect upon fixed costs. It should thus be noted that *fixed costs* do not necessarily have any relationship to what are often referred to as *fixed charges* in ordinary accounting procedure. For example, bond interest is usually classified as a fixed charge. However, a change in operations might conceivably result in increased or decreased total bond interest. Similarly, certain expenses that are ordinarily thought of as variable expenses, such as labor expense, may remain constant when a proposed change is made and thus be considered as fixed costs. Thus the term "fixed costs" must be considered in relation to a specific proposal.

Differential Costs. *Differential costs are those which arise as the result of a change in operations or policy.* Thus differential costs represent the actual increments or decrements of expense resulting from the change. They are the expenses that must be considered in determining the actual cost of carrying out the added operations. Like fixed costs, they are applicable only to the specific change from which they result. They may be either positive or negative in amount. Like fixed costs, they should be determined by fact.

A number of examples involving fixed and differential costs will now be examined to illustrate their effect and how they should be handled.

Unit Costs vs. Fixed and Differential Costs. Confusion has been caused by misuse of unit costs in economy studies by engineers. Unit costs are essentially accounting and control items. It is possible to use them in economy studies *if the correct unit costs are used.* Difficulty has arisen through attempts to use unit costs which apply accurately to only a given set of conditions. It is not always realized that many expenses are not affected in direct proportion to a change in output. A little thought should make this apparent. For example, one would not expect the salary of the president of the American Telephone and Telegraph Company to be affected by the fact that 50 phones were disconnected from the Bell System. Yet it would be theoretically possible to determine the unit cost of operating each telephone in the Bell System, and a portion of this unit cost would be a fractional part of the president's salary.

This same situation, to a more closely connected degree, exists in most businesses. It is customary to determine the unit cost of producing an article or rendering a service. It is necessary to do this in order to know the cost of production for each article. To obtain this unit cost all expenses of labor, material and overhead are determined and apportioned among the various units produced. They are thus based upon *existing* operating conditions and represent actual costs under those conditions. They may thus be used for determining profits or as aids to control.[1] Attempting to apply them to a different set of conditions, or use them for some purpose for which they were not intended, is much the same as saying that a Packard should cost the same as a Ford because they are both automobiles. An economy study is an entirely different process from routine accounting. While many of the same items of expense may be involved and many of the same things are considered in both, all items must be used in the light of the conditions that actually exist or will exist.

An excellent example of how a wrong decision may result from improper use of unit costs in an economy study is found in the following example. A large manufacturing plant consisted of 11 departments. In one of these automobile batteries were produced. The equipment for producing the hard rubber covers for the cells of these batteries occupied about 100 square feet in one corner of this department. This operation required only one workman per shift and was under the supervision of a man who also supervised a number of other operations. The daily production of cell covers was 576. The costs of operation were as follows:

Labor	$ 6.00
Material	4.32
Overhead	4.10
Total	$14.42

$$\text{Unit cost} = \frac{\$14.42}{576} = \$0.025 \text{ per cover}$$

A local company, which specialized in molding hard rubber products, offered to produce the cell covers from the existing molds for $1\frac{3}{4}$ cents each. The department manager computed that the saving involved through having the cell covers manufactured outside the plant would be as follows:

Present cost for 576 cell covers	$14.42
Cost if made outside (576 × $0.0175)	10.08
Daily saving	$ 4.34

This appeared to him to be a very worth-while saving since it could be obtained with no investment of additional capital. As a result the change was made and the cell covers were made by the outside company.

[1] See chapter on cost accounting.

After the change had been in effect a little over a month, the cost department made a check upon the savings that actually resulted from the change. The investigation showed that the actual saving in overhead was only $0.15 per day, which represented a saving in insurance. It was further found that a portion of the material which had been used for the cell covers was a waste product of another operation in the factory and that the actual saving in material was only $3.05 instead of $4.32. As a result the company was now paying for the 576 cell covers the following:

Remaining overhead	$ 3.95
Waste material	1.27
To outside company	10.08
Total	$15.30

Instead of a saving of $4.34 per day there was actually a loss of $15.30 − $14.42, or $0.88. Arrangements were made immediately to have the molds returned to the plant, and cell covers were again produced within the factory.

A little thought makes it apparent why the use of unit costs failed to give correct results. The unit cost of $0.025 per cover was based upon the assumption that 576 cell covers *were to be produced* each day. If the covers were not produced the unit cost had no meaning since it did not apply to this set of conditions. One might even do a bit of computation and say that the unit cost of *not producing* 576 cell covers each day would be:

$$\frac{\$3.95 + \$1.27}{576} = \$0.009 \text{ per cell cover}$$

It becomes apparent from the above example that serious errors may result from using unit costs in economy studies. For economy studies of this type one must determine the differential cost of producing the products. The actual (differential) costs which were incurred when the cell covers were produced, but which would not exist if they were not manufactured, would be:

Labor	$6.00
Material	3.05
Overhead (insurance)	0.15
Total	$9.20

Dividing $9.20 by 576 gives a unit differential cost for producing the cell covers of $0.01597. In other words, the actual cost of producing each cell cover, *compared to not making any cell covers*, was slightly less than 1$\frac{6}{10}$ cents. This result makes it obvious that an actual loss would result from paying 1¾ cents each for cell covers produced by an outside company. The department foreman had made the common mistake of using unit costs for a purpose for which they were never intended and failing to determine the facts which would reveal the differential cost for the alternatives of producing or not producing the cell covers.

Problem of New or By-Products. One of the great problems of industry is that of keeping all of its production facilities operating at capacity throughout the entire year. By thoroughly understanding the principles of fixed and differential costs and applying them to this problem it is often possible to lessen the effect of slack production. In many companies, because of increased use of heavy and expensive equipment and machinery, overhead costs are becoming a considerable proportion of the total cost of production. These expenses continue through periods of slack production. A great proportion of them are fixed costs; they do not change with temporary variations in production. If, during periods of business depression, the unused production facilities are used for the production of some new product, there is no need to charge this new product with more than a very small amount of overhead since the major portion of the plant overhead has already been charged to the existing production. Thus, if the new product does not have to pay any overhead expense, it can be produced at a relatively low cost. In many cases it may be possible to produce this new article at a considerably lower cost than could be obtained in plants where it is the main article of production and must therefore bear its share of the overhead. By producing an additional product in this manner the company may be able to market it at a price below the usual market price and still make a very substantial profit. Such a practice is obviously advantageous.

An example of this type of application of fixed and differential cost principles is found in the case of a company manufacturing blowers of various sizes. During the depression years the sales of large blowers were very low. As a result the company was faced with the necessity of operating at very low output and of laying off a number of its employees. A study of the situation revealed that they had all the facilities necessary for the production of small kitchen ventilating fans. It was found that there would be no fixed charges involved and that the men could work on this product at odd times when they were not employed on the production of blowers. The cost of producing each fan under these conditions was:

Material	$4.80
Labor	1.08
Total	$5.88

Other fans of this type were sold at about $18 retail, and the dealers were given a 40% discount from this price. This company placed their fans on the market at a retail price of $15 and allowed the dealers a discount of 50%. With this pricing the dealers were able to make more profit on a $15 fan than they had previously obtained from an $18 sale. The manufacturer obtained $7.50 from each fan. The profit to the manufacturer was:

Selling price to retailers	$7.50
Cost to manufacture	5.88
Profit per fan	$1.62

As the sales of the fans at $15 were considerably greater than had been anticipated, the company was able to show a profit throughout the entire depression. At the same time the entire working force was kept at nearly full-time employment. Thus, by taking advantage of the fact that the additional product could be produced for only the amount of the differential costs, the company was able to avoid a serious loss of profits and to maintain employment. Such a policy is of obvious advantage.

A similar situation exists in many plants in regard to scrap or waste products. In almost all plants where materials are converted into other forms there is accompanying waste and spoilage. Many companies have made profitable progress in converting these waste materials into income-producing goods. It is usually unnecessary to increase overhead costs in order to salvage these waste materials. The overhead charges go on regardless of whether the materials remain as useless waste or have a small amount of labor expended upon them in order to make them useful. The only actual expenses are the differential costs.

A case of this kind existed in a tire factory where a special grade of canvas was used as "liner" between the layers of calendered fabric in order to prevent the layers from sticking to each other. This liner was subject to hard usage and wore out quite rapidly. Previously the scrap liner had been sold as useless rags for $0.75 per hundred pounds. The foreman of the scrap department found on investigation that if this grade of canvas were cleaned and cut into certain sizes it could be sold to a furniture factory, for use in making upholstered furniture, at a price of $6 per hundred pounds. He found that the material could be laundered for $0.75 per hundred and that the necessary labor for cutting to the required sizes would be $2 per hundred pounds. Examination showed that 80% of the scrap liner could be made useful by this procedure. The profit to be obtained from each 100 pounds of scrap liner would be:

Income from sale of 80 pounds of reclaimed liner		$4.80
Expense of reclaiming		
Laundering	$0.75	
Labor	2.00	2.75
Profit per hundred pounds of scrap		$2.05

Such additional earnings through the conversion of scrap and waste products are becoming of great importance in industry. These savings are particularly attractive because in most cases they require little or no additional investment in equipment. In fact, the production of salable by-products out of waste materials offers one of the greatest possibilities of increased profits and stabilized production in many companies, especially those in the process industries. In most cases such by-products can be produced and sold at a profit because existing products are already paying the fixed costs and only the differential costs need be covered by the by-products. Of course, there must often be some additional investment in equipment in order to produce usable by-products.

Another recent example of the conversion of waste materials into profit-producing items is found in the paper industry. In the manufacture of the better grades of paper about half the wood pulp comes out as waste sulphite liquor. For many years this was considered to be worthless and was dumped onto vacant ground or into rivers and streams, causing pollution and impairing fishing. In several states legal action was threatened to force the mills to cease this dumping of sulphite liquor. Several paper companies have attempted to find a use for sulphite liquor. One of these, the Marathon Paper Mills Company, was particularly active in this respect. Research chemists were employed to find out what use could be made of the liquor. As a result this company is now producing a number of marketable products from their sulphite liquor, among them a synthetic vanilla flavoring, a chemical for tanning hides and a chemical for improving cement. Very recently they have announced a lignin plastic which is as strong for its weight as steel and can probably be sold for 5 cents per pound as compared with 15 cents or more per pound for most other plastics. This is an excellent example of what can be done by combining economy studies with engineering research.

Some unique circumstances may arise out of the production of by-products in an effort to utilize excess plant capacity or waste materials. When a new product is to be produced in this manner, it is assumed that the existing main products are the principal source of income and are therefore to continue to pay the fixed costs of the company. It is expected that the new products are to be more or less temporary items, or are to be considered as side lines. In this way they are to be the tail of the dog. But in numerous cases the tail has wagged the dog. A classic example of this occurred some years ago in a large sash and door mill in the northwest. This company was an old established manufacturer with its various kinds of doors well known throughout the trade. In an effort to use some of the pieces of scrap wood which resulted from the manufacturing processes, it was decided to produce a cheap door made out of these scrap pieces glued together to give the necessary thickness. It was thought that by selling these laminated doors at a price considerably below that of their other doors they might be able to sell enough to use up the waste pieces of wood. After a number of these "cheap" laminated doors had been sold and used it was found they were much superior to any of the ordinary doors the company produced, principally because the laminated structure prevented warping in damp climates. In a short time the main product of the plant was laminated doors which sold at a premium price because of their superiority. Since the by-product had become the main product, it was obvious that it would have to bear its share of the fixed costs of the business. It was necessary to revise the cost figures of the entire plant to fit the new conditions.

Another example of what may happen when a company attempts to expand the sale of by-products is found in the borax industry in this country. In former years a by-product of the borax industry was potash, used for the manufacture of soap and in producing glass and fertilizer. In recent years there has been an increasing demand for potash, which has principally been imported from Europe and mainly from Germany. The European producers, through their syndicates and cartels, attempted to maintain high prices for potash. As a result the borax producers in this country began experimenting with methods of obtaining a greater yield of potash from borax. They succeeded so well that they can now obtain two tons of potash for each ton of borax. The demand for potash had become so great that it was necessary to find some means of disposing of the excess borax which was produced, although this had originally been the main product. This problem was solved by halving the price of borax between the years 1926 and 1930 and introducing a number of new borax products. This is another, and admittedly somewhat extreme, example of how the fixed costs of an enterprise may have to be shifted from the main to the by-product.

Such examples illustrate the fact that fixed and differential costs must be related to a given set of conditions. Temporary changes of policy may be based upon such cost figures without further consideration. However, if the policy becomes permanent, or if the results affect the conditions considerably, honest accounting demands that the situation be restudied and the cost distribution be adjusted. The difficulty occurs in determining the line between temporary and permanent conditions. It is also true that many companies knowingly maintain an unfactual policy of cost distribution for many years. Certain products are allowed to bear more than their share of the fixed costs in order to allow other products to be marketed at lesser prices than they would normally have to bring. The wisdom of following such a course is open to question.

Economy of Shutting Down Plants. The principle of fixed and differential costs is of prime importance in decisions regarding shutting down plants during seasons of slack production. This situation was encountered by most companies following the crash of 1929. In some companies the situation was more acute than in others, but most were compelled to restudy their positions. A small manufacturer of specialized chemicals furnishes an example of this condition. This company produced a special line of chemicals which were used principally by one industry. In the year before the depression its net sales were $141,200. Operating expenses had been approximately as follows:

Raw materials	$ 42,500
Labor	27,600
Taxes, depreciation and maintenance	18,200
Managerial and sales expense	14,000
Total	$102,300

With these conditions, the net profit was:

Income from sales	$141,200
Expenses	102,300
Profit	$ 38,900

Because the industry which it served was affected seriously by depressed business conditions, the company estimated that its sales for the following year would be only $46,000. Examination made them estimate that their expenses for operating under these conditions would be as follows:

Raw material	$10,600
Labor	19,800
Taxes, depreciation, and maintenance	16,000
Managerial and sales	12,000
Total	$58,400

The loss which would be incurred by operating under these conditions would be:

Expenses	$58,400
Income from sales	46,000
Loss	$12,400

An alternative to operating the plant under these conditions was to close the manufacturing plant and maintain only their sales offices. Their products would be manufactured by a large general chemical plant. It was estimated that they could buy their products from the larger producer at prices which would enable them to resell them to their customers and break even on the individual transactions; that is, there would be no profit or loss from not producing the chemicals. Under these conditions their expenses for the year would be:

Taxes, depreciation, maintenance	$12,800
Managerial and sales	12,000
Total expense and loss	$24,800

After these figures were assembled, it was at once apparent that from a purely financial viewpoint it was much better policy for the company to operate its chemical plant and produce its own goods even though a loss would follow. The loss would only be $12,400 from this method of operating, whereas there would be a loss of $24,800 if the plant were closed. Even though a loss could not be avoided, if the company were to remain in business, it would be much better to have a small loss than a larger one. In addition to the purely monetary side of the question, there were the costs of rehiring and training new workers that would follow later; the possible loss of customers to the larger company from whom they were going to purchase their products; and the effect of unemployment on their workers. These were factors which had to be considered but upon which a monetary value could not easily be placed. It was decided that the plant should be operated at reduced capacity and considerable effort would be made to develop additional products and new markets for their existing products.

Many companies found themselves in similar positions in the years following 1929 and continued to operate at a loss instead of closing their plants. The effect of fixed costs is clear in such cases. If there had been no fixed costs it would have been possible to operate at reduced output and not have experienced large losses. Obviously, unit costs were of no value in making such decisions since they would indicate that if there were no production there would be no expense. The information for a correct decision can be obtained only by breaking all the expenses up into fixed and differential components.

Utilizing Excess Capacity by Dumping. Another method is often resorted to during periods of business depression by companies with a problem of excess plant capacity, particularly those which export a portion of their products. In a number of industries, especially the heavy equipment industries, there is an absolute maximum number of units of production which can be used in the domestic market during a given period. Reduction of the selling price would bring few, if any, additional sales. The only outlet for additional products lies in foreign markets. In such situations, sales can often be made in foreign markets only if the selling price is considerably reduced so as to compete with foreign produced goods. This price, at which the product must be sold on the foreign market, may be considerably less than is obtained for the same product on the domestic market. When goods are produced and sold in this market the procedure is known as foreign dumping.[2]

The economy of dumping is based upon the fact that fixed costs are present in nearly all enterprises. When a plant is operating at reduced output, a moderate increase in output will not affect the fixed costs. As a result these additional increments of production will actually cost less to produce than the others. This situation is illustrated best by an example.

Consider the case of the ABC Company which has plant capacity for the production of 100,000 units annually. Owing to depressed business conditions only 60,000 units can be sold in the domestic market at a price of $2.27 each. The unit cost for these products, on the basis of 60,000 annual production, is $2.34. Under these conditions there is obviously a loss of $0.07 on each unit, or a total loss of $4,200 on 60,000 units. The costs of producing 60,000 units, and other quantities between 60,000 and the plant capacity of 100,000, are shown in Table 16.

---

[2] The term "dumping" is also applied to cases where governments acquire surplus agricultural commodities and export them to foreign countries at prices which are often less than was paid to the producer. Many question whether, in the long run, dumping of manufactured goods is ever a sound economic practice. This is especially true in the case of heavy, producers' goods. There is always the danger that the foreign purchasers will use these goods, bought at low prices, to produce consumers' goods which will eventually compete with the domestic manufacturers. In this manner the domestic market for producers' goods might be destroyed.

TABLE 16. VARIATION IN UNIT COSTS WITH OUTPUT

(1) Output	(2) Material	(3) Labor	(4) Factory overhead	(5) Selling expense	(6) Total	(7) Unit cost	(8) Cost per unit of last increment
60,000	$31,200	$ 75,600	$22,800	$10,800	$140,400	$2.34	
70,000	35,700	88,200	24,000	10,950	158,850	2.27	$1.845
80,000	40,000	100,800	25,200	11,200	177,200	2.22	1.835
90,000	44,100	113,400	26,400	11,350	195,250	2.17	1.805
100,000	48,000	126,000	27,600	11,400	213,000	2.13	1.775

In Table 16 it will be noted that none of the costs are actually fixed costs in the strict definition that they are not affected by changes of output. However, factory overhead and selling expense are nearly fixed costs, varying only slightly with changes of production. Material expense is not exactly proportional to output since increased production makes it possible to obtain some economy in purchasing materials in larger quantities. This is a situation which usually occurs in economy studies of this type. There are actually very few fixed costs in the strict sense of the term. They usually vary slightly. Similarly there may be other costs which do not vary quite in proportion to production but are more nearly incremental than fixed. In this case only labor expense varies in direct proportion to output.

From Column 6 of Table 16, one may see that the total cost of producing 60,000 units is $140,400. The total cost for producing 70,000 units is $158,850, an increase of $18,450. Thus the cost of producing each of these additional 10,000 units is only $1.845, whereas each of the first 60,000 units costs $2.34 to produce. If 60,000 units are all that can be sold in the domestic market, any price above $1.845 that could be obtained for the additional 10,000 units in the foreign market would be profitable. From Table 16 it will be seen that successive increases of production above 70,000 units are accompanied with still lower unit costs for the additional increments of production. If the production were increased to plant capacity, the unit cost of the entire 100,000 units would be $2.13 while the increment cost of each of the 10,000 above 90,000 would only be $1.775. In this particular case it is estimated that 30,000 units could be sold annually on the foreign market for

$2.05 each. This is less than the unit cost of $2.17 for producing *all* of the 90,000 total production. The net effect upon the profits of the company is shown, however, by the following figures:

Income from sales	
60,000 units $2.27	$136,200
30,000 units $2.05	61,500
Total income	$197,700
Cost of producing 90,000	195,250
Profit	$ 2,450

Thus, although 30,000 units of production would be sold at less than the unit cost of the entire output, there is an actual gain of $6,650 by selling these goods on the foreign market, this gain being represented by the sum of the $2,450 profit on total sales and the loss of $4,200 which would be incurred if only 60,000 units were produced and sold on the domestic market. The immediate advantages of dumping become apparent from such an illustration. The practice is one which has been successfully followed by numerous companies while others have later suffered bad effects from such procedure.

Off-Peak Power Rates. Another situation that is familiar, and exists because of fixed and differential costs, is that of off-peak

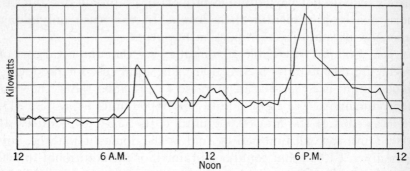

FIGURE 35. Daily load curve of a power company on January 5.

power rates. In public utility systems, such as light and power, water and gas companies, equipment must be installed which will be adequate to meet the maximum demands which will be placed upon it. In all of these fields there is a great fluctuation in the demand during each day. This is illustrated in Figure 35, which shows a typical demand curve of an electric power company for its peak winter day. It will be noted that the peak demand occurring between 4:30 and 9:30 P.M. is approximately twice that of any other time during the day. During the remaining 19 hours of the day much of the generating and distributing equipment is idle.

Since a great portion of the expense of delivering electric power to the consumer is due to the fixed charges resulting from heavy investment in plant facilities, any additional power which can be generated and sold during the 19 off-peak hours will not increase the fixed costs to any extent. These fixed costs will have been borne by the customary load. As a result, the differential cost of producing and distributing off-peak power will be very low. If the demand for such off-peak power can be stimulated by low rates which will yield some return above the differential cost of production, such a policy is of obvious advantage to the power company. Most power companies offer extremely favorable rates to consumers who will buy power only during the off-peak hours. For example, one company in the Pacific northwest has built up a very good off-peak load by establishing a rate of $0.0075 per kw.-hr. for power used for domestic water heating during the 19 off-peak hours. The water heaters are equipped with electric clock controls which turn the power on at 9:30 P.M. and turn it off at 4:30 P.M. Sufficient hot water storage is provided for the five peak hours by using a larger tank than would otherwise be needed and providing insulation. Although the average rate received by this utility for its power is about $0.026 per kw.-hr., the $0.0075 rate for off-peak power is very satisfactory from a revenue standpoint.

Off-peak rates should not be considered to be in the same category as dumping. In dumping there is no difference in the goods that are sold in the domestic and foreign markets at different prices. Off-peak power, on the other hand, is different from ordinary power since certain limitations are placed upon its use. Thus the consumers of off-peak power obtain lower rates than those who buy ordinary power because they abide by certain limitations. Thus the consumer benefits because he adjusts his demands to the requirements of the power company.

The possibility of utilizing off-peak capacity is present in numerous other industries. This is especially true in seasonal industries. Certain large manufacturing companies possess large and well-equipped machine shops which are used to capacity only a few months of the year for the production of jigs and dies for each year's models. Some of these companies are now turning out similar work for other concerns during the slack season. Since the differential costs of such production are low they are able to contract for such work at a low figure and still make a good profit. By keeping these departments operating at a much higher level than would otherwise be the case, they are able to maintain their equipment at a much more modern standard and at the same time earn more money.

Another practice is that of giving purchasers special discounts upon goods that can be produced during off-peak seasons. Obviously competent studies of differential costs are required in order to follow such a program advantageously.

The possible uses of the principle of fixed and differential costs are so many and varied that it is impossible to cover all of them.[3] However, they are all solved by determining what increases in expense will actually occur if a change is made. If such an approach to the problem is followed by sound reasoning little difficulty will be experienced in arriving at the correct solution.

Sunk Costs. The third type of cost which must often be considered in economy studies of going concerns is *sunk cost.* Sunk costs are somewhat different from other costs in that they are not in the nature of expenses which have to be paid in the future. Instead, sunk costs are those which *have already occurred* although they may not have been recognized as such. If money has been spent, or capital invested, which for some reason cannot be retrieved, such amounts are called "sunk costs." Regardless of what course is to be followed, the money has been spent and cannot be recovered. It is the result of *past* occurrences and therefore is a fact which should be recognized as a part of the past history of the business.

---

[3] An interesting case is arising on the air transport lines with the advent of substratosphere planes. Each descent for passengers has its differential cost. How far apart should the stops for passengers be, and what is the minimum number of passengers for which a transport can afford to come down? As yet there are not sufficient data available to answer this question.

Ordinarily the term "sunk cost" is applied to decreases in the value of assets beyond the normal rate anticipated and provided for by ordinary depreciation accounting. This excessive depreciation causes a decrease in value which is a very real "cost," but is one which is irretrievable.

Sunk costs are encountered most often in problems of replacement of existing equipment and facilities. They will be discussed in this connection in the following chapter.

REFERENCES

Clark, J. M.: "Studies in the Economics of Overhead Costs," The University of Chicago Press, 1923.

Eidmann, F. L.: "Economic Control of Engineering and Manufacture," McGraw-Hill Book Company, Inc., New York, 1931.

Grant, E. L.: "Principles of Engineering Economy," The Ronald Press Company, New York, 1938.

Harding, C. F., and D. T. Canfield: "Business Administration for Engineers," McGraw-Hill Book Company, Inc., New York, 1937.

PROBLEMS

124. The following quotation is from a magazine article on modern roads:

> If we cut down this hill and widen the two-lane bottleneck that piles up traffic seven days in the week, we'll save five and four-tenths miles of distance. The job will cost $410,000, but using three cents a mile as the average cost of operating passenger cars, trucks and busses, the saving will amount to 16.2 cents per vehicle trip. Multiply that by 1,460,000 trips and the saving will total $236,520 per year — enough to pay the whole cost of the project in two years' time.

Comment upon this method of computing the saving brought about by better roads.

125. During 1934 a machine tool manufacturer introduced a line of small power tools for home shop use. These were to be produced as a side line to utilize his idle equipment and were priced upon this basis. At the end of the year he found that his plant was operating at 90% capacity, and 75% of the plant capacity was being utilized for the production of the new line of tools. The plant had formerly operated at capacity in the production of large machine tools. Discuss the problem which this manufacturer faced with respect to his unit costs.

126. A college boy wishes to use his father's automobile to take a group of friends to a city 300 miles distant to attend a football game. His father says he may take the car if he will pay the actual expense incurred by operating the car over this distance. The father gives the son the following figures as the average costs of operating the car, based upon 20,000 miles operation per year.

	Cost per mile
Gasoline	$0.0120
Oil and lubrication	0.0025
Tires	0.0025
Depreciation	0.0100
Insurance and taxes	0.0025
Repairs	0.0015
Garage	0.0020
	$0.0330

How much should the son pay the father for the trip?

127. A man has $150,000 invested in a plant. Functional depreciation is 5% per annum. Physical depreciation is proportional to output, being 2% at full capacity. Material costs are $3.50 per unit of output and labor costs $5.80. Administrative and managerial expenses are $13,000 per year. The plant capacity is 800 machines per month. Taxes and insurance are 2% of the invested capital.

During a depression only 360 machines per month can be sold at $10.50 each. Should the plant be operated at this reduced output or shut down?

128. A man's electric light bill has averaged $3.60 per month. His average monthly consumption has been 120 kw.-hr., giving an average cost per kilowatt-hour of 3 cents.

The rate schedule of the utility company is as follows:

For all current used for residence purposes, including cooking and household appliances — 0 to 40 kilowatt-hours, per month, five cents per kilowatt-hour. The next two hundred (200) kilowatt-hours, per month, two (2) cents per kilowatt-hour. All in excess of two hundred forty (240) kilowatt-hours per month, three-fourths (¾) cent per kilowatt-hour.

He installs an electric range which consumes 260 kw.-hr. per month. What is the amount of his bill? What is the average cost per kilowatt-hour of the power used by the range?

129. A trucking company has a fleet of small delivery trucks which it is using to deliver packages of freight and express. Each truck is capable of 60,000 pound-miles of service each day. The company finds that the trucks are, on the average, rendering only 30,000 pound-miles per day. They are receiving $0.0005 per pound-mile for this service. Their operating expenses per truck are:

Overhead	$10.00
Driver	6.50
Operation and maintenance	$0.75 + $0.00005 × pound-miles

The company is making a bid to deliver packages for a group of local department stores. It is estimated that this business would be sufficient to increase the use of each truck to 54,000 pound-miles per day. What bid should be made per pound-mile for this service if the company wishes to make a profit of $4 per day per truck?

130. A manufacturer is preparing to produce a new product which will require one die casting. A company, specializing in this work and having excess capacity in equipment required for producing the casting, offers to manufacture the castings for the cost of the material, plus labor, plus 1 cent

per casting for power, heat and increment overhead, plus a profit of 25%, based upon the mentioned items of expense. They quote material and labor costs of 11 and 4 cents respectively, per casting. The quoted prices are to be good only if they are allowed to produce the required number of castings at off-peak intervals. This will necessitate the manufacturer's carrying an average stock of $550 worth of castings on hand. His capital is worth 8%.

The manufacturer dislikes the idea of paying the die casting company a profit of 25%. He therefore buys die casting equipment for $4,000. As he uses only a relatively small amount of material his material costs are 12 cents per casting. Labor costs are the same as quoted by the die casting company. He must write off his investment in the die casting equipment in four years. Other overhead costs will amount to 2 cents per unit. If he produces 10,000 castings per year, has he made a wise choice?

131. A department store has its own power plant which furnishes heat, light and power. The annual operating expenses are:

Fuel	$ 2,000
Labor	5,700
Repairs and maintenance	1,400
Depreciation	1,800
Miscellaneous overhead	600
	$11,500

120,000 kw.-hr. of electric power are generated annually. The salesman of the local power company has told the store management that they could save 1 cent per kw.-hr. if they would purchase their power instead of generating it in their own power plant. A careful analysis of their power plant costs shows that 12% of the fuel expense is attributable to the generation of power. Repair and maintenance of the generating equipment costs $200 per year. Power generation is charged with 40% of the depreciation of the power plant. No change would be effected in labor or overhead costs if no power were generated and the plant used only for heating. State your opinion of the accuracy of the salesman's claim.

132. A manufacturer of radio sets has estimated costs as follows:

Output	Labor	Materials	Overhead and administration	Selling costs	Total costs
0	—	—	$72,000	$18,000	$ 90,000
10,000	$ 40,000	$ 70,000	75,000	20,000	205,000
20,000	80,000	135,000	76,000	21,000	312,000
30,000	120,000	200,000	77,000	22,000	419,000
40,000	160,000	260,000	78,000	22,500	520,500
50,000	200,000	320,000	79,000	23,000	622,000
60,000	240,000	365,000	80,000	23,500	708,500

A survey of domestic sales indicates that he cannot sell over 30,000 radio sets during the current year at $14 per set. An exporting company makes an offer to buy 10,000 sets for export at $11 each, or 20,000 sets at $10 each. There would be no sales expense on these sets sold for export. Should the manufacturer accept either of these offers, and if so, which one?

Chapter XIII

REPLACEMENT

One of the common problems which is met in most businesses is whether or not some existing equipment or plant should be replaced by new or more modern and economical facilities. A great amount of confusion and argument has existed concerning this commonplace problem. Many businesses have failed to follow the correct policy in making replacements. Yet the correct solution depends only upon determining the facts and dealing with them in a straightforward manner.

Reasons for Replacement. One may name at least four common reasons for replacing existing equipment. These are:

1. Existing equipment is worn out.

2. The equipment does not have sufficient capacity of output to supply the demands which are placed upon it.

3. The equipment is obsolete owing to changes in the style or design of the products which must be produced.

4. More efficient equipment is now available which will produce at lower unit cost.

The first two of these reasons allow no alternative in the decision which must be made. If production is to continue at the necessary rate, new machines must be purchased. The only decision is in regard to the particular type of new equipment to purchase and the optimum capacity. The replacement problem does not exist under these conditions.

The third situation is one in which the necessity for replacing the existing equipment is usually apparent. If styles have changed so that the existing equipment can no longer produce salable goods, the only alternatives are to buy new equipment or go out of business.

With the fourth set of conditions, the correct course to follow becomes more obscure. While the equipment will still produce the needed products, the production costs, because of either obsolescence or excessive maintenance expense, are higher than could be obtained with new or more modern equipment. To determine whether or not such equipment should be replaced it is necessary to compare the operating expenses that must be met if the existing equipment is retained with those which would occur if new equipment were used. A correct answer depends, of course, upon a correct determination and analysis of the expenses in the two cases.

A Simple Typical Problem. A company which makes molded plastic products has a certain mold which cost $1,650. This mold has been in service for three years. Its estimated life at the time of installation was four years. The scrap value at the end of this time was assumed to be zero, and depreciation has been charged-off on a straight-line basis. Labor costs for operating this mold have been $4,900 per year.

A new type of mold will allow easier loading of the cavities and will eject the finished parts automatically. Such a mold costs $3,600. Its estimated life is three years. Labor costs with this mold would be $3,600 per year. Each mold will produce the same output. Overhead expense would be approximately the same with either one. The old mold could be sold for $150. This company will not invest in any new or replacement equipment unless a return of at least 10% can be obtained on the required capital. This company wishes to know whether or not the new type mold should be purchased.

This problem presents two alternatives. One is to continue to use the old mold. The other is to purchase the new mold. In order to decide which course should be followed one must determine what the total annual operating expense would be for each alternative.

In this simple problem the only expenses which must be considered are those due to labor cost and depreciation, since all others are stated to be approximately equal for both alternatives. If the old mold is kept in service, future labor costs will continue the same as in the past — $4,900 per year. In order to arrive at the correct value for future annual depreciation expense one should consider the definition of depreciation. This definition states that depreciation is the decrease in value with the passing of time. Thus it is necessary to consider the value of the mold at the beginning and end of the time which is being considered. The value of the mold at the present time, so far as is known, is $150, the amount for which it could be sold. Its value at the end of the next year will be zero. Thus, on a straight-line [1] basis, the annual decrease in value will be $150. The total annual expense of operation if the old mold is kept will be:

Labor	$4,900
Depreciation	150
Total	$5,050

Similarly, if the new mold is purchased the expenses which must be considered are labor cost and depreciation. It is estimated that labor will cost $3,600 per year. If it is assumed that this mold will also be worth nothing at the end of its estimated life, the annual cost of depreciation will be $\frac{\$3,600}{3}$ or $1,200. Thus the total annual expense will be:

Labor	$3,600
Depreciation	1,200
Total	$4,800

By buying and operating the new mold operating expenses will be decreased by $250 per year.

It is now necessary to decide whether this saving is sufficient to justify the investing of the capital which is required for the purchase of the new mold. This part of the problem is handled like any other problem in investment. The cost of the new mold is $3,600. However, the sale of the old mold will provide $150 which can be applied toward the purchase price of the new mold. Thus it will be necessary to invest only $3,450 in order to bring about the annual saving of $250. Therefore the $3,450 will earn an annual return of $250. This return is at the rate of 7.25% per annum. One must therefore decide whether this return is sufficient to justify the investment of the required

---

[1] Straight-line depreciation is used in this example for the sake of simplicity. Since the time involved is short, there is little error introduced.

capital. Ordinary procedure should be followed in arriving at this decision.

Unamortized Values. In analyzing the preceding example, one would find that the depreciated or *book value* of the old mold is $415. This is brought about by the fact that one-fourth of the original cost has been written off each year for three years. Yet in the previous analysis the present value of the old mold was stated to be only $150. At first glance there might appear to be an error in the economy study since $1,245 has been written off in previous years and the study provides for only $150 of additional depreciation charges, giving a total of $1,395. Previous accounting and future provision fail by $265 to provide for complete recovery of the capital which originally was invested in the old mold. Thus, if the old mold were sold and the salvage value of $150 obtained, there would still be an amount of $265 which had not been amortized. This amount is called *unamortized value*.

A little clear analysis reveals the exact nature of unamortized value. When the old mold was purchased, a depreciation rate was established by the use of which it was hoped the invested capital would be recovered. According to subsequent records this established depreciation rate has not been sufficiently high to fulfill the desired end. Either a mistake was made in setting the depreciation rate or some event has happened, such as an unforeseen technological improvement, which caused greater depreciation than it was reasonable to expect. The fact remains that, because of past mistakes, or uncontrolled events, some capital has not been recovered by ordinary depreciation accounting methods. At present the mold is not worth as much as the accounting records indicate it should be.

This situation is not particularly startling when one considers certain other assets. Take, for example, bonds. Assume that a company has some excess cash available and that it purchases a $1,000 bond for par as an investment. At a later date, owing to no fault of the company, the bond decreases in market value and is worth only $900. Obviously this asset is not worth as much as it was previously. The company's accounting records may show the value of the bond to be $1,000, and this same value is even printed upon the bond itself. Nevertheless, the fact remains that the bond is now worth only $900 to the company. To consider that the bond is worth any greater amount, and list it as such on the balance sheet, is only engaging in wishful thinking. The plain fact is that events have caused a decrease in the value of one of the company's assets. The only honest thing to do is to admit that the company has suffered this much loss. Any other course of action is not abiding by the facts.

Unamortized values represent decreases in the value of assets that were not anticipated or provided for but nevertheless have occurred. They cannot be brought back since they are in the past. Thus they are *sunk costs*. What has occurred is that past expenses were actually greater than the accounting records show them to have been. As a result the *actual* past profits were not as large as they were computed to be. A portion of the money which has been paid out under the heading of "profits" was in fact a part of the assets. Thus while the assets of the company have been depleted by the amount of the unamortized value, the owners of the business have received these funds, even though they mistakenly thought they were actual profits. Therefore the correct procedure is to recognize unamortized value as a sunk cost. As such it has no place in an economy study, where only future expenses are of significance. Following this principle, *the future depreciation expense of existing equipment should be based upon actual present value*.

If equipment is replaced and unamortized value exists, two separate transactions have taken place. In the first transaction an existing asset is sold or written off the books. Any loss resulting from this transaction must be charged against the Profit and Loss account. This closes the accounting records of the old asset. The second transaction consists of the acquisition of a new asset. New accounting records are established to record the financial history of this asset. It therefore has no connection with any past events which were related to the replaced equipment. Thus the correct handling of unamortized value in economy studies is in accordance with the correct accounting procedure for such an item.

Methods of Handling Losses Due to Unamortized Values. One of the most common methods of handling losses due to unamortized value is to charge them to the Profit and Loss account. This considers them to be a loss of the current operating period and thus deducts them from current earnings. This is a satisfactory procedure except for the fact that unusually large losses will have a serious effect upon the profits of the current period.

A more satisfactory method is to provide a surplus against which such losses may be charged. Thus a certain sum is set aside each accounting period to build up and maintain this surplus. When any losses occur from unamortized values, they are charged against the Surplus account. In this manner current profits are not affected seriously. The periodic contribution to the Surplus account is in the nature of an insurance premium to prevent profits being affected by losses from unamortized values.

Other methods which are used should more accurately be described as methods to avoid having unamortized values. These consist, essentially, of writing off investments in equipment in a very short time. This practice is becoming more prevalent throughout industry. For example, a recent study of 200 business firms revealed that over 60% of them expected an investment to pay for itself within three years. Five per cent expected the pay-out period to be a year or less. By requiring very short pay-out periods (high rates of depreciation) the likelihood of any unamortized values arising becomes less and less. One can readily appreciate this attitude when the rapid changes of industry are considered.

A further example of the tendency of industry to shorten the write-off period of investments is illustrated by the chart shown in Figure 36. This represents the method used by the engineering department of a large oil company for considering the advisability of replacing equipment. The new equipment is not considered to yield any profit until it has paid for itself out of the savings it brought about. After the equipment has paid for itself, the company considers that they are commencing to receive some profit from the replacement. The great difficulty with this method is that it is impracticable, if not impossible, to keep a record of each investment in this manner and pay profits to the stockholders only after each item of equipment has paid for itself. Applied to an entire enterprise it would mean that no profits could be paid until all the investment had been written off. The resulting accounting system would be most amazing.

A More Complex Replacement Problem. The fundamental procedure for handling replacement studies, which has just been discussed in connection with a simple problem, applies equally well to more complex cases. Consider, for example, the history

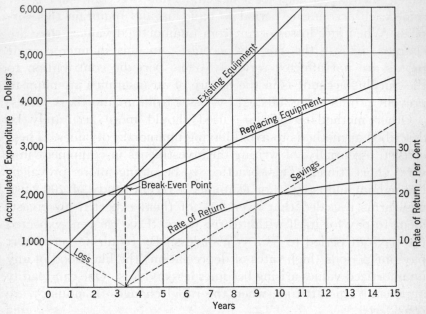

FIGURE 36. Graphical representation of the economy of a proposed replacement.

of the power plant which was discussed in Chapters X and XI. The 2,000-kw. Diesel plant was installed and operated successfully. The actual income and expenses of the plant were quite close to the estimated figures. An actual rate of return of 12.3% was obtained after the plant had been in operation for a few years.

When the plant had been in operation for eight years, an irrigation and power project was completed by the federal government in the near vicinity. As a result, the power company was offered the opportunity of purchasing electric power in wholesale lots from the government. This power could be purchased at the rate of $35 per kw.-year of maximum demand. To take advantage of this opportunity the power company would have to build a transmission line to connect with the main power line from the dam at the nearest point of contact. Of course, if power were purchased from the government project, there would be no further need for the Diesel engines and generators. The problem was, then, should the Diesel engines and generators be replaced by building a transmission line and purchasing power in wholesale lots from the government project?

The facts upon which the decision regarding replacement of the Diesel engines and generators with purchased power had to be based were as follows:

The plant had cost $431,500 to build. Of this amount, $240,000 was the cost of the Diesel engines and generators. The average annual operating expenses had been $116,815. Average profits for the past five years had been 12.3%. Taxes and insurance had been 4% of the initial investment. The maximum load on the plant had been a little less than 1,600 kw. and the average load was 1,060 kw. A straight-line depreciation "Reserve" was used for depreciation of all the investment, except the land, and based upon a life of 12 years. The plant had been in operation for eight years.

The cost of building the necessary transmission line and doing some modernization of the remaining equipment was estimated to be $75,000. The expenditure of this amount would make the entire plant capable of giving at least 10 years' additional service beyond the time of reconstruction, with ordinary maintenance expense. Power would cost $35 per kw.-year of maximum demand. The maximum demand would be 1,600 kw. The Diesel engines and generators could be sold for a net sum of $10,000. If the plan of purchasing power were adopted, it was felt that a reduction in power rates would have to be made which would result in a net annual loss of revenue of $2,600, in spite of the increase in power sales which the rate decrease might bring about. The expenses of operating with purchased power were estimated as follows:

Power costs	$56,000
Labor	9,200
Repairs	6,200
Taxes and insurance (4%)	10,670
Depreciation (life 10 years)	7,860
Miscellaneous	3,800
Reduced power rates	2,600
Total annual expense	$96,330

The above costs were analyzed as follows:

Power. The maximum demand was 1,600 kw. The annual cost, at the rate of $35 per kw.-year of maximum demand, would be:

$$1,600 \times \$35 = \$56,000$$

Labor and repairs. These were based upon the records of past experience and were therefore close estimates.

Taxes and insurance. In the past these had averaged 4% of the initial investment. The initial investment in plant, other than the Diesel engines and generators, was $191,500. The total amount to be used as a tax base under the new conditions would be:

Existing plant	$191,500
New plant	75,000
Total	$266,500

Taxes and insurance = $266,500 × 4% = $10,670

Depreciation. Since the average rate of return on the invested capital had been 12.3%, all depreciation estimates were made upon the basis of a 12% sinking fund. For this rate, the factor $s_{\overline{10}|} = 17.5$. The depreciation on the modernized plant was computed as follows:

Initial investment in plant	$431,500
Less cost of land	4,000
Depreciable investment	$427,500
Less cost of engines and generators	240,000
Initial investment in depreciable, remaining plant	$187,500
Less depreciation reserve (8 × $15,625)	125,000
Book value of remaining plant	$ 62,500
New investment	75,000
Total depreciable investment in modernized plant to be written off over 10 years	$137,500

Annual depreciation charge $137,500 $\times \dfrac{1}{17.5} = \$7,860$

$2,600 loss in revenue. This was not strictly an expense. However, it was felt that its incurrence was due to the utilization of government-generated power and the publicity attendant to the change. It was recognized that such a decrease in rates would probably have to be made at some future date but not for several years if no change were made. Therefore it was felt that this loss should be considered to be an expense of utilizing government-generated power.

The book value of the engines and generators at the time the replacement was being considered was $80,000. However, it was found that only $10,000 could be obtained from the sale of them as second-hand equipment. Thus there was an unamortized value of $70,000. This was a sunk cost which had to be recognized as such. The original estimate of the economic life of the Diesel engines and generators had not foreseen the building of the irrigation and power dam. The plain fact was that the immediate value of the Diesel engines and generators, *for purposes of replacement study*, was $10,000. The owners had suffered a loss in the value of their assets which had to be admitted and accepted.

If the Diesel engines and generators were kept in operation the annual operating expenses would be computed as follows:

Previous annual expenses	$116,815
Less previous depreciation charges	35,625
	$ 81,190
Plus depreciation of remaining plant with corrected value of engines and generators (total value = $62,500 + $10,000; $n = 4$ yrs.; $i = 12\%$; $s_4 = 4.78$)	15,150
Total annual expenses	$ 96,340

Comparison of the total annual expenses of the two methods of operation shows that the Diesel engines and generators should have been kept in operation. Expenses under replacement conditions would have had to have been several thousand dollars less to have justified the investment of the required $65,000 of additional capital.

It is interesting to note that the annual expenses based upon the existing salvage value of the engines and generators are considerably less than when the book value is considered. The

acknowledgment of the decrease in the value of the assets gives
a lower and more realistic annual expense figure for the future
years.[2]

Replacement Due to Excessive Maintenance. It is often found
that a saving can be made by replacing a piece of equipment
before the end of its physical life because of the excessive maintenance expense that is necessary to keep it in working condition.
In making a replacement study to determine whether such a
piece of equipment should be replaced by a new machine, it is
necessary to compare the cost of obtaining and operating a new
machine with the expense of maintaining and operating the old
one in a satisfactory working condition. The saving, if any,
must then be related to the investment required for obtaining
the new machine in order to determine whether such an investment is justified. In many cases it would be desirable, from the
standpoint of convenience, to have the new machine. But from
the economy side of the matter the investment may not be justified. It may be more economical to get along with a condition
which may be somewhat troublesome than it is to purchase the
new machine. The problem is well illustrated by the solution of
the following example.

A construction company owns a tractor that was purchased
two years ago for $2,200. The machine was estimated originally
to have a useful life of five years and to have no scrap value at
the end of that time. During the past year the repair costs for
the tractor have become quite large, and there are indications
that they will be even more during the coming years. Also the
machine has broken down twice during the past year, each time
causing a loss of $25 because of delay, in addition to repair costs.
The construction foreman believes it would be cheaper to replace
the tractor at the end of its second year of service and buy a new
one each two years. A new tractor of the same or slightly better
type could be purchased for the same amount as was paid for

---

[2] This is an interesting example of a case where the salvage value which could be obtained for a property is not a true measure of its worth to the owners as a producing
property. Actually the Diesel engines and generators were worth such an amount to the
owners that the total operating expense, including depreciation based on this value, would
be the same as could be obtained by using the most efficient competing method — in this
case purchased power. Such a value would be in accord with the best definition of value
and could well be used for future accounting purposes.

the old machine. The various expenditures for operating the old tractor during the past two years and the estimates for the next three years of its life are shown in Table 17.

TABLE 17. OPERATING EXPENSES OF A TRACTOR DURING
THE FIRST FIVE YEARS OF ITS LIFE

Expense	Year				
	1	2	3	4	5
Fuel	$1,100	$1,180	$1,290	$1,450	$1,650
Repairs	120	200	325	450	500
Breakdown	25	50	100	175	275
Total	$1,245	$1,430	$1,715	$2,075	$2,425
Trade-in value at end of year	$1,300	$ 850	$ 600	$ 400	$ 250
Book value at end of year	$1,760	$1,320	$ 880	$ 440	$ 000

The problem is to determine what saving, if any, would be made if the tractor were turned in at the end of the second year instead of being kept during the third year. The expenses for the third year by the two alternatives would be:

Keep Tractor the Third Year

Depreciation ($850 — $600)	$ 250
Operation	1,290
Maintenance	325
Breakdown	100
Total expense for third year	$1,965

Buy New Tractor at End of Each Two Years

Depreciation (write off $1,350 by 7% sinking fund in two years)	$ 652
Operation (average of two years)	1,140
Maintenance (average of two years)	160
Breakdown (average of two years)	38
Total annual expense	$1,990

The comparison shows that the approximate equivalent annual cost if the tractor were replaced at the end of each two years would be $1,990 per year. This amount would be the cost of operating a new tractor during the year corresponding to the third year of the life of the existing tractor. It is at once evident that there would be a loss amounting to $1,990 — $1,965 = $25 during the third year if the old tractor were sold and a new one obtained. Obviously, the tractor should be kept at least one more year.

If the same type of study is made at the end of the third year a different result is obtained. The values at this time would be:

Keep Tractor Fourth Year

Depreciation ($600 − $400)	$ 200
Operation	1,450
Repairs	450
Breakdown	175
Total expense for fourth year	$2,275

Buy New Tractor at End of Third Year

Depreciation (write off $1,600 by 7% sinking fund in 3 years)	$ 498
Operation (average of 3 years)[3]	1,190
Repairs (average of 3 years)	215
Breakdown (average of 3 years)	58
Total annual expense	$1,961

The estimated fourth year's saving is $2,275 − $1,961 = $314 by buying a new tractor at the end of the third year.

With the possible annual saving determined, this amount must be related to the investment which would be required in order to obtain it. The amount of this investment is obviously the difference between the purchase price of the new tractor and the trade-in value of the old one. This would be $2,200 − $600 = $1,600. The rate of return on this investment would then be:

$$\frac{314}{1,600} = 19.6\%$$

This is undoubtedly sufficient return on such an investment. The new tractor should be purchased at the end of the third year.

An item of interest in such studies is the fact that a number of engineers include interest on the value of the equipment at the beginning of the year as an item of annual expense and determine the total annual expense with this factor included. The

---

[3] The use of the average values for three years is justified when one examines the values which would be obtained if interest were considered on the amounts involved by determining equivalent equal annual expenses. The expenses determined in this manner would be:

Operation	$1,186
Repairs	211
Breakdown	57
Total	$1,454

The total by using average values is $1,463. The difference of $9 is only slightly over 0.5% and does not justify the extra work involved.

selection is then made by comparing the annual costs of the two alternatives. In a replacement study the interest on the total amount invested has no real significance or place unless money has actually been borrowed. One has decided that the return upon the investment is satisfactory or the original investment would not have been made. It is thus not necessary to include interest on the value of the property in replacement studies. One is interested in determining what saving will be obtained if replacement is made. The only amount of capital which need be considered is that which must be invested in order to bring about the saving. Therefore, if the sinking fund method is used for determining depreciation expense, the only interest to be considered is that which will be earned by the capital that must be invested in order to bring about the saving. This is actually not an interest return but a profit return which should be compared to the return that would be obtained from the capital if it were not invested in the replacing equipment. Of course, if it is necessary to borrow capital to finance the replacement, interest upon this borrowed capital is an expense which should be included as such.

Theoretical Replacement Policy. It is often desirable to be able to determine at what time a particular property should be replaced in order to obtain the most economical annual cost. Such a study must, of course, have many of the factors idealized, but it can produce information which may be of considerable value in establishing the actual policy of replacement. It is usually assumed that the equipment will be replaced with new equipment of the same type and price.

The question of when the ordinary passenger automobile should be replaced provides data for illustrating many of the items which must be considered in making such a study. The data for such a study are shown in Table 18. The figures were obtained for a car that cost $1,000 new. All of the values are very close to those ordinarily experienced for such a car with the possible exception of the amounts indicated for "Repairs." This item is somewhat higher than most people would experience since it is predicated upon the car's being maintained in the best possible condition at all times so that there would be no question of dependability of service over the period studied. If this were not done the question of dependability would have to be considered as an intangible item.

The problem is clarified by realizing that $1,000 is invested so that one may have an automobile. One then wishes to determine what annual expenditures will be required to operate the car and maintain the investment. In other words, it is assumed that one is going to operate a car continuously. Thus, he must always have an investment equal in value to the purchase price of the car. If all depreciation and operation costs are met annually, there will be no need for further consideration of the amount of the original investment. The return which can be obtained through replacement should be compared to the return which would be obtained through the necessary capital remaining in the invested depreciation fund.

Line A of Table 18 gives the trade-in value of the automobile at the beginning of the year indicated at the top of each vertical column.

Lines B through J, inclusive, list the annual expense items for operating the car.

Line K gives the gross operating expense for any given year.

The money which is set aside each year as the cost of depreciation is assumed to be invested at 3% interest. Thus the interest earned by the depreciation fund during any year would be available at the end of that year to help pay for a portion of the operating expense. The amount in the depreciation fund at the beginning of each year is shown in line L. Line M indicates the interest earned during each year.

Line N gives the net operating cost for each year, being the gross operating cost less the interest received from the depreciation fund.

In order to be able to determine annual cost, which may be compared when the car is kept for different lengths of time, it is necessary to have equivalent annual costs. These are determined by assuming that all of the expenses occurring in any one year are paid at the end of that year. Interest is then computed on these amounts up to the time the car is replaced. Line O gives the interest factor, $(1 + i)^n$, for the number of years indi-

TABLE 18. DETERMINATION OF MOST ECONOMICAL REPLACE-
MENT PERIOD FOR A PASSENGER AUTOMOBILE (BASED UPON
ANNUAL OPERATION OF 15,000 MILES)

		Year							
		1	2	3	4	5	6	7	8
A	Value at beginning of year	$1,000	$ 785	$ 640	$ 525	$ 440	$ 365	$ 300	$ 240
B	Depreciation	215	145	115	85	75	65	60	50
C	Gasoline	193	195	204	216	231	250	276	300
D	Oil	22	22	23	24	25	27	29	32
E	Lubrication	22	22	22	22	22	22	22	22
F	Repairs	5	10	25	50	75	100	130	160
G	Tires	—	60	60	—	60	60	—	60
H	Insurance	31	30	28	27	25	25	25	25
I	Taxes	12	9	8	7	5	4	3	3
J	Garage	30	30	30	30	30	30	30	30
K	Gross operating expense	$ 530	$ 523	$ 515	$ 462	$ 550	$ 583	$ 575	$ 682
L	Amount in depreciation fund at beginning of year	00	215	360	475	560	635	700	760
M	Interest from depreciation fund	—	6	11	14	17	19	21	23
N	Net operating cost	530	517	504	448	533	564	554	659
O	Interest factor $(1 + i)^n$	1.0	1.03	1.06	1.09	1.126	1.159	1.19	1.23
P		$ 530	$ 546 517	$ 562 533 504	$ 578 549 519 448	$ 596 564 534 461 533	$ 614 582 549 475 549 564	$ 630 600 567 489 565 581 554	$ 652 616 584 505 581 598 571 659
Q	(all operating expenses)	$ 530	$1,063	$1,599	$2,094	$2,388	$3,333	$3,986	$4,766
R	$s_{\overline{n}|}$	1.0	2.03	3.091	4.184	5.31	6.47	7.66	8.89
S	$\dfrac{Q}{s_{\overline{n}|}}$	$ 530	$ 523	$ 517	$ 500	$ 506	$ 515	$ 521	$ 537

cated. Each net annual expense, as given in line N, is then multiplied by the interest factor corresponding to the number of years which have elapsed between the time the annual expense was paid and the time the car is replaced. For example, at the end of the third year the value at the end of that year of all the expenses which had been paid up to that date would be:

First year's expense: $530 \times (1 + i)^2 = \$530 \times 1.06 = \quad\$562$
Second year's expense: $517 \times (1 + i)^1 = \$517 \times 1.03 = \quad\$533$
Third year's expense: $504 \times (1 + i)^0 = \$504 \times 1.00 = \quad\underline{\$504}$
Total value at end of third year (line Q) $\$1,599$

The summation of all of the annual expense items, with interest, is given in line Q.

Line R gives the values of $s_{\overline{n}|}$ for the various years. The interest rate used in this study was 3%, corresponding to the rate which could be obtained on funds deposited in a bank or in conservative securities. In a replacement study in a going business, a higher rate of interest would have to be used since the funds could earn a higher rate of return if allowed to remain in the business.

Line S gives the equivalent, equal annual operating cost if the car were kept for the number of years indicated at the top of each column. For example, if the automobile were kept for four years the operating cost for the various years would vary from a maximum of $530 to a minimum of $448, with the equivalent, equal annual cost being:

$$\frac{\$2,094}{s_{\overline{4}|}} = \frac{\$2,094}{4.184} = \$500$$

From Table 18 it may be seen that replacement at the end of each four-year period is most economical. However, in this case of a passenger car, the difference between replacement at the end of any of the first five years is not great. One can see how a good salesman may convince a person that replacement each year is desirable. The most economical replacement period would, of course, vary for any car of different value, or one operating under conditions different from those given in Table 18.

Theoretical vs. Actual Replacement Policy. As mentioned in preceding paragraphs, a theoretical replacement study along the lines which have been discussed is often useful in formulating an actual replacement policy. Because of the idealized conditions, the actual policy will usually vary somewhat from the theoretical. There are several reasons why this should be. In the first place, it is seldom possible, or desirable, to replace existing equipment with an exact duplicate. In nearly all cases improvements will have been made, and these must be taken into account in the replacement decision.

Another reason is the desire of business management to keep a plant in as up-to-date condition as possible so that their competitive position will be maintained. Thus a more liberal replacement policy is followed than would otherwise be indicated, so they will not find themselves in a position where they cannot take advantage of new opportunities which may arise but are dependent upon the use of the latest equipment.

A third reason is the willingness to pay just a little more in order to take advantage of a situation such as exists in Table 18 at the end of the first year. The difference between the equivalent, equal annual costs for replacement at the end of each year and at the end of each four years is only $30. In other words, by spending only $30 more each year it would be possible to have a new car every year instead of waiting for four years. The same situation often exists in industrial equipment. Two or more times may exist when replacement would offer nearly the same advantage from a financial view. Because of the relatively small additional expense required, it is easy to convince oneself that the earlier trade-in period is advantageous.

Another reason for actual replacement policy to differ from the theoretical is the personal whim of business executives. It is quite natural that prejudices should exist in such matters. Some companies believe that equipment should be operated as long as it can be made to run. Others wish to buy every new piece of equipment that is developed. Much of this is due to a lack of knowledge about the actual costs of keeping or replacing the existing equipment. The most successful companies usually have a well-formulated replacement policy and insist that it be followed.

Probably one of the most frequent reasons why theoretical

replacement is violated so often is the desire of most people to "keep up with the Joneses." How many people cannot be convinced by some smooth salesman that they owe it to themselves to spend the extra $30 per year in order to drive a new car each year? This same tendency is by no means unknown among "hard-headed" business executives. Many a businessman takes no little pride in showing his friends a new machine — "the latest thing out." Some companies explain such policies by insisting that it is good advertising for them to follow such a course. Witness some of the elaborate, streamlined oil trucks which drive through the cities, never going more than 30 miles per hour. Of course, in many cases there is a legitimate advertising value connected with the possession of the latest type of plant and equipment. But the fact remains that theoretical replacement policy can usually be used only as a guide for, or a check upon, the actual replacement policy. Probably the most important point is that the existing replacement policy should be examined to determine if it is economical. The present tendency of industry appears to be toward writing off equipment as soon as possible and using it as long as it is economical to do so.

REFERENCES

Barnes, R. M.: "When New Machines for Old?" Factory and Industrial Management, June, 1928.

Curtis, M. S.: "The Economics of Machine Tool Replacement," Trans. A.S.M.E., MSP–50–5, 1928.

Eidmann, F. L.: "Economic Control of Engineering and Manufacture," McGraw-Hill Book Company, Inc., New York, 1931.

Grant, E. L.: "Principles of Engineering Economy," The Ronald Press Company, New York, 1938.

Norton, P. T., Jr.: "Economic Lot Sizes in Manufacturing," Bulletin 31, Virginia Polytechnic Institute, 1934.

Norton, P. T., Jr.: "The Selection and Replacement of Manufacturing Equipment," Bulletin 32, Virginia Polytechnic Institute, 1934.

Rautenstrauch, W.: "The Economics of Business Enterprise," John Wiley & Sons, Inc., New York, 1939.

Raymond, F. E.: "The Fundamentals of Industrial Equipment Policies," Mechanical Engineering, July, 1933.

Vorlander, H. O., and F. E. Raymond: "Economic Life of Equipment," Trans. A.S.M.E., man–RP–54–2, 1932.

PROBLEMS

133. A rancher purchased a gasoline tractor four years ago for $1,200. He has provided for depreciation by maintaining a straight-line depreciation reserve based upon an estimated life of 10 years. He can now purchase a Diesel-powered tractor for $2,000. The total annual out-of-pocket operating expense of the gasoline tractor has been $450. He estimates the operating expense of the Diesel tractor to be $180 per year. He can sell the old tractor for $300. The salesman for the Diesel tractor claims it should last for 14 years. Conservative investments at this time are yielding 4%. Should the Diesel tractor be purchased?

134. A company has been generating its electric power with equipment that cost $8,000 when new. When this equipment was purchased 10 years ago, it was estimated to have a life of 16 years, and a straight-line depreciation reserve has been maintained. Each month, 10,000 kw.-hr. of power are used. The cost of producing this power has been $0.012 per kw.-hr.

The company can now buy power for $0.015 per kw.-hr. for the first 1,000 kw.-hr. per month, and $0.008 for each additional kilowatt-hour. To use the purchased power $1,000 must be spent for new distribution panels, etc. The old generating equipment can be sold for $500. The company now has an established policy that any new equipment must be written off within five years. Should they continue to generate their own power or change over to purchased power?

135. An oil company has a steam engine operating on a pipe line. The engine is six years old and cost $8,000 when new. Its estimated life at time of purchase was 10 years. A straight-line depreciation reserve has been maintained. The present second-hand value of this engine is $1,000. A natural gas engine can be purchased to replace the steam engine at a cost of $15,000. It would have an estimated life of 15 years and would operate for $1,500 a year less than the existing equipment. The average earnings of the company have been 8%. Would you advise the purchase of the natural gas engine?

136. A construction company is considering replacing two bulldozers with an earthmover. The bulldozers are three years old and cost $4,000 each when new. Operation and maintenance costs are $1,700 each per year. A straight-line Reserve for Depreciation account has been maintained, based upon a life of five years. Each can now be sold for $500.

The earthmover will cost $8,000. It will probably last at least five years. It will do the same work as the two bulldozers at an annual operating expense of $2,400. The average earnings of the company have exceeded 8%. Should the earthmover be purchased to replace the bulldozers?

137. A small factory, making a single product, has utilized a casting as the main body of the article. This is the only casting in the product. They have been making their own castings, having a small electric furnace and other necessary foundry equipment. The furnace cost $4,000 when new four years ago. A 6% sinking fund has been provided to write off this equipment over a 10-year period. The other foundry equipment has been entirely written off the books.

They now find that the casting can be eliminated by welding rolled shapes. The resulting saving in labor, material, maintenance and power will be $0.50 per article. The annual output is 600 machines. The necessary welding equipment will cost $2,000 and have an estimated life of eight years.

The electric furnace can be sold for $1,000 and the remainder of the foundry equipment for $250. Determine the rate of return on the investment if the change is made. Would you advise the change and why?

138. In connection with the annual survey of their production facilities, the managers of a washing machine factory are considering replacing two turret lathes with a screw machine. The essential facts about the turret lathes and screw machine are:

	Turret Lathes	Screw machine
Cost	$2,800 each	$4,200
Production	44 pieces per hour each	100 pieces per hour
Labor	1 man at $1.10 for each lathe	1 man at $0.90 per hour
Maintenance	$50 per year each	$50 per year
Power	$220 per year, total	$180 per year
Taxes and insurance	1% of first cost	2% of cost
Annual production	100,000 pieces	100,000 pieces

The cost of the turret lathes has been written off the books. It is found, however, that they can be sold for $125 each. A Surplus account is maintained for absorbing unamortized values. Capital is worth 8% to this company. They demand that all replacing equipment be written off within two years. Should they buy the screw machine to replace the turret lathes?

139. Following an earthquake, a gas company found that one section of their mains in a residential section was leaking at the rate of 3,500 MCF per year. The gas going into this main was worth 29 cents per MCF. This main had originally cost $5,200 and had been in service for 22 years. Depreciation had been computed upon a 35-year, straight-line basis. It has no salvage value.

A new main will cost $8,100 and will have an estimated life of 20 years before leakage would become appreciable, providing there were no serious earthquakes. Actually, the main should last for 10 or 15 additional years without excessive leakage.

If capital is worth 7%, should the main be replaced at this time?

140. All of the printing equipment of a large daily newspaper operates on direct current. Because of gradual changes this plant is the only direct current load of the local power plant. The power company wishes to eliminate their direct current power lines and has filed a notice of an increase of 20% in all direct current power rates. The newspaper's average annual power bill has been $17,420. They find that if they could use alternating current their power bill would be 10% less than in the past. Conversion of the entire plant to alternating current is being considered.

Investigation reveals that sale of all of the old direct current motors would bring only $750. This would still leave an unamortized loss of $3,800 on the direct current equipment. Complete installation of the new alternating current equipment would cost $21,000. Capital is worth 8%. No surplus account for adjusting unamortized values has been provided. Determine the advisability of making the conversion to alternating current drives if the investment is to be written off over a 10-year period.

141. An investigation reveals that an average of $1,800 per year has been spent to repair and maintain a certain piece of pavement in a large city during the past 10 years. A politician, campaigning for election, claims that the city could have had new pavement for less than was paid for repair on the old one. It is estimated that the new pavement would have cost $15,000. It would have been financed by the sale of $15,000 worth of 10-year, 4% noncallable bonds. Average maintenance expense on the new pavement would have been $250 per year. Was the politician correct in his claim?

142. In a certain process in an oil refinery, several types of crude stock are put through a particular piece of equipment. When a change is made from one stock to another, this portion of the plant must be shut down so that the equipment can be cleaned before the next stock is processed. This cleaning requires 20 hours, during which no production is obtained from this portion of the refinery. A manufacturer has developed a new piece of equipment which makes it possible to change from one stock to another in 2 hours.

The refinery estimates that it costs them $50 for each hour this portion of the refinery is not in operation. The existing equipment was installed two years previously at a cost of $20,000. Depreciation has been figured by the straight-line method, based upon an expected life of five years. The new equipment would cost $32,000. Although it would undoubtedly last at least five years, the refinery managers have decided that, because of recent rapid changes in the industry, any new equipment at this time must be fully depreciated within two years.

During the past two years the system has been changed from one stock to another twice each month. It is expected that this will continue in the future. Capital is worth 8%. Should the change in equipment be made at this time?

Chapter XIV

CAPACITY, LOAD AND FUTURE DEMAND FACTORS

The economy of a project may be affected by its size, by the variation of the load which is placed upon it or by the necessity of providing for future demands. It is, therefore, necessary to consider how these three factors may affect an engineering project so that they may be properly accounted for.

The most obvious effect of capacity is familiar in everyday experience. For example, a tube of shaving cream may sell for 43 cents. One may also be able to purchase the same shaving cream in a jar containing three times the amount of the tube for only 85 cents. One thus obtains three times as much shaving cream for less than twice as much money. Such instances are so common that they are accepted as a natural condition in our daily existence, little thought being given to the reason for such a situation. If such examples occur in our ordinary experience it is only reasonable to expect that similar conditions exist in engineering projects and must be accounted for if an enterprise is to be carried out with maximum economy.

Another effect of capacity is also experienced by everyone. For an example of this, consider a man and wife who own a two-passenger automobile. When only one of them is riding in the car the gasoline consumption may be one gallon for every 20 miles traveled. If both of them ride in the car the gasoline consumption will not be doubled. Instead they will probably obtain at least 19 miles to the gallon. In the first case the gasoline consumption is 0.05 gallon per passenger mile. In the second case the consumption is only 0.0263 gallon per passenger mile. Thus the fuel consumption per passenger mile varies greatly with the load that is placed on the car. This same effect is experienced in engineering work and has a very appreciable effect upon economy.

When permanent structures are to be erected, it is often desirable to build of sufficient size so that the needs of future years will be served, as well as the immediate demands. In such a problem, not only is it necessary to have information about what future demands may be, but the cost of meeting those demands must also be considered. If the structure is built large enough at the beginning to meet all future demands, there will be some economy owing to the utilization of larger quantities. However, if the structure is to be only partially used during most of its life, and then be completely utilized during the last few years, the expense of providing the larger amount of capital and the maintenance of the unused portion will detract from the economy. For example, in building the Golden Gate bridge it was proposed to finance the project by issuing 35-year bonds. A traffic survey estimated that at the end of 35 years the bridge would be used by 10,700,000 vehicles annually. However, during the first year after completion it was expected that only 2,000,000 vehicles would use it. How large should the bridge be? What would be the most economic size? If it were built only large enough to accommodate 5,000,000 vehicles it would be too small in a few years. It would then be necessary to tear it down and build a new one. On the other hand, if it were built large enough to accommodate the maximum load which would be placed upon it in the future years, the fixed charges accompanying the much larger investment would cause the bridge to lose money for a number of years. Would it be cheaper to build a smaller bridge and tear it down and rebuild a larger one in a few years than it would be to build the larger bridge in the first place and carry the excessive fixed charges? In all such cases it is necessary to compare the costs of several courses of procedure to determine which is more economic. However, to do this the different costs must be arranged on a comparable basis.

Importance of Fixed Costs and Fixed Charges. A little study of the problems involving capacity, load and future demand factors reveals that their effect is due to the existence of fixed expense items which must be met regardless of the capacity, load or demand. If all the expenses of an enterprise or business could be kept exactly proportional to the capacity, load or demand, these factors would have no appreciable effect upon economy. The fact that they are not proportional makes a careful consideration of the fixed expenses of an enterprise all the more important. It is, therefore, advisable for one to review in his mind the various items of fixed expense before passing on to a consideration of the effects of load, capacity and future demand.

Effect of Capacity on First Cost. Probably the most simple and apparent effect of capacity on engineering projects is in initial cost. This is illustrated in Table 19, which shows the cost of

TABLE 19.   COST OF GENERAL MOTORS CORP.   DIESEL ENGINES
OF VARIOUS SIZES DELIVERED IN SAN FRANCISCO

Horsepower	Cost	Cost per horsepower
82.5	$1,427	$17.30
110	1,745	15.87
165	2,445	14.82

various sizes of General Motors Diesel engines delivered in San Francisco. It is at once apparent that as the capacity of the engine is increased the cost per unit of capacity decreases. One may also observe that the decrease in cost per horsepower is not at all proportional. By increasing the capacity from 82.5 to 110 horsepower, an increase of 27.5 horsepower, the cost per horsepower decreases $1.43. A further increase of 55 horsepower decreases the cost per horsepower only $1.05. Both of these effects are quite typical and are matters of common experience. Figure 37 shows the effect of capacity on the price of turbine-generator units. The effect will be found in the majority of all products and projects.

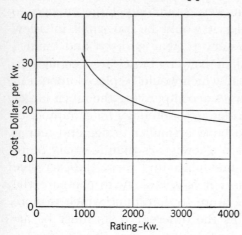

FIGURE 37. The effect of size upon the cost of 3,600 r.p.m. condensing turbine-generator units.

The reason for such an effect is readily ascertained. Consider some of the costs of producing 5,000- and 30,000-kw. turbines. The cost of originally designing a 30,000-kw. turbine would be little more than that required for the smaller one, and far from six times as great. The machining costs would have a somewhat similar ratio. Likewise, the labor and supervision costs would not be in proportion to the size. Even if the larger turbine required six times as much material, the total cost for materials should not be six times as great because they would be purchased in larger amounts and would therefore cost less per pound. Similarly, the various overhead charges of the plant making the turbines would not be six times as great for the 30,000-kw. machine. It is thus very easy to see why the 30,000-kw. turbine-generator unit should cost only half as much per kilowatt of capacity as the 5,000-kw. unit. Similar conditions will be found to exist for other products and structures. One may therefore say that a general effect of increasing capacity is to bring about decreased costs of production.

The effect of increased capacity in making it possible to use more efficient equipment and production methods should not be overlooked. While this is usually the direct result of larger scale production, the reduction in production costs is not due alone to the element of capacity. It is also due to this intermediate factor of more efficient equipment which the larger capacity makes possible. Therefore, savings brought about through the use of more efficient equipment and methods which are used to produce larger amounts of products are really an indirect effect of capacity. However, the result on the cost of production is the same, and the possibility of such savings should not be neglected when capacity is being considered. Very often the savings from this source are greater than from the direct factor.

It has been stated previously that the usual effect of capacity is to decrease first cost and production costs. The examples in Chapter II, in the discussion of the law of diminishing returns, show that this effect is not experienced in all cases. The possibility that the opposite effect may occur should never be neglected. When the effect of capacity is being considered one should always examine the circumstances and determine if the law of diminishing returns will reverse the more general effect.

Another item that must be considered with capacity is the fact that all capacities of a given article may not be made or available in comparable qualities. As a result, an increase in size at certain stages may mean an actual increase in cost. For example, the smaller size gasoline engines may be purchased in nearly any quality desired. The cheapest ones will operate, but not over long periods at full load. One may obtain such an engine of given size for about whatever he wishes to pay. On the other hand, when one wishes to purchase a gasoline engine of 100 horsepower, he will find that there are few, if any, low quality engines available. He may therefore find that he has to pay more per horsepower than he would for certain of the small engines. Obviously, quality must be considered when comparing the unit costs of small and larger sized products.

Capacity Factor. The usual effect of increased capacity has been stated to be a decrease in initial cost or cost of production. Accompanying this usually good effect is another which must be watched closely. This involves the extent to which the available capacity is utilized. The extent of the utilization of a capacity is measured by *capacity factor*. This is defined as the ratio of the average actual use to the available capacity. Discussions of the effect of capacity factor have most commonly been related to public utilities such as light and power, gas and water companies. Its effect is felt just as seriously by other industries. This effect was mentioned in the previous chapter when economic laws were discussed. Table 5 indicated the effect on unit costs when a tire curing unit was not operated at capacity. Whenever any capacity for production or service exists, the capacity factor at which the equipment operates has a vital effect upon the economy of the enterprise.

As a simple example of the effect of capacity factor, consider the case of automobiles. Compare a three-passenger coupe with a seven-passenger sedan. Even with the higher first cost and the greater operating expense, the cost per passenger mile probably would be considerably less for the seven-passenger sedan *if both cars were operated at capacity*. However, consider the effect of operating each car with only two passengers. The coupe is now operating at 66⅔% capacity factor and the sedan at 28.6%. Such a condition would not be serious in the case of a single auto. If the situation were extended to a company operating 100 cars, capacity factor would become of great importance. What would be the effect of operating 100 two-ton trucks where the maximum loads were only 500 pounds? Or the effect of owning 100 trucks when only 60 operate each day? The answer need not be given here.

Expand this situation so that it covers the entire automotive production industry. The total capacity of all the automobile factories in this country is tremendous. Through large scale production methods, specialized machines have been produced and great economies effected. Yet none of these plants ordinarily operates at maximum capacity for more than six months out of the year. During the periods of reduced output the charges for depreciation, taxes, insurance and supervision continue with very little decrease. What the effect of a 100% capacity factor in the automobile industry would be is difficult to say, but it is certain that a considerable reduction could be made in the selling prices of cars. The effect upon the nation through steady employment would be even more important.

Expand this condition again so as to include all of American industry. Some light has been thrown on this situation by the studies of the Brookings Institution. Their report [1] shows that in the peak year of 1929 American industry operated at a capacity factor of about 83%. In 1934 the capacity factor was only 60%. The cost of this idle capacity is as great as it is difficult to determine. It is significant that little has been accomplished in remedying this defect of our economic system. Numerous attempts have been made, some of them with some success. For example, one soap company has tried operating one of its plants at uniform volume throughout the entire year. Storage facilities and regulated sales effort were used to dispose of the output. Such efforts are worth more study in order to determine the exact cost to the country and the savings that could be effected.

Consider the case of the Blank Manufacturing Company, which

[1] See "Income & Economic Progress," Brookings Institution, 1935.

produces an article which it sells for $20. Their operating expenses are as follows:

Materials	$ 47,300
Labor	102,100
Taxes, insurance and depreciation	50,400
Maintenance	12,000
Supervision	17,500
Management and sales	31,700
Total	$261,000

They are producing 15,000 units per year and operating at a capacity factor of 79%. Total income from sales is thus $300,000, yielding a return of 7.8% on their capitalization of $500,000. It is believed that by reducing the price of their product 10% they will sell enough units to enable them to operate at 100% capacity. Would this be a desirable change?

From a study of the situation it is found that they could make a 4% saving on all of their materials if they purchase the larger quantities which would be required to produce the 19,000 units which correspond to 100% capacity. Their operating expenses at full capacity will be:

Materials	$ 57,500
Labor	129,200
Taxes, insurance and depreciation	50,800
Maintenance	12,800
Supervision	19,500
Management and sales	31,700
Total	$301,500

Total sales from the 19,000 units at $18 each will be $342,000. This will leave a net profit of $40,500 which will be a return of 8.1% on the capital investment. The change appears to be worth while, not only because a slightly greater profit will result but because the company will be placed in a better competitive position.

Economy studies of this type must take into account the effect of changing capacity factor upon the actual costs. Here, again, sunk, fixed and differential costs must be considered correctly. In this manner one may determine whether or not a decrease in price will be economically advantageous.

Load Factor. The second factor which must be considered in connection with available capacity is *load factor*. This is defined as the ratio of the average demand to the maximum demand. Obviously, if the maximum capacity were equal to the maximum demand, capacity factor and load factor would be identical. However, this is seldom the case, so load factor has special significance in measuring the effect of variations in demand.

In any attempt to measure the load factor it is necessary to decide which maximum demand shall be used. Should it be an instantaneous maximum demand or the maximum demand that lasts over several minutes? Thus in stating a load factor the period of the maximum demand should be given. Electric power companies commonly use the 15-minute maximum demand as the basis of determining the load factor of their individual customers.

Public utility companies pay particular attention to load factor. The reason for this is easily seen by looking at the power curve shown in Figure 35. As a result, most of the studies concerning load factors have been made by the utility companies. However, it can be shown that other industries are affected just as seriously by this factor. The majority of the customers of a public utility are limited as to the load they may throw on the system only by the maximum capacity of their equipment. The utility must make provision to supply whatever demand is placed upon its lines. Theoretically, the maximum demand which could be thrown on the lines would be the summation of the maximum demands of all the customers. For the modern utility company this would be a very great and serious load. In actual practice this condition never occurs.

Diversity Factor. Since a condition where the maximum load of a utility would be the sum of all the individual customers' maximum possible loads would be very serious, it is advisable to consider the circumstance that prevents this from occurring. This may be explained by a very simple example. Assume that a utility company has only two customers. One is a residence which uses the power for lighting. The other is a small factory which uses power for the operation of machinery between the hours of 8 A.M. and 5 P.M. Since the residence uses power only for lighting, it is unlikely that all of the lights would ever be turned on between the hours of 8 and 5 during the daytime. Similarly, the factory would not use any appreciable amount of power during the evening when the lights in the residence would be turned on. If the total connected load in the residence is 3 kw. and that of the factory 8 kw., the total possible load that can be thrown on the line is the sum of the two loads, or 11 kw. However, because of the diversity of the load, the maximum demand is actually 9 kw. It is thus seen that the maximum actual demand may be considerably less than the maximum possible demand because of the existence of two or more customers having different demand characteristics.

Ordinarily a utility has many customers of various types, such as residences, stores, factories, street lights, street railways, etc. No two of these have the same load characteristics. By having such a diversity of customers the utility is able to supply all of them satisfactorily with generating capacity which is considerably less than the sum of all the maximum demands of each consumer. Great effort is made to obtain customers who will use power during periods when others are using very little. Attractive rates are usually offered to those who will buy power during off-peak periods and not consume any during the peak hours.

Since the diversity of load is of such importance, a standard method of measurement has been adopted. This is the *diversity factor* which is defined as the ratio:

$$\frac{\text{Sum of the individual users' maximum demands}}{\text{Maximum demand actually experienced}}$$

Thus a diversity factor of 4 would indicate that the utility would need to have generating equipment of only one-fourth the capacity of the sum of the individual customers' demands.

The discussion of diversity factor has been in terms of an electric utility. Of course, diversity is just as important to other utilities. Water and gas companies must pay attention to the diversity of their consumers. These utilities do have one advantage in that they can provide some storage of their product during off-peak hours to meet the peak loads. Electric companies are unable to do this except in rare cases.

It is unfortunate that nonutility industries have given little attention, relatively, to their diversity factors. They are frequently in a much better position to control their diversity factors than are the utility industries. By producing a diversified line of products they may obtain a diversity in the demands of their customers. As a result, their productive capacities may be operated at much higher load and capacity factors, with attending economies.

A system with a high load factor may have a high diversity factor — but not necessarily. The effect may be just opposite. High load factor comes from continuous use of connected equipment. If all the customers on a utility system used all of their connected equipment all of the time, the company would have a 100% load factor. However, the diversity factor would be unity — a most undesirable situation. As a rule, a customer with a high load factor will have a low diversity factor. Thus it is desirable to obtain a high diversity factor by having many customers of different types.

Relationship of Load, Capacity and Diversity Factors to Utility Service Costs. From the load curve shown in Figure 35 it can be seen that a utility company must provide and maintain a vast amount of generating and distributing equipment which is not utilized during a large portion of the day. A large portion of the cost of any utility service is due to the fixed charges which exist because the company must at all times be ready to serve the maximum demand that may be placed upon it. Expensive generating stations must be built and maintained. Distribution lines, capable of carrying much more than the average load, must be built and kept in good condition. Administration and customers' expenses are nearly constant regardless of the load which is placed upon the system. In many cases the fixed expenses are more than 70% of the total cost of delivering power to the consumer. With such conditions existing, the expense of generating sufficient power to increase the plant load factor from 60 to 70% would be relatively little. The cost of such power is really only the differential expense of production. The utility can afford to sell such power for any amount greater than the increment cost. Many consumers will adjust their production processes so as to take advantage of such low-cost power.

Another method used by the utility companies to obtain greater load and capacity factors is to include penalty or bonus clauses in their rate schedules. These, in effect, enable the consumers to obtain decreased rates if they maintain a high load factor, or limit their maximum demands. For example, one company has the following rate schedule for commercial light and power:

Service charge: per month	$1.60
Energy charge (to be added to the service charge):	
First 1,000 kw.-hr. per month	2.7 cents per kw.-hr.
Next 2,000 kw.-hr. per month	2.3 cents per kw.-hr.
Next 5,000 kw.-hr. per month	1.9 cents per kw.-hr.
For all excess over 8,000 kw.-hr. per month:	
First 50 kw.-hr. per kw. of maximum demand	1.7 cents per kw.-hr.
Next 150 kw.-hr. per kw. of maximum demand	
but not more than 85,000 kw.-hr.	1.2 cents per kw.-hr.
All excess	0.7 cents per kw.-hr.

Utility companies attempt to obtain higher diversity factors by obtaining customers who have different load characteristics. Customers may be influenced to alter their load demands by the possibility of securing energy at very low rates during the utility's off-peak hours. One utility company includes the following clause in the rate schedule for general power consumers:

Any customer whose billing demand has exceeded 400 kw. for 3 consecutive months and thereafter until it has fallen below 300 kw. for 12 consecutive months may, upon request, have his maximum demand measured by a type of meter which records the demand at all hours, in which case demands occurring between 10 : 30 P.M. and 6 : 30 A.M. of the following day and on Sundays and legal holidays will be ignored in determining the billing demand.

Another company uses the following clause to allow discounts for off-peak power:

For current used for industrial power purposes, . . . the rate for peak hours shall be the same as for commercial purposes and for off-peak hours the rate shall be twenty-five per cent (25%) less on all loads of 21 horsepower and over. The peak hours shall be between 4 : 30 P.M. and 9 : 30 P.M.

Gas companies have an additional complicating factor in connection with the load factor of their pipe lines. This is the effect of weather. Electric transmission lines are affected very little by changes of temperature. This is not true of gas and oil lines.

The temperature has a great effect upon the amount of gas or oil that can be transmitted. In some cases the transmission capacity may be maintained, but only at greatly increased pumping expense. In order to transmit oil or gas during cold weather increased pumping costs must be met. Yet this is the time of year when the demands are heaviest. Thus these companies are faced with the problem of providing equipment which is adequate to meet their peak cold weather demands. During the summer months this equipment will be operated at a very low capacity factor. In most localities it is very difficult to find customers who can use large quantities of gas or oil during only the summer months, no matter how low the price.

While gas companies can provide for the storage of certain amounts of their product during the off-peak hours, the amount of storage that must be provided is determined by the load factor and diversity factor of the system. Therefore, these factors are of great importance to these companies.

It can be seen that load, capacity and diversity factors are related to fixed costs which must be met regardless of output. These fixed costs are due to the necessity for large investments in generation or production capacity. It has been shown that the fixed costs are often the largest portion of production expense. In such cases it may be desirable to employ a production unit which is less efficient but has a much lower initial cost than some other unit. The decrease in fixed costs will more than offset the increased variable expenses. It has been said, truly, that the possession of the capacity for production is accompanied by the obligation to use that capacity to its fullest extent.

Capacity and Load Factor in Manufacturing Industries. Considerable has been written concerning the effects of capacity and load factors in the utility industries. Apparently, much less thought has been given to the effect of these same factors in the manufacturing industries. Modern industry is characterized by large investments in plant and equipment. The fixed charges which must accompany such investments are a very appreciable part of the cost of production. Most manufacturers know that their fixed charges must be met regardless of the rate of production. However, it appears that only a few have determined the exact amount of savings that would result if their production facilities were operated at 100% capacity factor.

The problem is illustrated by a consideration of one of the large automobile companies of this country. This company can easily produce 50,000 cars per week. For a 50-week year the annual production at this rate would be 2,500,000 units. The actual annual production of this company during the past few years has been less than 1,000,000 cars. Thus their plants were operated at a capacity factor of about 40%. Their load factor was approximately the same as the capacity factor since the plants were operated at capacity for a few weeks. One cannot help but speculate on what reduction in the selling price of this company's cars could be made if the operations could be carried out in a plant which was 40% of the size of the existing plant but operating at 100% capacity factor. The further effect upon the national economy through providing steady employment by such a plan is almost beyond speculation.

A few companies have made excellent progress in moving their capacity factors toward the 100% point. Notable among these is a manufacturer of specialized textiles. Through careful study, he has determined the "least, economical" size of plant for his business. By this term, "least, economical," is meant the smallest size of plant that can be operated with a good degree of efficiency. These plants are built in various localities. No new plant is built until sales have reached a sufficient amount beyond existing capacity to assure that the new unit can be operated with a good capacity factor. Orders beyond the existing capacity are sublet to other manufacturers, if necessary.

Another notable example of maintaining an approximately uniform capacity factor is that of the Nunn-Bush Company.[2] In this case the attempt to obtain a uniform rate of production was made, primarily, to provide uniform employment for the workers. The variations in retail sales are absorbed, largely, by the stocks that are maintained in the retail stores.

An interesting result occurred in some of the canneries of Wisconsin, where manufacturers were practically forced to better

[2] See the article "Fifty-two Pay Checks a Year." *Fortune*, November, 1938, for a complete discussion of this.

their capacity factors. When this state put unemployment insurance laws into effect, it was apparent that the canneries were going to be in difficulty, because of heavy unemployment insurance assessments, unless they were able to stabilize their employment. A great many changes were made in order to spread out the canning season and thus give more uniform employment. Without realizing it, they were increasing their capacity factors. Many of the canneries found that the savings which resulted from better utilization of their production facilities more than offset the cost of the unemployment insurance payments.

Figure 38 shows the variation in unit cost with percentage of operation for one company in the field of heavy manufactures. These figures assumed no change in wage rates or other direct costs of operation. The company had no bonded indebtedness so that the variation in unit costs is less than would be experienced by many companies. The advantage of high capacity factor is apparent.

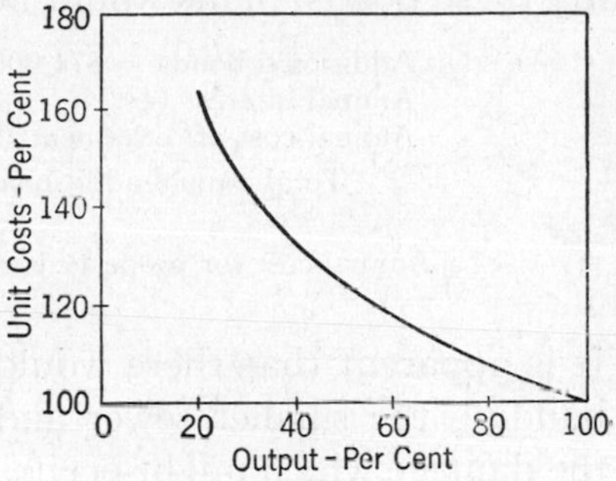

FIGURE 38. Variation in unit costs with percentage of operation for a company manufacturing heavy equipment.

Capacity Factor in Sewers and Flood Control Projects. Capacity factor has a somewhat different significance when applied to structures which must be operated at loads beyond the control of man. Sewers and flood control projects are good examples of such structures. Here the capacity factor cannot be controlled by varying the load. The only possibility of control is in varying the size, or capacity, of the structure. In most cases of this type the loads vary greatly. The maximum loads are usually much greater than all the others. For example, there might be 100 cases of rainfall in one year. One of these might be twice as great as any of the other 99. Should a storm sewer be built adequate for the peak load, or only to take care of the 99 cases of ordinary rainfall?

An example of this kind occurred in a mountain community in the west where "flash" floods were experienced on an average of once every four years. A storm sewer of sufficient size to handle all loads except those caused by the flash floods was estimated to cost $50,800. A sewer which would be large enough to handle all possible demands would cost $74,000. It was estimated that if the smaller sewer were built, the damage resulting from the excess water which would not be handled by this sewer would average $3,000, occurring once each four years. This damage would be to city property, such as streets and walks. The sewer was to be financed by the sale of 20-year, 4% bonds. A decision had to be made as to which sewer would offer the greater economy.

The cost of building the larger sewer would be the expense of interest on the additional amount of bonds, plus the cost of retiring these bonds. This would be:

$$
\begin{aligned}
\text{Additional bonds} &= \$74,000 - \$50,800 &&= \$23,200 \\
\text{Annual interest } (4\%) &&&= 928 \\
\text{Annual cost of retirement } (s_{\overline{20}|} = 29.78) &&&= \underline{780} \\
\text{Total annual additional cost} &&&= \$1,708
\end{aligned}
$$

$$
\text{Annual cost for property loss} = \frac{\$3,000}{s_{\overline{4}|}} = \frac{\$3,000}{4.25} = \$706
$$

It is apparent that there would be an annual saving of $1,002 in building the smaller sewer and making provision for paying for the damage which might occur. Where private property might be damaged, lives endangered, or great inconvenience caused the public by the occasional floods, the monetary saving might be a small item in the final economy of such a project. However, the necessity for considering the capacity factor of such projects is indicated.

Power Factor. An additional factor, which accompanies the use of alternating current electric power, should be considered. A detailed explanation of the cause of the *power factor* is outside the purpose of this book. It is sufficient for this discussion to say that the measured power consumed per phase by an alternating current device is equal to $E \times I \times \cos \Theta$, where E is the voltage, I the current and Θ the phase angle between the voltage and current maxima. Power factor is equal to the value of the cosine of Θ. It may also be defined as the ratio of the kilowatts per phase to the kilovolt-amperes per phase. The effect upon the utility company is to make it necessary to provide excess capacity in generating and distributing equipment since they do not receive payment for some of the current generated. Increased costs result, owing primarily to this necessity for increased capacity of all current-carrying apparatus, the increased losses which occur in this equipment, and the poor voltage regulation in the system. Thus the power company incurs additional expense due to heavy inductive loads which are placed on the system and cause low power factor.

Low power factor may be corrected in several ways. One is to eliminate improperly loaded induction motors from the system. Another is to substitute synchronous or unity-power-factor motors for induction motors. Improvement may also be had by placing static condensers or synchronous condensers on the lines. All of these methods are used. It will be noted, however, that the use of the first two methods is limited to the extent to which the users of the power may wish to cooperate with the power company. In other words, the power factor of the system would be improved, at no expense to the power company, if the consumers would substitute synchronous motors for induction motors in their plants.[3] Since synchronous motors are more expensive than induction motors, it is natural that few consumers are willing to make this substitution unless given some monetary consideration.

In order to influence consumers to help the power company improve their power factor, most utility companies grant certain rate reductions to consumers who maintain a high power factor. For example, the rate schedule of one company includes this clause:

When the billing demand has exceeded 300 kw. for 3 consecutive months and thereafter until it has fallen below 200 kw. for 12 consecutive months, charges for energy will be adjusted for weighted monthly power factor, as follows.

If the power factor exceeds 80%, bills should be reduced by 0.3% for each 1% of such excess up to and including 90% power factor and by 0.2% for each 1% of such excess over 90% power factor. If the power factor is less than 65%, bills shall be increased by 0.5% for each 1% of such deficiency in power factor, provided that the maximum increase shall not exceed 5%. In no case, however, shall the total charge, after adjustment for power factor, be less than the minimum charge.

---

[3] The power factor could be improved by the installation of synchronous or static condensers, but this would necessitate investment by the utility.

For determining the weighted monthly average power factor for the purpose of this schedule a meter to measure the reactive kilovolt-ampere-hours of the load shall be installed in conjunction with the kilowatt-hour meter. The power factor computed from the ratio of the monthly reactive kva-hr. to the kw.-hrs. shall be computed to the nearest whole percent. In any case, where the power factor is likely to be leading at any time, the reactive component meter may be ratcheted to prevent reversal.

With such bonus and penalty clauses applying to the power consumed by manufacturing establishments, it is often necessary to consider the economy of installing equipment which will improve the power factor and thereby enable lower power costs to be obtained. For example, assume that a company is considering the installation of a 100-horsepower motor which will operate at 85% of capacity during 8 hours per day and an average of 22 days per month. An induction motor may be purchased for $800 which would have an efficiency of 91% and operate at 79% power factor. A synchronous motor would cost $1,100, have an efficiency of 90% and operate at unity power factor. The power output of each motor would be 11,260 kw.-hr. per month. The cost of the power consumed would be at the rate of $0.007 per kw.-hr. before any adjustment for power factor penalty or bonus. If the power were purchased under the power factor clause cited previously, the two motors would be compared as follows:

Induction motor:

$$\text{Power consumed} = \frac{11,260}{0.91} = 12,380 \text{ kw.-hr. per month}$$

Cost of power $= 12,380 \times \$0.007 = \$86.60$ per month

Synchronous motor:

$$\text{Power consumed} = \frac{11,260}{0.90} = 12,500 \text{ kw.-hr. per month}$$

Cost of power:

Base cost	$12,500 \times \$0.007 =$	$87.50
Bonus for power factor		
From 80 to 90%, $10 \times 0.3\% = 3\%$		
From 90 to 100%, $10 \times 0.2\% = \underline{2\%}$		
Total bonus	$5\% =$	4.37
Net bill		$83.13

Saving per year by use of synchronous motor = ($86.60 − $83.13)12 = $41.64. This saving should be related to the added cost of the synchronous motor, in the usual manner, to determine the advisability of purchasing this motor.

The Effect of Future Demand. Another very important type of problem in economic selection is that of determining what provision should be made for meeting future demands. Mention has been made of this problem in connection with the building of the Golden Gate bridge. Similar circumstances exist in the public utility industries. For example, the telephone companies must decide to what extent they will install cables of sufficient size to provide adequate service during future years. Water companies must install mains of sufficient size to supply the customers who may ask for service during future years. Power and light companies are unable to know exactly what their customers' demands will be in the future.

In all of these cases, the utility companies are obligated to provide service to any customer who asks for it. In order to supply the first customer in a given district, pipe or cable must be installed. It is obvious that it would be uneconomic to install pipe or cable of sufficient size to supply only this initial customer. When another customer applied for service, the installation would have to be duplicated. Such a practice would be extremely expensive and result in prohibitive rates for service. An alternative would be to build service lines of sufficient size to provide adequate service for any possible loads that might be placed on them in future years. Such a solution introduces a number of complications, some of them similar to those encountered in considering depreciation.

Determination of Future Requirements. The first question which would come to one's mind in connection with future demand would be, "What will the future demands be?" In nearly all cases the answer to this question must be an estimate. Since it is usually impossible to have an estimate 100% correct, it is to be expected that some error will exist in the result. The demand for goods or services is connected closely with the existence of human population. Thus one of the factors which must be considered is the growth or change in population. A second factor is the amount of service that will be demanded by the population. The methods of predicting these factors are varied, and their details are beyond the scope of this book. Some of the references at the close of this chapter give information on the methods which are used by various companies. However, most of these may be divided into two types.

The first method is that of using past experience. Thus a company predicts its future load upon the way in which its load has changed in the past. Or the prediction for the future may be made by considering what change was experienced in another locality or company where the initial conditions were similar to those at hand. The disadvantage of such a procedure is apparent. There is no guarantee that things in the future will follow those of the past. In fact, one can usually be quite certain that this will not be the case. Thus past experience can usually be used only to determine the *trend* of the changes that are taking place. This trend must then be projected into the future.

The other method consists of studying the factors that will affect future demand, and basing the prediction upon these items. For example, in order to determine what the electric power consumption will be in a certain city during the next 10 years, it is necessary to study the growth in population, the migration of people from other areas into the city, the increase in use of labor-saving and power-consuming equipment, the general economic and business conditions in the city and throughout the country, etc. The extent to which each of these factors will affect the demand for electric power must be estimated by one who has considerable knowledge about the subject. Thus a great amount of judgment is required. This is true of either method, although statistical methods may be applied to some parts of the problem.

All of the successful methods of prediction have been the result of much experience and trial and error. Those methods which are most successful are the result of years of experience during which the difficulties could be determined and proper correction made. It is usually impossible for a company to start out on a course of predicting future demands and have immediate success, except by accident, or by having spent a number of years in establishing the system and trying it experimentally before attempting to put it into actual practice.

One very important factor in predicting future demands should not be overlooked. This is the necessity of examining the method each year and ascertaining to what degree it has succeeded or failed and making whatever corrections are indicated. Most successful methods make use of a periodic correction to their estimates. This is one of the most important phases of planning. Thus, while a company may make predictions for 20 years in advance, the predictions are corrected each year in the light of the amount by which the actual values for that year have differed from the predicted values.

The discussion thus far has dealt with the necessity for utility companies determining future demands. The problem is just as important for many companies which are not utilities. For example, consider a company which is contemplating building a new factory. Should the building be large enough for only the immediate needs, or should it be of sufficient size to accommodate operations 10 years from the date of construction? It is apparent that future demand is of vital importance in making the proper selection. The main difference between the problem of the utility and the nonutility is that the latter may regulate the demand placed upon it by refusing to accept business for which it is not equipped.

It may appear to some that the attendant inaccuracies make attempts to predict future demands somewhat futile. It is true that the results will not be all that might be desired. However, it is much better to have some information of reasonable accuracy than none at all. It is well to remember that a number of companies who have done work along this line for a number of years are now estimating demand for several years in advance with an accuracy of over 90%. Such figures are of great value.

Determining the Economy of Investment for Future Demand. The method of making economy studies, where future demand must be considered, is the immediate purpose of this discussion. Even if the future demands are known with great accuracy, the problem is not a simple one. This fact can probably be best illustrated by a simple example.

A certain water reservoir of sufficient capacity to supply all the loads which will occur during the next 20 years will cost $40,000. This reservoir will last 20 years. An alternative would be to construct a smaller reservoir having sufficient capacity to meet all the demands of the next 10 years, and adequate to supply one-half of the demand for the following 10 years. This reservoir would cost $27,000. At the end of the first 10-year period it would be necessary to build a second reservoir, large enough to meet the other half of the demand during the second 10-year period. This reservoir would cost $23,000 to construct. The first of these smaller reservoirs will last 20 years and the second for 10 years. Let it be assumed that all operating and maintenance expenses of the two alternatives would be the same. How should these two alternative installations be compared in order to determine which should be used?

The most obvious method of comparison would be to consider the amounts of capital required by the two alternatives. The first proposal requires the investment of $40,000. The second would require the ultimate investment of $50,000. But the fact that the required investment varies with time makes it apparent that this method of comparison is not satisfactory.

A refinement of the above method would be to determine the present value of the investments required for each alternative and compare these. The present value of the investment required for the first proposal would be $40,000 since it must be invested at once. The present value of the investment required for the alternative method would be computed as follows:

$$\begin{aligned}
&\text{\$27,000 required now; present value} &&= \text{\$27,000} \\
&\text{\$23,000 required in 10 years;} && \\
&\quad \text{present value} = \text{\$23,000} \times v^{10}(i = 5\%) &&= \underline{\quad 14,130} \\
&\quad \text{Total present value} &&= \text{\$41,130}
\end{aligned}$$

This method of comparison makes it appear that the first proposal would be the more desirable since the present value of the required investment is less than for the alternative. One should remember that the validity of this conclusion is dependent upon the interest rate which was used in determining the present value of the investment required for the second proposed installation. For example, if an interest rate of 8% had been used, the present value of the investment for the second proposal would have been only $37,650. In this case the second proposal would appear to be less expensive. The importance of the interest rate in problems of deferred investments should never be overlooked. The greater the interest rate, the greater will be the likelihood of the deferred investment appearing to be the more economic. It is difficult to set any hard and fast rule as to what interest rate should be used in such calculations. Certainly the rate of interest should never exceed the average rate of earning of the business. The average rate of earning of the business is probably the correct one to be used *provided the enterprise can actually make use of any capital which would be available if investment is deferred*. If this is not the case, the correct interest rate is either the cost of obtaining additional capital, or the return which might be obtained from the investment of idle funds. The correct rate for each case must depend upon the circumstances. Another justification in using the average earning rate of the business is that it is usually higher than other rates that might be used. This tends to favor the alternative which involves a deferred investment. As will be pointed out later, this is the alternative which usually should be favored.

Determination of the Present Value of All Expenses. The method of comparing the present values of the required investments is quite satisfactory for the problem given, because of the assumptions which were stated. These were that the future operation and maintenance expenses of the two alternatives would be identical. This is seldom the case in actual practice. Of course, the amount of investment required for two alternative proposals is of importance and should be considered. But after a structure is built it must be operated and maintained. The factors which are the best for comparing the economy of two projects are the total costs of operation.

Obviously, if costs extending throughout different periods of time are to be compared, the most simple method is to determine the present worth of the costs of each method. Thus, in order to make a valid comparison between two alternative methods of providing for future demands, one must determine the present value of the cost of possessing and operating each. One assumes that at the beginning the first cost and all of the future operating expenses are going to be provided for.

Now consider the application of this method of analysis in order to determine the correct choice between two proposals where the annual operating and maintenance expenses are different. A company is contemplating the building of a new power plant. Two plans are being considered. Plan A would be to build a power plant of sufficient size to meet all of the needs of the next 10 years. Such a plant would be of 5,000 kw. capacity and cost $400,000 to build. Plan B would be to construct a plant of 3,000 kw. capacity at the present time and at the end of six years enlarge this plant by an addition of 2,000 kw. The 3,000-kw. plant would cost $310,000 and the additional 2,000 kw. would cost $180,000. Taxes and insurance on the plants would be 2% of the invested capital in each case. Annual operating and maintenance expenses for the two plants would be as follows:

	Plan A	Plan B
First and second years	$48,000	$45,000
Third and fourth years	54,000	52,000
Fifth and sixth years	61,000	60,000
Seventh and eighth years	78,500	80,000
Ninth and tenth years	96,000	97,000

To compare the economy of the two alternative plans the present value of all of the future expenses of each must be determined. For plan A this would be done as follows (7% interest rate being used):

Present cost to possess: $400,000
Present value of taxes and insurance: $400,000 \times 0.02 \times a_{\overline{10}|} = 56,200
Present value of operation and maintenance expense:

First and second years	$48,000 \times a_{\overline{2}|}$	$ 86,900
Third and fourth years	$54,000 \times a_{\overline{2}|} \times v^2$	85,300
Fifth and sixth years	$61,000 \times a_{\overline{2}|} \times v^4$	84,200
Seventh and eighth years	$78,500 \times a_{\overline{2}|} \times v^6$	94,600
Ninth and tenth years	$96,000 \times a_{\overline{2}|} \times v^8$	101,100

                                                                                      $452,100
Present value of cost to possess and operate $908,300

For plan B the present value of the total costs would be:

Present cost of 3,000-kw. plant: $310,000
Present cost of 2,000-kw. addition 6 years hence:
    $180,000 \times v^6$ 120,000
Present value of taxes and interest:

First 6 years	$310,000 \times 0.02 \times a_{\overline{6}|}$	$29,600
Last 4 years	$490,000 \times 0.02 \times a_{\overline{4}|} \times v^6$	22,150
Total		51,750

Present value of operation and maintenance expenses:

First and second years	$45,000 \times a_{\overline{2}|}$	$ 81,400
Third and fourth years	$52,000 \times a_{\overline{2}|} \times v^2$	82,100
Fifth and sixth years	$60,000 \times a_{\overline{2}|} \times v^4$	82,800
Seventh and eighth years	$80,000 \times a_{\overline{2}|} \times v^6$	96,500
Ninth and tenth years	$97,000 \times a_{\overline{2}|} \times v^8$	102,100
Total		$444,900

Present value of cost to possess and operate $926,650

By a comparison of the present values of the total costs of the two methods it is apparent that plan A will be less expensive than plan B.

If the present value of the total cost of alternative B had turned out to be less than that of A it would have meant that B was cheaper than A and that the extra capital required would earn something greater than the 7% rate which was assumed. When using this method the interest rate used should be the minimum rate of return which is desired from the investment of additional capital.

Other Factors Affecting Deferred Investment Studies. A number of other factors complicate studies of deferred investments. The first of these is the life of the structures. In the examples considered it has been assumed that the structures in the alternative plans would cease to render service at the same time. In actual practice this is not often the case. Alternatives must be compared which utilize structures and equipment that have different lives. If one attempts to account for the difference in life too rigorously, the problem becomes so complicated that the results are practically impossible to compare. Therefore, it is often assumed that the structures will become useless, or at least have no book value, at the same time. This assumption may be made more valid in extreme cases by adding an expense for keeping the shorter lived structure in service up to the time when the other would become of no value. Another method is to include only those expenses, both to possess and operate, of the longer lived alternative which do not extend beyond the life of the other plan. By these methods no appreciable error is introduced.

Another factor which should be considered is the necessity for obtaining the additional capital that may be required if a more expensive plan is followed immediately. Of course this is a financial matter and does not directly change the economy of the alternative. Indirectly, however, it may be an important item. If it is difficult for a company to obtain capital, an alternative permitting deferred investment may be the correct one, even though it is ultimately more expensive. As in other economy studies, however, it is best to determine the true economy of the proposed plans and then take this financial factor into account in making the final decision.

The last factor, but a very important one, is the element of time. Time always favors the plan calling for a deferred investment. Studies of this type are based upon estimated future results. The actual results will usually deviate to some extent from the predictions. Unless the immediate investment of additional capital offers the possibility of a considerable return, good judgment requires one to take advantage of the possibility of waiting before investing. Possible exceptions to this rule are when public inconvenience, or favor, is involved, such as when streets have to be torn up to install additional sewer or utility facilities. However, investments for future demand must always receive the utmost caution and consideration.

REFERENCES

Clark, J. M.: "Studies in the Economics of Overhead Costs," The University of Chicago Press, 1923.
Eidmann, F. L.: "Economic Control of Engineering and Manufacturing," McGraw-Hill Book Company, Inc., New York, 1931.
Grant, E. L.: "Principles of Engineering Economy," The Ronald Press Company, New York, 1938.

PROBLEMS

143. List five instances where the selling price of articles is affected by size.
144. What is the difference between capacity factor and load factor?
145. Explain the connection between capacity and load factors and overhead costs.
146. The annual overhead expenses of a business are equal to $24,000 + $5,000 × C.F., where C.F. is the capacity factor. The output capacity of the company is 10,000 units per year. It is estimated that a decrease of $0.50 per unit in selling price would increase the capacity factor from 80 to 90%. If all other expenses remain fixed, will this be a good plan to follow? The present selling price is $10 per unit.

147. The load on an oil pipe line varies as follows during the year:

Load	Hours
3,000 gal. per minute	1,400
2,250 gal. per minute	3,600
1,500 gal. per minute	3,760

In selecting the pump for a section of this pipe line two alternative installations are being considered. Alternative A is to use a 3,000 g.p.m. pump. Alternative B is to use two 1,500 g.p.m. pumps. The power required for these pumps at various loads is:

Load	Pump A	Pump B
750 g.p.m.	4.7 kw.	2.7 kw.
1,500 g.p.m.	5.2 kw.	4.2 kw
3,000 g.p.m.	7.8 kw.	—

If power costs 2 cents per kw.-hr., which alternative should be used?

148. A foundry which buys power under the rate schedule shown on page 252 has been paying an average of $150 per month for power. They contemplate the installation of an electric furnace which will use 17,000 kw.-hr. per month. What will be the cost of the power used by the electric furnace? Maximum demand will be 50 kw.

149. The foundry can secure a reduction of 22% in the cost of the power used by the electric furnace by not using it during peak hours. Such operation will increase the amount of power consumed by 10% and necessitate paying overtime pay of $30 per month to various workmen. Should the furnace be shut down during peak hours?

150. A factory has a large number of induction motors. The resulting power factor is 81%. A new mill is being installed. If this mill is driven by an induction motor the power factor for the entire plant will be lowered to 79%. If a synchronous motor is used, the power factor of the plant will increase to 92%. The synchronous motor will cost $1,200 more than the induction motor. Its economic life is five years. The average monthly power bill has been $470. Capital is worth 8% to this company. If the company buys power under the rate schedule quoted on page 257, which motor should be installed?

151. A department store is building the first unit of a new building. Adjacent ground is owned for the second unit of the building. It is expected that the second unit will be built in five years. If the foundation for the second unit is built to the street level at this time it will cost $11,000. It is estimated that the same foundation will cost $17,000 if built five years later. The foundation will be used for parking space for customers' cars if built now. Otherwise a parking lot would be established on the unoccupied ground. If capital is worth 7% to this company, should the foundation be built now?

152. A state highway commission is planning to build a bridge on a new highway. At the present time a three-lane road is to be built. It is expected that in 10 years a second three-lane strip will be added, giving a divided six-lane highway.

A decision has to be made between building a bridge wide enough to carry six lanes of traffic or build a narrower bridge which will carry three lanes and build another three-lane bridge when the additional three lanes are added to the highway at the end of 10 years. To build a six-lane bridge now will cost $82,000. The three-lane bridge will cost $58,000. Upkeep for the three lane bridge will be $3,000 annually, while that for the six-lane bridge would be $4,600. It is assumed that the second three-lane bridge can be built in 10 years at the same cost as if it were built now. The project is to be financed by 4%, noncallable, 40-year bonds. Assume that the end of the life of all structures will occur at 40 years from the present date. Which alternative should be used?

153. A power company is designing a new steam-electric plant to supply a growing community. The initial load when the plant is completed will be 5,000 kw. This load will increase 500 kw. each year for 20 years. Two alternatives are being considered for supplying this demand. Plan A:

Build a 15,000-kw. plant at a cost of $1,200,000. This plant would consume 1.18 pounds of coal per kw.-hr. Plan B: Build a 10,000-kw. plant at a cost of $950,000. This plant would supply all the needs for 10 years and have an efficiency of 1.21 pounds of coal per kw.-hr. At the end of 10 years build an additional plant of 5,000 kw. capacity at an estimated cost of $550,000. This plant would probably have an efficiency of 1.15 pounds of coal per kw.-hr.

Assume that all plants are to be written off at the end of 20 years from the present time. Coal will cost $4.50 per ton and have a heat value of 13,500 B.T.U. Capital is available for either plan and is worth 7% to the company. Taxes and insurance amount to 3% annually. Which plan should be adopted?

Chapter XV

THE USE OF GRAPHICAL METHODS OF ANALYSIS

There are a number of places where the use of graphical methods of analysis and portrayal is a distinct aid in economic selection. A simple case of this is illustrated in the following example.

A company finds that in its generating plants a certain coal will produce 1 kw.-hr. of electricity per pound. A second grade of coal always sells for $0.50 less per ton than the first grade. However, this lower grade of coal will produce only 0.856 kw.-hr. of electricity per pound consumed. Overhead and fixed costs are $0.005 per kw.-hr., regardless of which coal is used. They wish to know at what prices the two coals will be equal in economy and be able to determine which coal to use at any time.

In order to obtain a solution to this problem the graphical method illustrated in Figure 39 may be used. The cost of production when using the cheaper grade of coal is plotted, using as abscissas the price of the cheaper coal per ton, and as ordinates the unit production cost in dollars. Thus the total cost of production per kilowatt-hour is shown by the solid line on the graph. The unit cost of production when using the higher priced coal is then plotted, using as abscissas the cost of this type of coal per ton. Double abscissas are necessary, since the price of this type of coal is always $0.50 greater than for the lower quality coal. Thus, when one grade of coal can be purchased for $2 per ton the better grade will cost $2.50. The total unit cost when using the higher priced coal is shown by the dotted line on the chart. The chart reveals that the unit cost will be the same, regardless of which coal is used, provided the cheaper grade of coal is selling at $3 per ton and the higher grade at its corresponding price of $3.50 per ton. The two coals are said to "break even" at prices

269

of $3 per ton for the cheaper coal and $3.50 per ton for the more expensive grade. Charts that show relationships of this type are often called "break-even" charts.

The break-even chart in Figure 39 has an additional advantage, beyond showing the "break-even" point, in that the effect of using either grade of coal is shown for any selling price of the coals. When the cheaper grade of coal is obtainable at less than $3 per ton, it is more economical to use the less expensive grade.

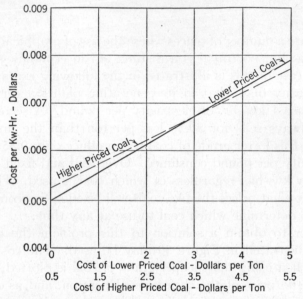

FIGURE 39. Break-even chart for two different priced coals.

When the price of the cheaper coal goes above $3 per ton, this coal is not the most economical grade to use. For any given prices of the two coals, the difference in the cost of producing 1 kw.-hr. of power by the use of the two coals can be determined from the chart. In this manner the break-even chart may be used to show more information than could be given by a single mathematical solution of the problem.

Graphical solutions to economy problems also offer a method of obtaining fairly precise general solutions to problems involving numerous factors that change in magnitude as the conditions vary. By obtaining the solutions to a few specific cases, sufficient data are made available so that curves may be drawn from which the most economic conditions may be determined. The curves shown in Figure 41 are examples of this use of graphical representation.

Another advantage of graphical solutions of economy problems is the fact that the correct solutions for varying conditions may be shown. This is an important feature of the solution shown in Figure 39. Not only are the break-even prices of the two grades of coal shown, but the grade which should be used when prices change is also indicated. Thus it is often possible to have the solution for changed conditions at hand in pictorial form before the conditions have actually come to exist. This is important in problems concerning management practice. One is enabled to know what course of action should be followed if conditions change. Since business is changing constantly, it is often advantageous to have a graphical solution which covers a range of possible conditions.

Economic Lot Size. Graphical representation may be used to advantage in determining the effect of the quantity of goods manufactured at one time upon the unit cost. In the production of most goods the unit cost is composed of some expenses which are constant and others which vary with the quantity produced in one run. For example, unit material and labor costs may be the same regardless of the number of units produced at any one time. If there is any appreciable expense due to getting the machinery ready for production and issuing the necessary orders, forms, etc., these expenses are about the same whether one or one thousand units are produced for each setup of the equipment. An equation may be written which will enable one to determine the most economical quantity in each lot of production. To obtain such an equation let

X = the lot size
S = a safety factor — the minimum number of days for which supplies should be on hand at all times
M = the quantity needed to supply one day's demand
N = the number of days of operation per year
C_a = unit cost for materials and labor, direct charges

C_p = cost of setting up the production equipment and originating the order

I = cost of depreciation, taxes, insurance, interest, etc., in per cent

W = cost of storing one unit for one year

y = total unit cost

Y = cost of one year's requirements

Total direct costs for one year's supply = NMC_a

Total cost of setup for one year = $C_p \dfrac{NM}{X}$

Average number of units on hand = $SM + \dfrac{X}{2}$

Investment costs = $\left(SM + \dfrac{X}{2}\right)\left(C_a + \dfrac{C_p}{X}\right)(I)$

Storage costs = $\left(SM + \dfrac{X}{2}\right)(W)$

$$Y = NMC_a + C_p\frac{NM}{X} + \left(SM + \frac{X}{2}\right)\left(C_a + \frac{C_p}{X}\right)(I)$$
$$+ \left(SM + \frac{X}{2}\right)(W) \quad (48)$$

$$= NMC_a + C_p\frac{NM}{X} + SMC_aI + C_a\frac{IX}{2} + SMC_p\frac{I}{X}$$
$$+ C_p\frac{I}{2} + SMW + \frac{WX}{2} \quad (49)$$

To determine the optimum value of X, Equation (49) is differentiated with respect to X and set equal to zero.

$$\frac{dY}{dX} = -C_p\frac{NM}{X^2} + C_a\frac{I}{2} - SMC_p\frac{I}{X^2} + \frac{W}{2} = O \quad (50)$$

$$X^2\frac{(C_aI + W)}{2} = SMC_pI + C_pNM \quad (51)$$

$$X = \sqrt{\frac{2\,MC_p(SI + N)}{C_aI + W}} \quad (52)$$

By the use of Equation (52) the correct number of units to be produced in one lot in order to obtain the lowest unit cost may be determined. After the number of units to be produced in one lot has been determined, the unit cost may be found by solving

Equation (49) for the computed value of X and dividing the answer by the quantity NM.

Equation (52) is entirely satisfactory for determining the correct number of units to be produced in one lot. However, in using this equation it is difficult to determine the effect upon unit costs of producing a lot size other than the optimum. This is very often the information which is needed. Many times it is convenient to produce goods in quantities somewhat different from the optimum economic size. Under such circumstances it is desirable to know what the effect upon unit costs will be.

Equation (49) may be divided by the quantity in order to obtain unit costs. Performing this operation and rearranging, it becomes

$$y = \left[C_a + SC_a \frac{I}{N} + \frac{C_p I}{2\,NM} + \frac{SW}{N} \right] + \frac{1}{X}\left[C_p + \frac{C_p SI}{N} \right]$$
$$+ X\left[\frac{C_a I + W}{2\,NM} \right] \quad (53)$$

For any given set of cost conditions the quantities inside all of the brackets are constants. It is thus quite simple to obtain the unit costs for any lot size. By determining the unit cost for three or four different lot sizes a curve can be drawn similar to the one shown in Figure 40. This particular curve was for the following cost conditions:

$$M = 200$$
$$N = 300$$
$$S = 10$$
$$C_a = \$1.00$$
$$C_p = \$75.00$$
$$I = 20\%$$
$$W = \$0.02$$

The values of y were determined for lot sizes of 1,000, 5,000, 10,000 and 30,000 units by substitution in Equation (53). From the resulting curve it can be seen that the most economical lot size is approximately 6,400 units. This value checks very well with the value of 6,420, which is obtained from the solution of Equation (52).

From this same curve one can readily see the effect of lot size upon unit costs. It is apparent that the lot size may be decreased by about 2,000 units before the unit cost is increased one cent. However, the lot size may be *increased* by nearly 8,000 units before the unit cost increases one cent. Thus the graphical method of solution not only indicates the most economical lot size but also makes the effect of lot size on unit cost available for effective use.

Graphical Representation of Kelvin's Law. The problem from which Kelvin's law originated furnishes a good illustration of the

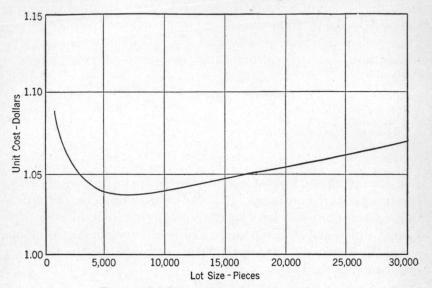

FIGURE 40. Effect of lot size on unit costs.

use of break-even or minimum-cost-point charts. The energy lost in an electrical transmission line is I^2RH, where I is the current in amperes, R is the resistance of the line in ohms, and H is the number of hours during which the line is used. This lost energy represents a loss in dollars and may be considered one of the expenses of operating the line.

Additional expenses which exist are the fixed charges of depreciation, taxes, insurance and interest. These are proportional to the amount of money invested in the transmission line. If the size of the conductors is increased, the resistance of the line is decreased and the resulting energy loss becomes less. Thus the amount of this expense is lessened. However, as larger conductors cost more money, the fixed expense items become greater. Therefore, by increasing the size of the conductors one expense is decreased but another is increased. If these two expenses do not change by the same amounts there will be some size of conductor for which the sum of the two types of expenses will be less than for any other size. A minimum-cost-point chart offers a convenient method of determining the most economical size.

TABLE 20. ANNUAL COST OF LOST POWER AND INVESTMENT CHARGES FOR VARIOUS SIZES OF COPPER WIRE; PER 1,000 FEET

		0000	000	00	0	1	2
A.	Wire size	0000	000	00	0	1	2
B.	Resistance, ohms	0.049	0.0618	0.0779	0.0983	0.124	0.156
C.	Weight, lbs.	641	508	403	320	253	201
D.	Kw.-hr. at 50 amp. and 4,500 hr. per yr.	551	695	876	1,107	1,397	1,757
E.	Cost of lost energy at 1.5¢ per kw.-hr.	$8.26	$10.43	$13.14	$16.60	$20.95	$26.35
F.	Investment at 18¢ per lb.	$115.30	$91.50	$72.60	$57.60	$45.50	$36.20
G.	Annual investment expense (Dep., taxes and ins.) 16%	$18.43	$14.64	$11.62	$9.21	$7.28	$5.79
H.	Total annual cost	$26.69	$25.07	$24.75	$25.81	$28.23	$32.14

Table 20 shows the computed values of the two types of expenses for three sizes of copper conductor. The values in Lines E, G and H are plotted on the minimum-cost-point chart shown in Figure 41, being shown in relation to wire size. The two expense curves, "Cost of Lost Energy" and "Annual Investment Expense," intersect at a point corresponding approximately to size 00 wire. The third curve, "Total Annual Expense," has its minimum value at this same point. Thus it is noted that a minimum total expense is obtained when the cost of lost energy is equal to the invest-

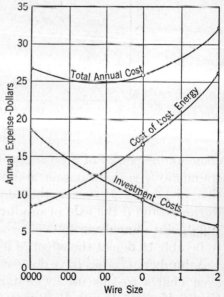

FIGURE 41. Break-even chart for determining the most economical size of copper conductor.

ment charges upon the conductor. This corresponds with the statement of Kelvin's law as given in Chapter II. The minimum-cost-point curve gave the required wire size with only three sets of computations. At the same time it gives a graphic representation of the effect of wire size upon economy.

Break-Even-Point Charts. One of the most satisfactory uses of break-even charts is in showing the relationship between in-

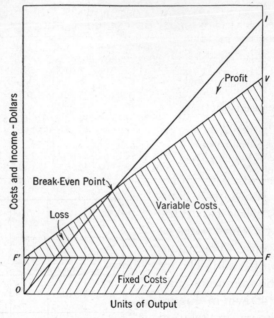

FIGURE 42. Break-even chart for a business enterprise.

come and expenses of a business. The balance sheet and income statement give information about a business for one particular time or period. However, they do not show what would happen to the profits if the rate of production should change. From the standpoint of analysis and control it is of considerable advantage to be able to depict the effect of a change in production rate.

A number of people have done excellent work in adapting break-even charts to this use. Outstanding among these have been C. E. Knoeppel and Professor Walter Rautenstrauch. Such charts may be very simple or quite complex. Figure 42 shows a simple break-even chart for a typical business. Fixed costs.

variable costs and income are plotted against percentages of sales capacity. Thus, the line $F'F$ represents the fixed expenses of production. The line $F'V$ shows the variation in total variable expense with production, being drawn with its starting point at F', so that it actually represents the sum of all production expenses. The gross income from sales is represented by the line OI. Since $F'V$ represents the total expense of production and OI the total income from sales, the intersection of these two lines at E is the point at which income is exactly equal to expense. This point is often called the *break-even point*. At the production corresponding to this point the business will make no profit and have no loss. For production greater than that of the break-even point a profit will result. For production rates less than that of the break-even point a loss will be sustained. By representing the income and expenses of a business in

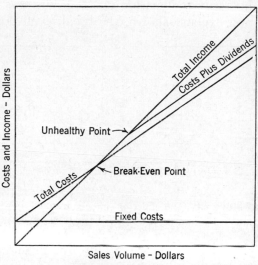

FIGURE 43.   Break-even chart for a business, showing provision for dividends.

this manner the possibility of profit for any rate of production can be determined easily.

A more elaborate break-even chart for a business is shown in Figure 43. Here the income and expenses are plotted as functions of the amount of sales in dollars. When plotted in this manner the income line always makes an angle of 45 degrees with the vertical and horizontal axes. This chart has an added feature in that provision for dividends is shown. This adds another significant point to the chart — the "unhealthy point." This indicates the sales volume at which the business will be able to pay exactly the desired rate of dividends. The location of the unhealthy point is, of course, dependent upon an arbitrary setting of the desired rate of dividends. Break-even charts drawn in this manner make the effect of production rate on profits very apparent and afford an excellent method of representing this relationship.

Effect of Changes in Fixed and Variable Costs. One of the most satisfactory uses of break-even charts is in showing the relative effects of changes in fixed and variable expenses of a business. This is illustrated in Figure 44. Figure 44a shows the break-even chart for a certain business. For the values of income and expense shown, the break-even point occurs at 50% of sales

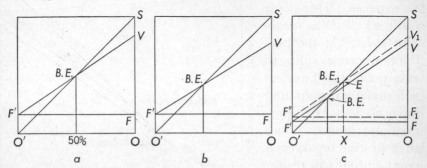

FIGURE 44. The effect of changes in fixed and variable costs upon the location of the break-even point.

capacity. For any volume of sales over $150,000 the business will make a profit.

The chart in Figure 44b is drawn to determine what the effect will be if the variable expenses are decreased 10%, with all other factors remaining constant. It is apparent, of course, that the profits are increased by $20,000 when the business is operated at 100% sales capacity. However, a more significant effect is the change in the break-even point volume of sales. The 10% decrease in variable expenses lowers the break-even point to approximately 41% of sales capacity. This means that not only will the company make greater profits if the plant is operated at capacity, but more important, some profit will be earned if operations are greater than 41% of capacity whereas before the saving was effected the business had to operate at greater than 50% capacity in order to make a profit. In times of depression it is usually more important that a business be able to earn some profit, or not go in the red, when operating at partial capacity than it is for it to be able to earn a very large profit if operated at a capacity which is entirely beyond the realm of possibility.

The third break-even chart, Figure 44c, was drawn to determine to what extent the break-even point will be shifted if the same saving of $20,000 is effected out of the fixed expenses. The solid lines in Figure 44c give the solution to this question. It is shown that this change in fixed expenses will lower the break-even point from 50% to approximately 29% of sales capacity. This makes the importance of controlling fixed expenses very apparent. The saving of $20,000 in fixed expenses lowers the break-even point nearly 12% more than would be the case if the same saving were made in variable expenses.

Unfortunately, it is usually easier to effect savings in variable expenses than in fixed costs. One might wish to know what saving in fixed expenses would give the same result as a greater economy in variable costs. The dotted lines in Figure 44c give the answer to this question for this particular company. A vertical line XE is drawn upward from a point corresponding to 41% of sales capacity until it intersects the income line $O'S$ at point E. Through point E a line $F''V_1$ is drawn parallel to $F'V$. $F''F_1$ is the fixed expense line which will give the required break-even point of 41% of sales capacity. The fixed expenses are determined by the ordinate $O'F''$. $O'F''$ corresponds to $42,000. This means that a saving of only $8,000 in fixed expenses will lower the break-even point as much as a saving of $20,000 in variable expenses. Thus the effect of fixed expense upon the break-even point is evident.

It should be noted that in each case illustrated in Figure 44b and c the profit at 100% capacity is the same. The difference lies in the percentage of capacity at which some profit can be earned. It should also be remembered that the changes in percentages apply only to the conditions of the example given. Other cases will, however, show a similar change.

Break-Even Chart Representation of Economic Characteristics of Businesses. An interesting use of break-even charts has been developed by Professor Walter Rautenstrauch. It was thought that for many business enterprises the total expenses over a period of years would tend to be equal to a fixed amount plus a certain percentage of sales income. Thus the total expense line of a business would be approximated by a line having the equation

$$\text{Total cost} = a + bx$$

where

a = the constant portion of the total expense

x = the annual output in dollars

b = ratio of variable total expense to output

By taking the data given in the annual reports of businesses, the total sales volume and total expenses for the various years may be determined. If these are plotted and straight lines drawn

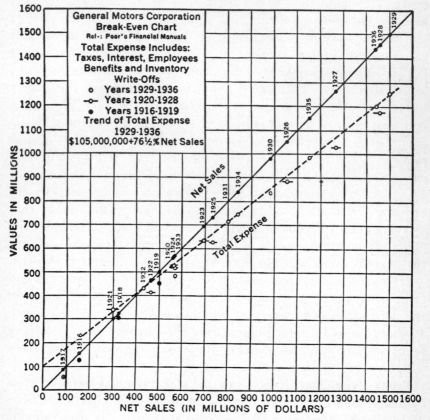

FIGURE 45. The break-even chart of the General Motors Corporation. (Reprinted by permission from *Economics of Business Enterprise* by Walter Rautenstrauch, published by John Wiley & Sons, Inc.)

through the plotted points, break-even charts result. Two such charts, compiled by Professor Rautenstrauch, are shown in Figures 45 and 46. These two charts show how closely the actual total expenses agree with the theoretical relationship. It often happens that the total expenses will follow a certain trend for a period of years and then change in management policy will cause a new expense trend to be established. This is shown in Figure 46.

Once the break-even chart of a business has been obtained by plotting the values of total sales and total expenses for a period of years, and the trends established, valuable information about the business may be obtained from the chart. The sales volume corre-

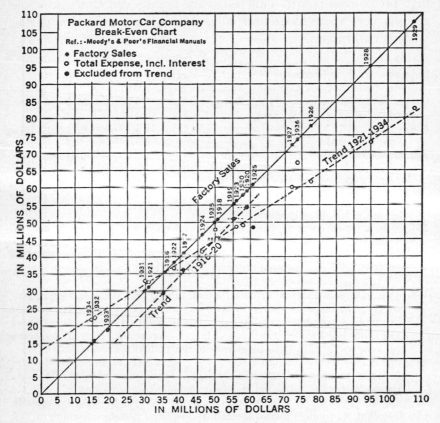

FIGURE 46. The break-even chart of the Packard Motor Car Company. (Reprinted by permission from *Economics of Business Enterprise* by Walter Rautenstrauch, published by John Wiley & Sons, Inc.)

sponding to the break-even point of the business may be determined. Second, the fixed portion of the total expenses can be found. Third, the angle between the sales and expense lines gives an indication of the profit possibilities of the business after the break-even point has been reached. By obtaining the break-even charts of several business enterprises in this manner, the relative profit possibilities of each may be determined. Thus a business which is found to have a low break-even point, but small divergence of the sales and expense lines, will probably possess better profit possibilities during depression years than one which has a large divergence between the sales and expense lines but a very high break-even point. This use of the break-even chart principle gives a very convenient and enlightening method of comparing various enterprises.[1]

REFERENCES

Eidmann, F. L.: "Economic Control of Engineering and Manufacturing," McGraw-Hill Book Company, Inc., New York, 1931.

Grant, E. L.: "Principles of Engineering Economy," The Ronald Press Company, New York, 1938.

Knoeppel, C. E.: "Profit Engineering," McGraw-Hill Book Company, Inc., New York, 1933.

Rautenstrauch, Walter: "The Economics of Business Enterprise," John Wiley & Sons, Inc., New York, 1939.

PROBLEMS

Solve the following problems graphically.

154. A coal which costs $8 per ton contains 13,800 B.T.U. The furnace in which it is burned has an overall efficiency of 45%. One kilowatt-hour of electricity is equivalent to 3,412 B.T.U. Assuming the electricity to be 100% efficient, at what price per kilowatt-hour must electric energy sell to be equivalent to the coal?

155. Two pumps, with their driving motors, are 70 and 60% efficient respectively. The output required of each is equivalent to 25 horsepower. A, the more efficient, costs $700 and B only $500. Electric energy costs $2\frac{1}{2}$ cents per kw.-hr. Each has a life of four years. How many hours per year would each have to operate to have equal operating costs?

156. A privately owned interoffice telephone system costs $100 + $40 N, where N is the number of connected stations. The system will last 10 years. Extension phones furnished by the telephone company cost $2 each per month. How many interior stations would have to be served to justify installing a privately owned interoffice telephone system? Assume capital to be worth 6%.

[1] A number of interesting analyses of this type are shown in Professor Rautenstrauch's excellent book, "Economics of Business Enterprise."

157. An untreated telephone pole costs $30 and will last 10 years. Treated poles cost $34. How long must the treated pole last to justify the added investment if a 7% return is desired?
158. Solve Problem 13, page 40, graphically.
159. What is the most economical size of copper conductor to carry 25 amp. continuously throughout the year? Copper costs 14 cents per pound. Assume interest at 6% and taxes and insurance at ¾% of first cost. Assume a life of 15 years with no scrap value. (Consult electrical handbooks for values of weights and resistances.) Electric energy is worth 1 cent per kw.-hr.
160. The setup cost for producing a certain article is $200. The annual output is 600,000 pieces. The plant is operated 300 days per year and can produce 3,000 pieces per day. Cost of labor, material and other overhead is $2.50 per unit. Rental cost for storage space is 0.5 cent per piece per year. Return desired from capital is 10%. How many pieces should be produced in one lot for greatest economy? Assume shipment of finished product is constant each day throughout the year. It is desirable to keep a minimum of 1,000 pieces on hand at all times.
161. Solve Problem 17, page 40, graphically.
162. Draw the break-even chart for the following company.

Capital stock	$4,000,000
Total labor costs	$0.41 per $ of sales
Material costs	$0.31 per $ of sales
Fixed charges (interest, depreciation, etc.)	$700,000 per year
Dividend policy — 10% per year on capital stock	

  a. Determine the sales volume to break even.
  b. Determine the sales volume to pay usual dividends.
  c. Determine amount of surplus if practical sales limit is $6,500,000.
163. Solve Problem 162 on the basis of fixed charges of $100,000 per year.

Chapter XVI

ECONOMY STUDIES OF GOVERNMENTAL PROJECTS

Growing Importance of Governmental Financing. During recent years rapid expansion of governmental financing has taken place. The increase has occurred in types of projects financed in whole or in part, and in the number and size of the undertakings. There has also been a notable shift in the source of funds from the city and county to the state, and from the state to the federal government. Main highways of a state are now usually part of the federal system and, as such, receive grants of federal funds for construction or reconstruction. Maintenance is provided from local revenues. Housing construction projects involving as many as several hundred units each are federally financed, for sociological or military reasons. Water supply, sanitation, irrigation and power projects are built with public capital. Industrial plants, particularly for production of war materials, are similarly built or enlarged. Beneficiaries of aid in one form or another have included railways, banks, life insurance companies, waterways, flood control structures, soil erosion reduction works and many other types. The shift from local to federal financing is noteworthy. Public construction, represented by expenditures from city, county and state taxes, bond issues, and other revenues, amounted to $2,469,000,000 in 1930 and to $1,314,000,000 in 1939. In the meantime, similar federal expenditures rose from $307,000,000 in 1930 to $2,206,000,000 in 1939.[1]

A clearer picture of the changes during the 1930's is given in Figure 47.[2] Note that the upper curve includes private, as well

---

[1] The figures for 1940 are affected by defense expenditures and so are not quoted.

[2] Taken from National Resources Planning Board, "The Economic Effects of the Federal Public Works Expenditures, 1933–1938," p. 35.

as state and local public, construction expenditures. In the preceding decade, the average for private construction alone for the years 1925–1929 was 8,341 millions annually. For public construction — federal, state and local — the corresponding annual average was 2,292 millions. It is apparent that all construction combined did not mount to capacity or near-capacity levels during the period 1933–1938. Defense activities called for such a shift in types of construction and in manufacturing that figures for 1940 and later years must be interpreted as part of a new cycle.

Clearly the engineer will find it important to know the conditions under which projects in which he is interested may be built and financed. To do so he must become a student of governmental agencies. He must know which agencies are authorized

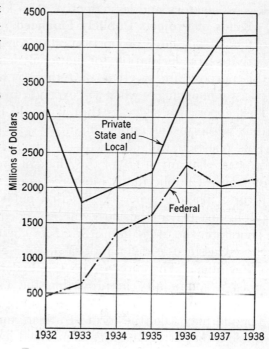

FIGURE 47. Private, State, Local and Federal expenditures for the years 1932 to 1938, inclusive.

to work in given fields of activity, what financial aid they can give and what criteria must be met to secure the aid. He will need to make economy computations to determine the best possibilities for projects in which he is interested. He may be employed by a public agency to assist in a public project, he may represent a governmental agency dealing with local or private bodies seeking aid, or he may serve a private company.

Two suggestions for procedure are made. First, the interested engineer should secure the printed material which the appropriate governmental agencies provide concerning their activities, including where feasible the acts creating them and defining their activities. Second, he should discuss the problem with the local representatives of the agency where possible. Local representatives can often save time and money for the inquirer. A trip to the headquarters office may later prove desirable, but it is often less satisfactory and less effective than local inquiry.

Kinds of Projects Publicly Financed. Public finance has been extended to a large proportion of all construction and production activities by legislation for national defense. Expenditures for this purpose are so great that there is widespread concern over postwar financing — when war expenditures diminish from the peak. Past experience suggests that it would be erroneous to assume that all forms of public financing provided for war will stop. This question will be discussed later. It is mentioned here to indicate that any study of the kinds of projects eligible for grants or loans of public funds must recognize the uncertainties of the future. There is general belief that public aid for many forms of public and private business will be needed for a long time to come. Therefore, the discussion of kinds of eligible projects will include those classified as defense projects.

Facilities. The director of the Federal Works Agency may assist a community in providing the facilities needed for war activities to the extent of funds appropriated by the Congress. The aid may take the form of a loan, an advance, or a grant in whole or in part. Facilities mentioned in the act include schools, highways, water supply and distribution, sewers and sewage disposal and facilities generally. The aid may be provided on account of needs due to the presence of the armed forces or of war industries.[3] The War and Navy departments also contribute to facilities or construct them under the special provisions in their own appropriation acts.

---

[3] See: Public Law 137, 77th Congress, as amended June 28, 1941 H. R. 4545. Among other things, the law provides:

". . . the activities authorized under this title shall be devoted primarily to schools, waterworks, sewers, sewage, garbage and refuse disposal facilities, public sanitary facilities, works for the treatment and purification of water, hospitals and other places for the care of the sick, recreational facilities, and streets and access roads." ". . . Whenever the President finds that in any area or locality an acute shortage of public works . . . necessary to the health, safety, or welfare of persons engaged in national-defense activities exists or impends . . . the Federal Works Administrator is authorized. . . .

(a) To acquire . . . lands . . . by purchase, donation, exchange, lease . . ., or condemnation . . . for such public works.

Housing. Housing — the building of home units — is aided by several related agencies. For the person who is able to pay for and own his home, the Federal Housing Administration (FHA) insures loans which may be made by ordinary financial institutions, generally banks and building and loan associations. The valuation is made by the FHA, and loans up to 90% of the value of house and lot are made where the total value is $6,000 or less. Where the value is higher, the limit is 80%. Time loans are made, repayable in monthly installments over 10-, 15- or 20-year periods. Payments are set to include estimated insurance and property tax requirements. The loans are insured in a pool under government management, for which an insurance premium of ½% is charged. The interest rate is 4½% nominal plus the insurance premium, plus ½% service fee.

To construct homes for those unable fully to pay the cost of good quality living quarters, housing administrations have been established in many places. These agencies generally construct and operate large blocks of apartment houses or groups of modest homes at rental rates which would not justify the investment if made by private builders. The usual plan is to sacrifice return on the investment, in whole or in part, and to set rentals so as to pay operating costs, depreciation and replacements. Original capital is supplied by the United States Housing Administration (USHA) under stipulated conditions as to policy of operation and facilities to be supplied. The selection of site and standards of construction are intended to improve slum districts and blighted areas of cities. More than 200 cities have such areas, according to current surveys.

To provide housing for war workers, a housing coordinator provides for the construction of family and bachelor units in localities where war industries cause influx of workers beyond available facilities. The policy attempted in 1941 is to encourage construction by private capital to the extent feasible. Investors

---

(*h*) By contract or otherwise . . . to plan, design, construct, remodel, extend, repair, or lease public works . . ., provide proper approaches thereto, utilities, and transportation facilities, . . .

(*c*) To make loans or grants, or both, to public and private agencies for public works and equipment therefor, and to make contributions to public or private agencies for the maintenance and operation of public works, upon such terms and in such amounts as the Administrator may consider to be in the public interest. . . ."

cannot be expected to construct homes for sale or rent if the period of repayment by the buyer is too short or if the probable income of the buyer is too low to repay the investment and to give a satisfactory return. Uncertainty as to the duration of a war effort is a major influence in discouraging investors. If a time limit of five to seven years is set for recovery of investment, the payments or rentals must be higher than wage scales will support. Under these conditions the government finds it necessary to construct homes and to assume the risks. Generally, efforts are made not to overbuild a city which is presumably experiencing a forced growth. Hence some of the units provided are permanent, some are demountable and some are house trailers.

War Industries. Industries are profoundly influenced by the defense effort required in modern warfare. Production of equipment and supplies for mechanized forces requires the maximum output of existing and specially constructed facilities. It has been estimated that the investment per worker in mechanized industry is now about $7,000. It is probable that the investment per man of the armed forces will presently exceed this. It may do so already. Industry finds itself obliged to participate in war production to a continually increasing extent. Raw materials are not sufficient for both peace and war industries. Peace industries are obliged to accept smaller and smaller supplies of such materials. To maintain themselves and to augment war production they convert facilities to the production of munitions. Existing equipment is often unsuited to the job and must be supplemented by new buildings and tools. This means expansion of plant and increase of invested capital. Moreover, the ordinary valuation of the new facilities by the methods of engineering economy is not the controlling factor under national emergency conditions. Facilities may thus grow beyond peace needs and investment beyond the limit for satisfactory return upon it.

To meet these conditions, the government advances necessary funds for plant enlargements from defense appropriations and, if desired, retains title for five years, during which period profits may be utilized to amortize the enlargements. At the end of the period the industry may purchase the supplementary plant at an agreed depreciated value or may elect to leave it with the government. What the government is to do with facilities so acquired is one of the unsettled problems to which consideration must later be given. If a manufacturer succeeds in amortizing a plant expansion within the five-year period, he has acquired this enlargement essentially as a gift from the government. If it should prove valuable for postwar production, he will be in a more favorable competitive position than his rivals who did not so benefit. It is to be presumed that numerous plant extensions represent more recent and more efficient design than the original plants of which they form a part. If so, they may become the future main production units of the industries concerned. On this account some movement of sea-coast industries to the interior sections of the country where plant extensions have been made would not be surprising. The extent to which the new buildings and plant extensions prove profitable will be affected by the valuation for income tax purposes assessed to them. As far as stockholders are concerned, however, a portion of the plant which has been completely amortized need not add to the capital value on which dividends must be earned.

Many large organizations have acquired capital for purposes of munition production. One motor car manufacturer produces tanks, another operates an airplane assembly plant. A builder of railway cars is fabricating gun carriages, shells and tank parts. General contractors for heavy construction are operating shipways and building ocean-going vessels. The initiation of a munitions industry of such size as is now under way will greatly modify postwar industrial operation. Therefore, it is appropriate to record these observations of emergency developments for the benefit of students at later times.

In some cases, conditions closely prescribe the location of a plant. This may mean the creation of a new town or the enlargement of an existing one beyond recognition. A magnesium plant is authorized in a western state. It must be close to a large power source and to the ore which it is to reduce. Consequently, the plan as approved includes a complete new town near by for the workers. The contract includes the plant itself, the town, and facilities. These include streets, sewers, water supply, access roads, power, schools, homes and civic buildings.

Financing this type of undertaking is generally by the Defense Plant Corporation, on recommendation of the War Production Board (WPB).

Public Works. The term public works may be assumed to include (1) highways, (2) water ways, (3) harbors, (4) irrigation, (5) flood control and other structures, (6) public buildings, including schools, and (7) utilities.

Many famous public structures may be called to mind. The Panama Canal, the harbor works of the great seaports, the levee system of the Mississippi River, the George Washington Bridge over the Hudson River, Boulder Dam and Grand Coulee Dam in the west, the works of the Tennessee Valley Authority in the south, the water supply systems of New York City, Los Angeles, San Francisco and many other cities, the rapidly developing national highway and airway systems, the post offices of the country and the defense works of the army and navy are only samples. As indicated earlier in this chapter, the defense policy of building at public expense private plant extensions to which the government may retain title under certain conditions greatly extends the range of potential future public works. The Facilities Act mentioned earlier gives a broad definition of public works for its purposes. No distinction is made here between public works and public construction, although it might be desirable to emphasize durability as a commonly held property of public works. It is on this account that public works construction during periods of extensive unemployment is emphasized. Something durable is added to the capital structure of the nation as a result of work aid provided.

From the point of view of engineering economy, great interest lies in the financing provisions of the public works provided or the private undertakings aided. It is therefore desirable to discuss the kinds of financial aid available to public or private agencies and the significance of each.

Kinds of Financial Aid. In determining the desirability of an enterprise, the analyst must consider the obligations assumed in obtaining capital. In the cases heretofore treated in this book, it has been generally assumed that all capital invested must earn a satisfactory return. Financial aid from governmental sources in nearly all cases is designed to relieve or reduce the requirement of earned returns. For example, if money is lent to build a home, it must be fully repaid. But the interest rate of FHA is lower than that which was charged by regular private sources when the plan was inaugurated. Also, the permissible maximum amount of the loan was set at a higher than customary percentage of the valuation of the property, 80 or 90%, instead of 50 to 70%, as formerly. Further, the period of repayment without intermediate refinancing was materially increased. Clearly, these elements of the plan amount to governmental encouragement of home building. They were designed to aid persons without other assets with which they might secure capital at low interest rates.

This may be called the first plan of government aid. The effects of the plan on the decisions of a prospective homeowner and of one who is building houses for rent are definite. The amount of rental one can afford to pay in lieu of owning his home is obtained by computing the net annual cost in both cases and comparing them. The cost of borrowed money is one of the principal items of cost to the buyer who owes a large fraction of the home cost. Likewise, the return obtainable from houses built for rent must drop if they are to compete in an open market with homes which can be bought for small monthly payments. Thus, a very simple form of governmental aid, that of money for long periods at low interest rates on easily provided security, may have profound effects. It should be mentioned that the record of capital repayment to 1941 on home loans under the FHA plan is extremely good.

A second form of aid is the loan without interest. This is had by colleges and universities when they receive grants or gifts for buildings. It is clearly noted in the case of gift dormitories for students. Here, the costs of operation are expected to be paid from income, and sometimes, depreciation or replacement funds are accumulated. No return on the capital is expected. Governmental grants of this type are made in reclamation projects. The cost of a project may be advanced to a properly constituted irrigation district to be repaid within a period of 40 years without interest. If the money so advanced is obtained by governmental borrowing, then the amount of the interest paid by the government for the amount of capital so utilized is a grant in aid. It may be interpreted as a developmental cost or a subsidy to a needed activity or as an operating cost. Those who interpret this as a developmental cost expect the resulting development and related activities to increase the business and incomes of those directly and indirectly concerned to such an extent that increased tax revenues and reduced relief expenditures will pay the amount of the annual grants. In any case, the determination of the feasibility of a district's assuming the costs of a given irrigation development is modified from the usual type of investment.

A third form of aid is the direct grant. Since 1936 the federal government has assumed the responsibility for flood control on streams. Flood control surveys are conducted and control structures installed by the War Department (the Corps of Engineers) and the Department of Agriculture (Soil Conservation Service and Forest Service). Lands which are no longer subject to flood damage rise in value. In effect, the cost of flood protection is taken from the property owner and the community and assumed by the government. A similar policy is reflected in navigation works, especially on inland waterways, and in aids to air navigation. In the latter case the government provides airway beacons, radio ranges, emergency landing fields and weather service without charge. These are available for all users. They constitute an aid to national air transportation and an impetus to its rapid development. Similarly, payments to air lines for the transport of air mail for the Post Office Department have been set high enough to aid air transport companies to break even or to earn a profit during years of development. This has permitted lower passenger rates for air travel during this period than would otherwise have been the case. Americans dislike the word "subsidy" when used to describe this form of aid, but other peoples commonly call it that. Without such aid, the air lines could not have developed to their present high state of service and efficiency. For the five-year period ending with June, 1940,

Post Office revenues from domestic air mail approximated payments to the carriers. Including Post Office expenditures other than transportation, apportioned to the air mail service, however, gross income on domestic air mail in 1940 was about 65 percent of gross postal expense; and for foreign air mail, 45 percent.[4]

Combinations of the three forms of financial aid here listed are not uncommon. Some illustrations will be listed and discussed in the section dealing with multiple-purpose projects.

Self-Liquidating Projects. The designation "self-liquidating project" is commonly applied to an undertaking by a governmental unit which earns revenue estimated to be sufficient to repay the cost in a specified or estimated time. It is often a utility, such as a municipal water supply, a municipal or regional hydroelectric, steam or Diesel power plant. Water supplies for cities are notable examples. Similarly, highway toll bridges or tunnels are frequently initiated as self-liquidating projects. The Holland Tunnel under the Hudson at New York City, the Golden Gate Bridge at San Francisco, the Pennsylvania Super Highway are well-known examples.

Economy studies of self-liquidating projects under public operation should take account of several differences from conditions for the same projects under private operation. Profits and taxes are not required to be earned. As a matter of policy, they may be earned. One prominent municipal electrical utility reports turning into the city treasury sums amounting annually to from 10 to 20% of the annual income in lieu of taxes. The U. S. Government has undertaken to pay annually to the states of Arizona and Nevada $300,000 each for 50 years in lieu of taxes which might have accrued to those states if Boulder Dam had been privately constructed and operated. It is not intended to discuss here the question of whether or not payments should be made in lieu of taxes or whether profits should be earned. The question to be considered is one of engineering economy. "What items must be paid from revenue?" If charges are accumulated annually for a fund to repay capital expenditures it would be incorrect also to charge depreciation for the same structures. However, some communities under favorable conditions have decided to retire rapidly the bonds issued to pay cost of construction instead of reducing rates.

---

[4] "Rationale of Air Transportation," by J. Parker Van Zandt, p. 28. This is an unpublished report to the National Resources Planning Board, 1940.

Multiple-Purpose Works. It is to be expected that consideration of by-products, so to speak, will affect governmental projects as it does private industrial plants. In the construction of a rayon factory, for example, there is a minimum size for economic operation [5] which is determined in part by the amounts of by-products produced. When the quantities are sufficient to justify their recovery, the rate of return of the entire plant is raised to a satisfactory level. The rayon plant thus becomes a "multiple-purpose project." Similarly, generation of electricity as a combined undertaking of electrical utilities and oil refineries becomes part of a "multiple-purpose project." The project includes (a) use of refinery wastes as fuel, (b) generation of process steam for refinery use and (c) generation of electricity for refinery use and public sale.[6] The compound result is one of excellent economy. Similarly, a dam constructed by the Bureau of Reclamation, like Boulder Dam, may provide (a) flood control, (b) regulated water for irrigation, (c) water for municipal use and (d) electric power. Often the benefits for a single purpose, such as irrigation, may not be sufficient to justify the cost. However, the sum of the benefits may be ample. The problem of assessing a proper charge against each benefit becomes a delicate one when some of the benefits must be repaid with interest, some repaid without interest and some are outright grants or governmental responsibilities. The subject of this breakdown of cost into charges is under study by a special committee of the American Society of Civil Engineers.[7]

Most governmental projects which come to mind are single-purpose projects. They include municipal water supply, sewage treatment, irrigation, highway, bridge, harbor and other improvements. It is natural that the increasing complexity of a country passing out of the pioneer period should be revealed in the need for multi-purpose projects. Not merely from the point of view of justifying cost is this to be expected, but also to conserve resources. An industrial nation is dependent on its resources of

[5] See Tyler, "Chemical Engineering Economics," p. 6. Cost of minimum size for economic operation is given as $3,500,000.

[6] The Pacific Gas and Electric Company has several generating plants of this type in operation or under construction.

[7] Dean Samuel B. Morris of Stanford University is chairman of the committee, which is attempting to suggest standards for the segregation of charges.

energy and materials. Conservation of petroleum and natural gas calls for use of available hydroelectric power. Conservation of power calls for reduction of useless transportation — the type that may occur if raw materials are needlessly shipped from the source for processing and then returned for use. Just as the automobile has acquired a number of accessory gadgets and automatic controls to improve its operation and economy, public works will become more complex. The multiple-purpose work is becoming commonplace.[8] Many of these are likely to be government sponsored, not merely as a result of public policy, but because the government is in some cases the only agency with adequate authority to undertake the project and the only one in a position to supply the funds. This is especially true where part of the cost is a governmental grant. It is even more true for national defense production with its uncertainties.

Evaluation of Projects as to Benefits. Evaluation of governmental projects may include:

1. Classification. Does the project satisfy the requirements of acts governing approval and financing? May it be classified under one of the acts? Is it, for example, a flood control project, an irrigation project, a federal highway project or a combination of these, as they are defined in the acts?

2. Benefits. If a flood control project is under examination, are the annual benefits equal to or greater than the annual costs? If a multiple-purpose project, what percentages of cost are applicable to the several benefits? Does each partial cost meet the requirements? If one part is for reclamation, can the beneficiaries reasonably undertake the repayment required?

3. Financial Plans. Where local participation in cost is required, are the amounts to be contributed locally adequate, and are they properly assured? If a structure is of the self-liquidating type, is the operating agency properly constituted with adequate authority to establish rates and, if necessary, to make up deficits — possibly, by taxation?

[8] Examples are: Boulder Dam for flood control, irrigation, municipal water supply and power; Grand Coulee Dam for irrigation, power and navigation; and most dams under consideration. The public forests, when maintained jointly for recreation, timber production and erosion control, are of this type. In private enterprise, an automobile manufacturer who runs his own transportation, mines his own ores and grows some of his other raw materials operates a single-purpose industry with multiple-purpose results.

Some examples will clarify these questions.

1. The Bonneville Dam on the Columbia River was approved as a navigation project. It is primarily of aid to navigation and power. The Boulder Dam on the Colorado River was approved as a navigation project, but it is primarily for irrigation, water supply, flood control and power. The Pennsylvania Turnpike was undertaken as a federal highway project. Most cases are clear enough, but legal questions result in classification or justification by a minor and even negligible use. Boulder Dam was justified in testimony as a navigation structure, presumably because of the legal freedom enjoyed by navigation structures. Such procedures, which are due to historical developments, are irritating and illogical to most engineers. They are numerous and significant, however, and one must be prepared to understand them. Some historians explain that this stretching of legislation to cover new developments is normal.

2. The method of appraising benefits for a flood control project is illustrated by the Report of the Chief of Engineers, United States Army, on the Connecticut River at East Hartford, Connecticut.[9] The report concerns the realignment of an earth dike north of the railroad so as to increase the area to be protected against floods by an authorized project. The estimate for the authorized project is $1,163,000; the estimated increased cost for the modified plan is $249,000. The criterion used for justification of the change is the ratio of annual benefits to annual costs. The comparison is made clear by study of Table 21, parts a, b, c. It will be noted that the ratio of annual benefits to annual costs is greater than unity for the authorized project, for the proposed addition, and hence for the revised total project.

The technique of computing costs and benefits for these projects is worthy of study. It is affected materially, like other financial determinations, by changes in assumptions. Those about which there is considerable discussion include: rates of interest to be charged, time periods chosen for depreciation and replacement, and methods of estimating damages. The Corps of Engineers is pioneering in this work. The details of the analysis in this Connecticut River example are worthy of study. Space will

---

[9] Senate Document No. 32, 76th Congress, 1st Session, presented February 9, 1939.

not permit presentation here. The student is referred to the printed report cited.

3. The method of appraising a waterways project is illustrated by a report of the Chief of Engineers on the Lake Erie and Ohio

TABLE 21. COSTS FOR FLOOD CONTROL PROJECT AT EAST HARTFORD, CONNECTICUT

a. Total and Annual Costs of Protection

Description	Cost to United States	Cost to local interests	Total cost	Total annual cost
Realignment of dike north of railroad	$ 333,000	$ 14,000	$ 347,000	$18,900
Dike part in authorized plan to be abandoned	84,000	5,000	89,000	4,300
Net cost of protection for area north of railroad	249,000	9,000	258,000	14,600
Cost of authorized project for protection of the area south of railroad	1,163,000	226,000	1,389,000	79,000
Cost of protection for total area in proposed project	1,412,000	235,000	1,647,000	93,600

b. Annual Benefits in East Hartford from Project

Dike area	Natural average annual damage	Benefits due to dikes alone	Benefits due to reservoirs alone	Benefits due to dikes after reservoirs	Total benefit
Area protected by authorized dike	$219,300	$211,100	$87,800	$130,400	$218,200
Additional area proposed to be diked	18,400	17,000	2,400	16,000	18,400
Area outside of authorized and proposed dikes	1,200	—	900		900
Total, town of East Hartford	$238,900	$228,100	$91,100	$146,400	$237,500

c. Relation of Benefits to Costs

Description	Total average annual benefits	Total average annual costs	Ratio of benefits to costs
Protection for the area north of railroad	$ 16,000	$14,600	1.09
Protection for the area south of railroad (existing project)	130,400	79,000	1.65
Protection for the entire area by proposed project	$146,400	$93,600	1.57

River Canal.[10]   This is an exhaustive report analyzing alternative routes, costs of construction and operation and benefits. The chief values of the canal are potential reductions in transportation costs, especially of iron ores and coal to and from the Great Lakes, and availability as an addition to the national transportation system. At the time the report was prepared, it appeared that the railways might easily carry the load without reaching their capacity. Under national defense conditions, the additional capacity would probably be useful. The cost of the canal and related works is estimated by the Chief of Engineers at $207,257,000 to the United States and $12,472,000 to local interests. It is thus a major project. The report is comprehensive and thorough. Some of the complexities faced by the engineering staffs may be understood by the recommendations for allocation of charges. Each required prior analysis.

Costs chargeable to United States: [11]

(a) All locks, dams, and appurtenances.
(b) All channel improvements.
(c) Railroad (common carrier) relocations and bridges.
(d) Public utility relocations, including relocation of power, telephone, telegraph, and pipe lines.
(e) Grand River Reservoir, dam, and dikes.
(f) Dredging and breakwater for Lake Erie Harbor.
(g) Operation and maintenance of the completed waterway.
Costs chargeable to local interests:
(a) Highway relocations and highway bridges.
(b) Revision of all privately owned facilities, including railroad and foot bridges.
(c) Reconstruction of drainage facilities (storm and sanitary sewers).
(d) Water rights.
(e) Rights-of-way, disposal areas, and flowage damages (canal).
(f) Rights-of-way, land and improvements (Grand River Reservoir).
(g) Such annual operation and maintenance in connection with the above as may be necessary.
(h) Local interests to guarantee indemnification to the United States from all claims for damages incident to the improvement.

[10] "Lake Erie and Ohio River Canal," House Document No. 178, 76th Congress, 1st Session. Referred to Committee and ordered printed February 21, 1939.
[11] Loc. cit., p. 30.

Annual charges and savings for the principal routes investigated are:

Route	Prospective annual commerce (tons)	Prospective annual savings (dollars) [a]	Annual economic charges (dollars) [b]	Ratio of annual charges to annual savings
Allegheny-French Creek	12,510,000	7,811,000	9,091,000	1 : 0.86
Pittsburgh-Ashtabula	22,480,000	[c] 14,185,000	10,484,000	[d] 1 : 1.34
		[c] 13,225,000		[e] 1 : 1.26
Portsmouth-Sandusky	4,087,000	2,429,000	12,994,000	1 : 0.19
Cincinnati-Toledo	375,000	296,000	13,957,000	1 : 0.02

[a] With allowance for interest on investment at 6%, and allowance for terminal charges, winter closure and degradation, where applicable, in the case of coal.

[b] Including amortization; and interest on Federal investment at 3½% and on local interest's investment at 4½%.

[c] Including flood control benefits at $275,000.

[d] With full back haul credit.

[e] Partial back haul credit only.

Space does not permit further analysis of this interesting report. The student will find the one-page Syllabus of the Report of the District Engineer [12] an excellent example of summarizing assumptions and conditions of a complex problem.

This report has been chosen for comment for two reasons, in addition to those mentioned. First, the annual savings are based upon freight rates then existing and estimated future water rates. This is perhaps the most logical basis for the study. The water rates would probably be realized. The shippers could then utilize water transport or rail as they might prefer. If the railroads should reduce average charges per ton 29 cents for the Pittsburgh-Lake Erie haul, the computed savings would disappear. On this account, the President of the United States asked to have published in the Report a memorandum which he sent to the Interstate Commerce Commission, asking its advice concerning this phase of the problem. Thus, analysis of the project by the Corps of Engineers within its field of duty may not cover a more general problem, such as national policy concerning waterways in competition with railways. The subject is complex, but full of interest as a problem of balance in national transportation facilities. The second reason for special comment is the importance of including explicit statements of assumptions made so as to permit a new judgment of the merits of the project to be made

[12] *Loc. cit.*, p. 36.

when conditions change. Problems of national defense and change in the volume of industry in the region may present reasons for a change in the recommendations made and in the official attitudes taken. The report can be modified to show the effects of such changes.

Policies Controlling Government Aid. The discussion of types of financial aid as given above is probably the best beginning for a study of public aid policies. It is difficult to generalize, but many believe that whatever forms of financial aid are deemed by legislatures or the Congress to be in the public interest will receive the sanction of the courts. Changing public opinion concerning the propriety of governmental aid, whether as loans, with or without interest, as partial or full grants for construction deemed in the public interest, or as grants for relief, is revealed by examination of the acts inaugurating these policies together with the dates of their enactment. The Reconstruction Finance Corporation was authorized in 1933 to make loans to private and public agencies without requiring the type or amount of security that private lending agencies would expect. As its name implies, it was intended to furnish capital to reconstruct or revivify the businesses concerned, whether banks, railways, insurance companies or others. The Public Works Administration undertook its program of public works as a stimulus to employment. The program was intended to furnish valuable public works for water or power supply, sewage disposal, highways and the like which would require large use of labor and materials and thus serve to stimulate industrial recovery. Partly because of local legal debt limitations and of local depletion of tax revenues, the PWA program combined partial grants of capital with interest-bearing loans. The Works Progress Administration was authorized as an agency to provide relief labor. It undertook construction projects as secondary to the relief of unemployment. Officers of that agency commonly interpreted its primary purpose as the furnishing of relief through employment. It was believed that the psychological effect on the worker and the total sociological effect would be better if work were exchanged for relief than it would be if a dole were given. Sociologists report that much support to morale followed wise application of this principle, although serious damage occurred when the projects undertaken were trivial or of doubtful value. The development of policies with reference to housing has already been mentioned.

The depression years of the "30's" caused widespread study of differential costs, as discussed in Chapter XII. Industries added new products or emphasized side lines in order to break even or make a profit when otherwise a deficit would have been experienced. The profit ratio acceptable for undertaking production of some items was strongly influenced by the state of the business. If necessary to keep going, management would accept increased business where the possibility of no profit or even a deficit existed. Similar influences led administrators of self-liquidating public projects to seek increased business through rate cutting or development of new services. Similarly, the power to meet deficits from public funds possessed by some public works agencies led to rate determinations with little or no contemplated profit. For example, the directors of a public toll bridge cut the rates for automobiles several times in the course of three years. Increased traffic followed each cut, but the prospective margin over necessary payments for bond interest and redemption, maintenance and operating expenses was materially reduced. It was held that the service rendered to the community by cheaper transportation justified intentional cutting of income to the break-even point, and that the bondholders were adequately protected by the guarantees which the state concerned had given the agency operating the bridge. This is an illustration of the no-profit policy applied to a public structure.

Policies for War Industries. In war industries, national policy shifts from emphasis on minimum bids and costs for given orders to maximum production from available materials with available labor. It is assumed that the necessary cost must be met. Waste and extravagance are to be avoided to the extent possible, but production must be had. In peacetime, an industry does not usually limit its production by the available supply of steel or aluminum or nickel, for example, or by the limited number of welders or die makers available. The optimum output for production of profit is sought. For national defense, the whole country must cooperate to get the maximum output of munitions with available plant, materials and labor supply. Where possible, these must all be expanded. It should be recognized that the armed forces themselves have taken on aspects of a huge production industry. Each man is operator, repair man or administrator of equipment. The number of men to operate an airplane, a tank, a field gun or a ship is the minimum efficient number. Hence, a man must manage or maintain as much equipment as he can. The transportation and supply systems become large and elaborate. Interruptions of supplies must be short and infrequent. Continuity of operation must be assured by small but definite local supplies. Hence, a Diesel-operated tank may be preferred to a gasoline-driven model if it gains in radius of operation without refueling. Under the conditions of combat, there must be high-speed flow of the maximum possible quantities of expendable munitions from industrial and storage areas to the movable combat zone. It is reported that the final checks for one of the greatest battles of history were with the transportation division and the weather bureau chiefs. These conditions of warfare are stressed because the engineering economy of war industries, from the factory to the combat divisions, is one where the capacity for continuous consumption of materials is much greater than the potential supply. The engineer need not fear that he is overproducing for the munitions market, except where unbalance is caused. Engineering analysis to get the maximum movement of equipment and supplies from raw materials to penetration of enemy lines must be a continuing study. The military officer is a military engineer.

Works Planning for Postwar Period. In a sense every normal agency of government is a postwar agency. It is clear, however, that just as the planning staffs of the arms of national defense devote themselves to planning the use of industry for defense in times of national emergency, appropriate national agencies should consider the transition to postwar conditions. It is generally recognized that the dislocation of industry for war is now far greater than in the past and that the character of postwar America will be modified by the manner of the transition which will occur as well as by its character. In 1941, the national agencies giving consideration to phases of the problem number at least 30. Some of the most prominent are (a) The National Resources Planning Board, (b) The Federal Works Agency, (c) The War Production Board and the Federal Reserve System. These are concerned with general questions. The National Resources Planning Board is concerned with national development and is charged with determination of the relationships between employment and the stabilization of industry. Its reports are excellent for the student.[13] The Federal Works Agency is administering under the WPA the Public Works Reserve, a list of public works for the entire country, mainly as proposed by local agencies of government. Although the study is made on the assumption of continuing local financing over a six-year period, the program could be readily modified to take account of any acceleration which might be desired and be facilitated by additional funds. The WPB is concerned with the reconversion of industries to peacetime activities. Since this agency is responsible for the shifts to war materials production, it is in a good position to appraise the problems caused by the shifts and to consider the probable difficulties of postwar industrial adjustment.

Numerous other agencies have had their normal activities reduced and their construction projects delayed or suspended by reason of the primary demands of national defense for money, men and materials. The current period may permit them to prepare more adequate plans and to put in better order their lists of public works. Among these are (a) the War Department (Corps of Engineers) with both navigation and flood control projects, (b) the Bureau of Reclamation with water projects, (c) the Department of Agriculture with land use and conservation projects. Many others could be cited. The Public Roads Administration is building its list of needed extension and reconstruction to make a national highway system. Most of these agencies and the Federal Power Commission have many projects that are vital to national defense as well as lists for normal development. It has been estimated, for example, that the war production program requires about 2.75 kw.-hr. for each

[13] See National Resources Planning Board, "Development of Resources and Stabilization of Employment in the United States, Part I," Government Printing Office, Washington, 1941.

dollar of contract let. The power production of the United States in 1940 amounted to about 143,000,000,000 kw.-hr. If defense production reaches $3,000,000,000 per month in 1942 as scheduled, the defense requirements for power might approximate 8,000,000,000 kw.-hr. per month, or two-thirds the national output of 1940. Considering regular needs for power, it would not be feasible to divert so large a percentage. Hence, the FPC recommends addition of power capacity at the maximum possible rate, 6 or 8% per year, consistent with other defense needs for steel and construction materials. It estimates the possible rate of increase at 2,500,000 kw. per year for steam power and 1,000,000 kw. per year for water power. (See Table 22.)

The availability of additional power for postwar America is one of the factors which will probably accelerate the mechanical age. It will, like the airplane, influence profoundly the trend of development for the next generation. The need for study of postwar possibilities by industry, government and education is a challenge. Many of the large problems cannot be fully resolved in advance, but it will be serious if inadequate attention is given to those which can be solved by planning.

Coordination of Projects by Governmental Bodies. Engineers have recognized for many years the importance of coordination of projects to secure maximum return. It is characteristic of the pioneer period in a country that the need for development is so urgent that coordination is largely left to care for itself. Now that the United States is out of the pioneer stage, coordination is recognized as essential. A city which is stabilized in population, even though it continues to grow, recognizes the need for adjusting itself and its services. The transportation system is highly expensive. It is usually inadequate — at least for the automobile. The city needs a highway plan to meet the needs of its commuters, shoppers, tourists and merchants. The plan must be adjusted to neighboring communities, the state and the nation. Account must be taken of past and prospective developments of residential sections, of industrial sections, of business and shopping quarters, and of technological development. Past developments have been experimental, but many things have been learned. Future solutions can be greatly improved over

TABLE 22. NEW GENERATING FACILITIES FOR LOADS THROUGH 1946 [14]

(Based upon $36,000,000,000 annual defense expenditure)

Region		Amounts of new capacity kw. by years			
		1943	1944	1945	1946
1	Steam-electric	240,000	700,000	680,000	880,000
	Hydroelectric	42,000	576,000	362,000	242,000
2	Steam-electric	325,000	820,000	650,000	505,000
	Hydroelectric	173,000	60,000	50,000	290,000
3	Steam-electric	385,000	111,000	385,000	195,000
	Hydroelectric	210,000	259,000	500,000	310,000
4	Steam-electric	60,000	725,000	540,000	480,000
	Hydroelectric	15,000	0	0	0
5	Steam-electric	180,000	0	95,000	90,000
	Hydroelectric	127,000	90,000	154,000	60,000
6	Steam-electric	0	0	20,000	75,000
	Hydroelectric	0	0	0	0
7	Steam-electric	25,000	55,000	215,000	30,000
	Hydroelectric	324,000	198,000	108,000	360,000
8	Steam-electric	0	70,000	140,000	0
	Hydroelectric	358,000	150,000	105,000	90,000

Key to Regions:
  Region 1: New England and North Atlantic
  Region 2: Great Lakes and south thereof
  Region 3: South Atlantic and Tennessee Valley
  Region 4: North Central
  Region 5: Western Gulf Region
  Region 6: Northern Plains and Intermountain
  Region 7: Pacific northwest and Greater Columbia Basin
  Region 8: Pacific southwest

past ones. The method requires democratic acceptance of the use of experts. One of the most promising modes of approach is the use of a city planning commission, cooperating with the offices of the street department, the water department, the school department, the finance department and the other operating agencies of the city to study the problems, consider plans and

[14] Summarized from " Plan for Adequate Power Supply by Federal Power Commission," a report to the President, July 16, 1941.

stimulate programs to solve present problems and to direct future development. Such agencies need technically trained men. They use many engineers, architects and city planners. They are developing procedures which are gaining steadily in promise and reliability.

The national government has a double task of coordination. The national programs of many agencies require integration. On a river the problems of power, irrigation and flood control are not independent, although the programs for their solution may be separately administered. Progress has been made in coordinating these programs through exchange of data and plans by the agencies involved and through coordinating committees. The task is difficult because of the size of the programs, the dual administration by Congress and the President and the necessary relations with the states and localities. The second coordination necessary is that between local and national programs. Much of the stimulus and support for development is local. Some states have well-advanced plans for development. A few have administered and financed these programs. All of them are concerned to maintain the practice of local initiation and determination of a large proportion of all developmental works, even though the financing and construction are federal. Therefore, a large share of the planning for highways, housing, public buildings, water and power projects is initiated locally, then proceeds to federal agencies for achievement in whole or in part. The process is two-way: from national to local and from local to national. The engineer should understand this and should not be surprised at the limitations imposed on the authority or procedures of the agencies he may deal with. State planning has been stimulated by the federal programs of the past decade, but national planning has probably advanced more rapidly. The urgency of better coordination of both types here mentioned is likely to increase with time. Any advance in coordination will require more engineering. The interest of the engineer in the process is obvious.

Extensions and Differential Costs. Large projects often require considerable time for market development. A long and expensive aqueduct for city water supply must be built for future needs. If half its length is in tunnels, as is the case with the Colorado

River aqueduct to southern California, engineering economy determinations show that the tunnels must be built to full or possibly half ultimate capacity at the beginning. Similarly, water power dams must usually be completed to capacity even though the power demand will not be reached for a period of years. This is one reason why public agencies build them. Private capital could not face the losses of the long periods of partial use. The agencies operating the works must decide what to do about rates. To obtain sales before the general need is urgent, they may find it necessary to adopt plans of dumping or of differential costs. The problems are similar to those discussed for other businesses with surplus capacity. There are two points of special interest. If the agency is distributing water, for example, over which public bodies have a monopoly in the area involved, the effect on total public revenue of all water companies in the area will need to be studied, as well as the economy of the single agency with the surplus. If the agencies include privately owned ones, as commonly occurs where public power is distributed, it may be determined as unfair to distribute at a price which will permit no profit to the private companies, unless the public agency is prepared to buy up the private ones at equitable prices. Except for considerations like these, the problems of excess capacity are precisely those discussed before.

Relation of the Engineer to Changing Public Policies. As the machine age advances, more and more governmental operations will involve engineering. The fact that every large building needs a building engineer, in addition to general maintenance men, the continuing problem of adjusting street and roadway design to the city and the automobile, the problems of competing modes of transport, the interconnections of city and country, all of these and many other factors cause problems that require public attention. Settlement by court decrees of relations between public and private operation of many types has been unsatisfactory because the decision is often delayed until the questions decided are no longer the most urgent ones and because such decisions rarely furnish a means of adjustment to change. Whether these or other reasons lead to increasing governmental financing, construction and operation of utilities and services, such a movement is clearly to be seen. Also, as intimated above, the older operations of governmental agencies are themselves becoming more technical. The changes in policy which result from actions of public bodies and which affect the ownership and operation of engineering works may or may not accord with the political philosophy of the engineer. It is the writer's belief that the engineer will do his best work and live in mental health if he adopts a philosophy that permits him to render the best possible service to public activities which he may or may not have favored but which have been adopted. If he can help his city, state or nation to get efficiency and good results from a work that has been undertaken, he would seem to meet the ethical standards of his profession. As an individual, he is likely to be an amateur in political economy and governmental structure. He can seldom be as confident of his judgment concerning correctness of governmental policy as he can concerning the design of a bridge or a highway, or his analysis of the operation of a power plant. He is, in fact, a professional man rendering professional services, and he wants his government to have the best.

REFERENCES

National Resources Planning Board: "The Economic Effects of the Federal Public Works Expenditures, 1933–38," Government Printing Office, November, 1940.

National Resources Planning Board: "The Development of Resources and Stabilization of Employment in the United States," — Parts I, II, III, Government Printing Office, 1941.

Galloway and Associates: "Planning for America," Henry Holt and Company, Inc., New York, 1941.

Boutwell, William Dow, and others: "America Prepares for Tomorrow," Harper & Brothers, New York, 1941.

Finney, Burnham: "Arsenal of Democracy," Whittlesey House, New York, 1941.

Public documents of the Congress relating to many well-known public works.

The references by Galloway and Boutwell contain extensive reference lists on many national and economic policies.

PROBLEMS

164. Define "multiple-purpose project." List three public and two private projects which meet your definition, explaining how each one does so.

165. What is the nature of the federal financial aid to public roads? To what class of roads is it applicable in the state with which you are most familiar?

166. Ascertain the terms available to you to secure an FHA loan for building a home. Assume that you own a lot valued at $1,200 and that you estimate the cost of building the house at $6,000. Assume property taxes at $90, insurance at $12 per year, and estimate your monthly payment on a 15-year loan, a 20-year loan.

167. With the data of Problem 166, estimate your monthly payments, if taxes and insurance costs remain unchanged, but money costs become 6% nominal for a loan equal to 50% of the total value of house and lot, 8% nominal for additional amounts. You must borrow all but the value of the lot. Compute for the 15-year loan only.

168. Make a brief analysis of some one of the following reports of the Chief of Engineers, War Department, explaining the economic justification given in the report and commenting upon the assumptions made and conclusions reached. (This should not exceed 1,000 words, with any tables used.)

Navigation:	H.D.[a] 337/77/1
Ashland Harbor, Wisconsin	
Ohio-Lake Erie Canal	H.D. 178/76/1
Flood Control:	
Ventura River, California	H.D. 223/77/1
Connecticut River at East Hartford	S.D. 32/76/1
Multiple-Purpose:	
White River, Missouri and Arkansas	H.D. 917/76/3
Whitney Dam, Texas	H.D. 390/76/1

[a] H.D. means House Document; S.D., Senate Document. 337/77/1 means Document 337, 77th Congress, 1st Session.

169. Make a list of the types of public works which to your knowledge have been undertaken by cities, counties, states or the nation, indicate by suitable notation which ones seem to you desirable or justifiable, and give, in addition, the grounds for your classification.

Chapter XVII

PERSONNEL FACTORS

The effect which the workers of an industry may have upon its economy has probably received less attention than any other of the production factors. It is only in the last few years that this portion of the field of engineering economy has received more than a small percentage of the attention it deserves. Now that some idea of its importance has been realized, very few data are available for use in such economy studies.

Undoubtedly the worker is the most important factor in industry today. Yet few economy studies are made of the personnel factors which affect production costs. A great proportion of the improvements introduced in factories and stores are the result of labor agitation or governmental regulations. Relatively few companies appear to know the exact effect of labor turnover, strikes, accidents, poor lighting and noise upon the economy of their enterprises. Yet in most cases the effect can be determined in dollars and cents. Economy studies which reveal such information enable management to deal with these problems in a sane and logical manner. This allows the proper course to be followed and all the benefits to be obtained. The possession of the actual figures regarding these personnel factors enables the company to act intelligently when changes are requested by labor groups. But even better, it usually results in the employer's providing conditions that are conducive to satisfactory labor relations and economical operation.

Labor Turnover. The number of separations from service to an employer during a given period is referred to as *labor turnover*. Its measurement is not entirely standardized, although two methods are generally employed. One is that specified by the

Bureau of Labor Statistics of the United States Department of Labor. This bureau's formula is:

$$\text{Labor turnover ratio} = \frac{\text{Number of separations}}{\text{Average number in the working force}}$$

Another formula which is used by a number of industries is:

$$\frac{\text{Labor turnover per}}{100 \text{ employees}} = \frac{\text{Separations} \times 100}{\text{Average number on the payroll}}$$

The greatest weakness of both of these formulas is that they give no indication of what percentage of those who were employed at the beginning of any period were employed continuously throughout the period. For example, assume that an average of 1,000 persons were employed during a given period and that the number of separations from employment during that period was 200. The labor turnover would be 20%. This does not mean that only 800 of the 1,000 people who were employed at the beginning of the period would be on the payroll at the end of the period. If the period were 200 days, the 20% labor turnover might have been caused by hiring one man at the beginning of each day and discharging him at the end of the day. Thus, although 999 of the 1,000 original employees had been employed continuously, labor turnover, as computed by the formula, would be 20%.

Only a little thought is required to realize that there is considerable expense involved in hiring a new worker and training him to do his work efficiently. The exact cost of this procedure is sometimes difficult to determine, but it is certain that it is becoming more costly all the time as industry becomes more complex. Numerous surveys have been made in order to determine the cost of labor turnover for various companies. These estimates have ranged from $2 to $250 per man turnover. Obviously, the cost will vary with the type of labor involved and the task which is to be performed. A number of estimates place the average cost of labor turnover at $50. As an average this figure is probably quite conservative. This cost is made up of employment and personnel office expense, cost of training the worker, medical examination expense, unemployment insurance, decreased production during the learning period, possible breakage of equipment because of inexperience, increased supervision, inferior production and many other items.

By using the measure of labor turnover and the average cost of each change in personnel it is possible to obtain some idea of how much could be spent profitably in order to reduce labor turnover. For example, if a company normally employing 600 workers experienced a labor turnover of 50%, the yearly cost of this turnover would be

$$600 \times 50\% \times \$50 = \$15,000$$

If the turnover in labor could be reduced to 25%, the annual saving would be $7,500. Thus the company could well afford to spend $5,000 or $6,000 to obtain such a reduction in labor turnover. In fact, it could afford to spend the entire $7,500 since there are always other profits to be obtained from reduced labor turnover above those which can be measured directly in money. Practically all companies that have spent considerable sums of money to obtain low labor turnover have found that such expenditures have turned out to be very good investments.

Executive Turnover. There has probably been less attention given to the cost of executive turnover than to that for ordinary labor turnover. This has undoubtedly been due to the fact that the number of executives who leave companies is rather insignificant in comparison with the actual number of ordinary workers. However, if the average cost of labor turnover is $50 per case, the cost of executive turnover is probably from five to ten times this amount. It is not at all uncommon for the cost of changing one executive to be several thousand dollars. This is due to the fact that the entire organization of the business may have to be changed and disrupted. If one executive leaves a company he may take several minor executives with him. When a new executive is brought in from outside the business he may bring several new men with him. He will also, in most cases, wish to introduce new ideas and procedures which will necessitate considerable expense. The entire cost of such changes is difficult to determine, but it is no small amount. While the turnover of executives may result in gain in the long run, it is apparent that considerable immediate costs do attend such turnover.

Expenditure of money to assure executive loyalty and low turnover usually results in many indirect returns. For example, satisfied and loyal executives will usually be interested in the welfare and loyalty of those who work under them. This will be reflected in the turnover of the ordinary workmen.

Another phase of labor turnover is worth considering. This is the turnover of young college graduates who are just entering the industrial world. This is particularly true of young engineers and technically trained graduates. It is usually considerable time before these workers really earn a profit for their employers. Many companies use the first six months or more of their employment as a training period. As a result, the expense of turnover of this class of workers is very high. Yet it is surprising to note how many companies are not greatly concerned about the great turnover of their employees of this class. It is true that the turnover among this group must necessarily be considerable. However, more care in hiring young graduates and more effort in their behalf after they are employed would do much to reduce this loss.

Wages. The matter of wage payment is an entire subject in itself. It has a very real connection to economy. The most obvious of these is the manner in which labor is compensated for its efforts. All of the various methods of wage payment fall into three essential types: *time wages, piece work* and *bonus systems.* The extent of the use of these types is the same as the order in which they are given.

The basis of *time wages* is that the worker is paid for the amount of time he works, regardless of the amount that he produces during this time. All salaried workers and those who work by the day, week or month are paid upon this basis. From the viewpoint of determining the payroll its advantages are obvious. Similarly, the worker always knows how much he is to receive for his work during a given period. Its great weakness lies in the fact that it is very difficult to predict or determine production costs when this method of payment is used, since there is no assurance as to what amount of goods will be produced during any given period. Since the worker receives the same amount, regardless of what he produces, there is not much incentive for him always to do an equal amount of work for the same amount of wages. The effect of variations in production upon the workers' earnings is shown in Figure 48. With this method of wage payment there is, of course, no effect. The effect of variations in production upon labor costs for each unit produced is shown in Figure 49. It is apparent that any attempt to predict unit labor costs would be very difficult with this method of wage payment.

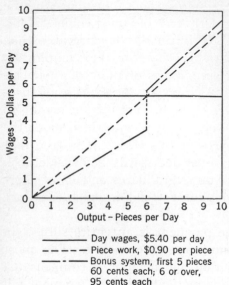

Day wages, $5.40 per day
Piece work, $0.90 per piece
Bonus system, first 5 pieces 60 cents each; 6 or over, 95 cents each

FIGURE 48. Variation in wages with output for three wage payment systems.

Time wages are usually advantageous where work of very high quality is to be done. This is especially true when inspection of the completed product would be difficult. Where a worker is being paid according to the time consumed he is more likely to do a good grade of work. This method of wage payment is also needed where workers are constantly performing different tasks so that they have no chance to standardize their methods, or the amount of time required for the task would be difficult to predict.

Piece work payment is used where workers are performing the same operations repeatedly so that a standardized method of work may be established and the amount of time which should be required may be determined with considerable accuracy. In this method the worker is paid a definite sum for each unit which he produces. His wages are therefore in direct proportion to his output. The results of this method of wage payment are also shown in Figures 48 and 49. Since the worker's wages vary with his production, payroll accounting is considerably more complicated than for time wages. However, this is offset by the fact that unit labor costs are constant and the employer receives the same amount of work for a given amount of money. Similarly, the worker who attains great skill and produces more than the average receives extra compensation for his efforts.

There are two serious objections offered by workers to this method of wage payment. First is the fact that the worker does not know in advance what his earnings will be. This is usually met by the employer's guaranteeing a certain minimum wage, regardless of output, as long as the worker makes a reasonable amount of effort. This guaranteed wage, in many cases, is about 75% of what would be earned by producing a normal day's output. There should always be assurance that the worker will not be penalized for delays that are beyond his control.

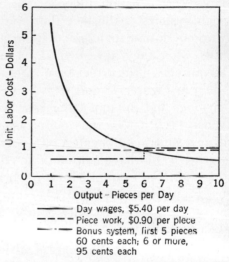

Day wages, $5.40 per day
Piece work, $0.90 per piece
Bonus system, first 5 pieces 60 cents each; 6 or more, 95 cents each

FIGURE 49. Effect of wage payment systems upon unit labor cost.

The second objection is due to the piece rates being set too "tight." This is usually due to insufficient or incorrect time studies, or to unfairness on the part of the management. The remedy in both cases is apparent. The fault does not lie in the method of wage payment.

Several recent surveys have shown that the piece work method of payment is becoming more widely used. Its simplicity, both to the management and the worker, is one of its great advantages. The worker understands it readily and realizes that he is being paid in proportion to what he produces. It is probably the most satisfactory method of wage payment when all viewpoints are considered.

Bonus or *incentive wage systems* attempt to obtain greater productive effort from the worker by giving him some type of bonus when his output exceeds a certain arbitrary amount. The systems vary widely, each having been originated by some person with an idea as to what the bonus should be and how it should be paid. Among these are the Taylor Differential Piece-Rate Plan, the Halsey Premium Plan, the Gantt Task and Bonus Plan, the Emerson Efficiency Bonus Plan and the Bedaux Plan. It is characteristic of these plans that the worker's wage is not directly proportional to the amount of his output, nor is the unit labor cost constant. One of the very serious disadvantages of such systems is the fact that they are so complicated that the workers do not understand them and are often not able to compute what they have earned. They are also subject to the disadvantages of incorrect base rates.

From Figures 48 and 49 it can be seen that both the worker's earnings and the unit labor cost are dependent upon the output. When such a wage payment system is used the accounting becomes quite complicated. It is apparent that the output per worker would have considerable effect upon the economy of production. For example, if each worker, under the plan illustrated by Figure 49, produced five units per six-hour day, the unit labor cost would be only $0.60. However, if each worker produced six units per day the unit labor cost would be increased to $0.95, an increase in labor cost of over 58%. Of course, this would be offset to some extent by a decrease in overhead, but this decrease would be small in comparison to the increase in labor cost.

The bonus plan illustrated in Figures 48 and 49 is probably the most simple of those which exist and as a result the effect upon the economy of production is not as great as if one of the more elaborate plans were used. A number of them are so complicated that their application is often not understood by the workers, and sometimes it appears that even the management is not fully aware of their effect. Labor unions have been quite universally opposed to the bonus methods of wage payment.

Other Effects of Wage Payment. A number of other items in connection with wage payment sometimes affect economy. The effect is often indirect through their increasing labor turnover. Some of these often seem insignificant but have been found in many cases to have real importance. One of these is the time at which the workers are paid. For many years it was customary to pay the workers on Saturday. This custom is still followed in many plants. A number of investigations indicated that the workers were more apt to squander their earnings over the week-end when paid on Saturday than if payment were made in the middle of the week. In other cases, where payment was made on Saturday by check, the workers were unable to get their checks cashed as the banks were closed. Numerous check cashing agencies came into existence in industrial areas, and the workers were forced to pay exorbitant fees to get their checks cashed. The effect of these conditions upon the workers was far greater than most had suspected.

A number of companies have caused themselves real economic loss by poor timing of announcements of wage increases. This is well illustrated by one company which gave wide publicity to its stockholders' meeting where announcement was made that the past year's profits had exceeded those of any previous year. Considerable agitation had existed among the workers for an increase in wages, and it was generally admitted by all the management that an increase would have to be granted. Yet the announcement of the wage increase was delayed for two months after the stockholders' meeting. The effect on the workers was anything but good. One cannot help but wonder how much employee good will could have been gained by announcing the wage increase at the same time the increased profits were publicized.

Strikes. The economic effect of strikes is one which is extremely difficult to determine accurately. This is due, to a great extent, to the fact that both parties to such arguments are usually extravagant in their claims, and truth usually goes out the window. Nearly everyone realizes, however, that such industrial conflict has a tremendous effect upon the companies involved. The effect upon the economy of the workers is usually lost sight of.

A number of estimates of the total cost of various strikes have been made. Unfortunately such figures have not been considered very seriously by those who could profit most from their study.

An idea of how much anyone usually profits from a strike may be had from a consideration of one fairly recent instance. Approximately 4,000 workers of a certain company were on strike for six weeks. The average earnings of the workers of this company were nearly $0.90 per hour for a 30-hour week. Being off the job for six weeks meant a loss of $162 for each worker. When the strike was finally settled the workers had won a wage increase of five cents per hour, or an average of $1.50 per week. This meant that 108 weeks would have to pass before the workers would get back the wages they had lost during the strike. Those who were familiar with the situation were convinced that the workers would have received the same increase within one year if no strike had been called.

From the viewpoint of the company the strike was said to have caused an actual loss of $10,000 per day. This was a total loss of $300,000 during the duration of the strike. Dividing $300,000 by the cost of giving each worker an increase of $1.50 per week, one finds that such an increase could have been paid for 50 weeks for the amount which the strike cost in actual dollars. It does not take much study to become convinced that the statement "nobody wins in a strike" is no idle platitude. While it is not the correct basis for lasting industrial peace, it is quite possible that considerable progress may be made toward this goal when adequate figures regarding the cost of industrial strikes are available and understood by all parties concerned.

Accident Reduction. At first thought it seems strange that it should be necessary to make an economy study of accident reduction programs. Accident reduction work should be carried on by all companies in the most intensive manner without regard to cost. Undoubtedly, at the present time, most of such work is done in this manner. However, this was not always the case. It is a shameful fact that in the beginning accident reduction work had to be forced upon certain companies by indignant social workers, employees and legislatures. On the other hand, many companies entered upon such work from a purely humanitarian interest in the welfare of their workers and were much surprised to find that actual profits were obtained from their money and efforts. In spite of the progress which has been made, it is still

probably true that many companies would make less effort along
the lines of accident prevention if they did not realize that such
programs are real economy.

From another viewpoint studies of the economy of accident
reduction programs are advisable. When a company is interested
in reducing accidents, without regard to profit, economy studies
of the work give an indication of how efficient their efforts have
been and indicate where additional expenditure is needed.

It is impossible to place a monetary value on the loss of a life
or injury to human beings. Thus the actual cost of accidents
can never be determined. It is possible to determine, with some
degree of accuracy, the actual cost to the company involved.
The direct cost in compensation, medical and hospital bills can
usually be found with little effort. The indirect costs, represented
by lost time of workers who were not directly involved in the
accident, damage to machinery, spoiled work, training new employees, preparation of reports or attending hearings of industrial
accident commissions, etc., are usually much greater than the
direct costs. One investigator states that the indirect costs are
four times as great as the direct costs. The Travelers Life Insurance Company, which has made extensive studies of this matter,
states that the indirect costs are at least four times as great as
those of the insurance company which was affected by the accident. The National Bureau of Casualty and Surety Underwriters
has stated that the direct cost of claims, medical service and
hospitalization arising out of industrial accidents in this country
is in excess of 600 million dollars per year. They also estimate
the indirect costs to be at least four times the direct costs. This
would make the total bill for industrial accidents in this country
amount to over three billion dollars per year.

The highway department of the state of Pennsylvania found
that the average cost of compensation for serious eye accidents
was over $2,000. Addition of the indirect costs would make the
total cost of each such accident amount to $10,000. A study in
the state of New York showed that the average cost of compensation in 23,000 cases of handling[1] accidents was $211. Again

---

[1] Handling is defined as lifting, carrying or manipulating an object or material by
human strength.

adding indirect costs the total cost of each such accident would be $1,055. These are among the most common accidents occurring in industry.

That accidents can be reduced by continued and intensive accident prevention work is proved by the experience of numerous companies. Typical of these is that of the United States Rubber Company. In 10 years this company reduced the number of lost time accidents from 1,100 to 158 per year. It operated its factories for 34 consecutive months without a fatality. One of its subsidiary plants, employing 2,000 workers, operated for 15 consecutive months without a lost time accident. The cost of accidents was reduced from 60 to 36 cents per $100 of payroll. This represented a saving of over $50,000 per year to this company.[2]

Another outstanding record is that of the Western Clock Company, where 2,300 employees worked for 10,000,000 hours without a lost time accident. This record was the result of 25 years of safety work. Every operation in the factories was studied carefully, and safety appliances and guards were installed wherever possible.

Another excellent example is that of the United Parcel Service in Los Angeles whose 18 truck drivers drove over 310,000 miles in one year without a single accident. Equally impressive records have been attained by other companies which have made determined efforts to eliminate needless injury and loss of life.

The railroads of the United States have long been ardent advocates of accident prevention and have established excellent records for safety. The air transport companies of this country recently completed an entire year of service without a single passenger fatality. This record has had a very good effect upon their business, their operating costs and their profits.

The United States Steel Corporation has spent large sums for accident prevention work with excellent results. During a 10-year period they spent over $9,700,000 and obtained an actual saving of over $14,600,000.[3] This is just one more indication of the economic aspect of accident prevention work.

[2] E. W. Beck, "Safety Engineering," vol. 66.
[3] W. H. Cameron, "Factory and Industrial Management," vol. 77, No. 1.

A recent example of the success of a somewhat spectacular safety appliance was the use of a rope safety net under the entire span of the Golden Gate bridge during construction. This net was responsible for the saving of 19 lives. The chief engineer stated that the saving that resulted from the workers' increased output, owing to lack of fear of falling, paid for the net many times.

In connection with industrial accidents it is well to point out that accidents are more prevalent among very new workers and those who have been on the job for many years. Inexperienced workers are not acquainted with possible sources of danger, while long-experienced workers tend to become careless.

At the present time there is probably no place where the cost of accidents needs to be considered more than in regard to our streets and highways. The loss of human life should be enough to cause all concerned to adopt radical measures to eliminate this evil. However, it appears probable that vast expenditures could be made to make the highways and streets safer on the basis of the monetary savings which would result. Some progress is being made along this line, but entirely too little.

Lighting. Lighting has two primary effects upon economy of production. First is its relationship to accidents. The second effect is upon quality and quantity of production. The United States Department of Labor has stated that 15% of all industrial accidents are due to faulty lighting. This department has estimated the cost of industrial accidents caused by poor lighting to be in excess of $150,000,000 annually. It is interesting to note that this amount would pay for the power for one 100-watt light for each of 30 million workers for fifty 40-hour weeks if such power were worth 2½ cents per kw.-hr. The actual cost of providing adequate lighting to eliminate this cause of accidents is usually very little. In most cases it does not exceed 1% of the payroll. In industrial work any such increase in lighting usually produces large dividends in increased production, as will be mentioned later.

Lighting has a very vital connection to the accident rates upon public streets and highways. The effect is probably more pronounced than in industrial work. The experience of the city of

Detroit in the years 1931, 1932 and 1933 gives vivid testimony of the effect of street lighting upon automobile accidents. Table 23 gives the results of a decrease in the amount of street lighting as an "economy" measure and the effect of again utilizing more adequate lighting. Figure 50 shows the data of Table 23 in

TABLE 23. EFFECT OF VARIATIONS IN STREET LIGHTING UPON TRAFFIC FATALITIES IN THE CITY OF DETROIT, 1931, TAKEN AS 100% (Courtesy of *Safety Engineering*)

	Fatalities	
	Night	Day
Street lighting at 100% in 1931 (10 months)	124	119
Street lighting at 65% in 1932 (10 months)	151	75
Street lighting at 85% in 1933 (10 months)	138	90

graphical form. This gives eloquent testimony as to the effect of lighting upon night-time accidents. It is interesting to project the curve beyond the 100% lighting value and note how little extra lighting would have to be added to eliminate entirely (theoretically) accidents caused by darkness.

Another example is found on Wilshire Boulevard in Los Angeles. On one five-mile section of this street (this section being much better lighted than other portions) there were no traffic fatalities during the year 1938, in spite of the very heavy traffic volumes and somewhat notorious high speeds which are encountered. Other streets, where traffic was relatively light but lighting inadequate, were the scenes of many accidents. Considerable education is needed to convince taxpayers that additional taxes for improved lighting are just as necessary as those used to provide fire and police protection. In fact, the return often would be greater.

The relationship of lighting to industrial accidents is well illustrated in an example given by

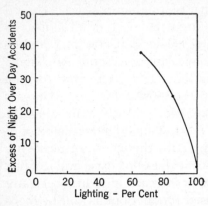

FIGURE 50. Effect of variations in street lighting on the excess of night accidents over day accidents in the city of Detroit (1931 lighting taken as 100%).

Mr. R. E. Simpson of the Travelers Insurance Company in an address before the Illuminating Engineering Society.[4]

The company . . . employed an average of 1,000 workers, had an annual payroll of one and three-quarters million dollars, and paid a yearly compensation premium of approximately $22,000. For some time the annual number of accidents (many of them minor, none of them fatal) was approximately 425. The compensation payments and medical fees averaged nearly $15,000 per year, or about $35 per accident.

The entire lighting system of the plant was revamped by substituting large lamps with approved reflectors in place of the original lighting equipment, and locating the units in a proper manner with respect to the work. The electric current consumption was increased from an average of 40 watts per employee to 100 watts per employee. The contract for the electrical work was $5,000, and the annual lighting bill increased from $1,900 to $4,700. The accidents, however, dropped from an average of 425 to 170 per year, and the compensation payments were reduced to approximately $6,000.

If we apply the four-to-one principle referred to earlier in this discussion, we find that with the original lighting system the company paid $1,900 a year for electric current and $59,500 to meet the hidden or uninsurable cost resulting from 425 accidents. With the new system the company paid $4,700 for lighting and only $23,800 for the hidden costs of 170 accidents. The direct and immediate saving amounted to $35,700, and in addition to this the favorable accident experience would have a weighty influence when the proper time came to adjust the compensation premium.

While improved lighting can nearly always be justified on grounds of its effect on accidents, such improvements are usually accompanied by additional savings through increased production or improved quality. It is estimated that 25% of all human energy is consumed in seeing. It is also well established that the amount of energy required for seeing is a function of the amount and quality of the light available. It is therefore reasonable to expect that the output of workers will be affected by lighting. Many cases are available to prove this effect. A number have been summarized by Munroe and Cook[5] and are shown in Table 24. It is important to note that from an average increase of only 2% of the payroll an average of 15% increase in produc-

[4] R. E. Simpson, "Accidental Lighting Costs," Trans. I. E. S., vol. XXIII, No. 6.
[5] C. C. Munroe, and H. A. Cook, Trans. A. S. M. E. Man., 51–8, 1929.

tion was obtained. It is doubtful if such results could be obtained by the expenditure of the same amount of money in any other way.

TABLE 24. COMPARATIVE PRODUCTION WITH OLD AND NEW
SYSTEMS OF FACTORY LIGHTING

Work and shop	Average foot-candles with old system	Average foot-candles with new system	Increase in production with new system, per cent	Additional lighting cost, per cent of payroll
Pulley finishing (Pyott Foundry Co.)	0.2	4.8	35.0	5.0
Soft-metal bearing (Foote Bros.)	4.6	12.7	15.0	1.2
Heavy steel machine (Lee Loader & Body Co.)	3.0	11.5	10.0	1.2
Carburetor assembly (Stromberg Carburetor Co.)	2.1	12.3	12.0	0.9
Plant manufacturing electric and gas irons (Dover Mfg. Co.)	4.0 at tool point	13.5	12.2	2.5
Semiautomatic buffing of brass shell sockets (General Electric Co.)	3.8	11.4	8.5	1.8
Manufacturing piston rings (Detroit Piston Ring Co.)	1.2	18.0	25.8	2.0
Letter separating (U. S. Post Office Dept.)	3.6	8.0	4.4	0.6
Inspection in roller bearing-plant (Timken Roller Bearing Co.)	2.0	20.0	12.5	2.5
Average	2.36	12.5	15.0	1.97

The effect of lighting upon quality is probably recognized to a greater extent than the effect upon production. Most companies are providing quite good lighting where inspection of quality is done. However, in many cases they fail to provide adequate illumination where the work is originally done so that quality might be improved at the source. The extent to which lighting may affect quality is illustrated by a situation in a tire factory. A worker was building 6.50–16 white sidewall tires which required great care to assure a perfect appearance. Suddenly defects started appearing in the tires which he built, averaging two tires per six-hour shift. These tires, being defective in appearance only, had to be classed as "seconds" and sold as such, resulting in a loss of over one dollar for each tire. An investigation disclosed that someone had substituted 50-watt bulbs for the two 100-watt bulbs which furnished light for this worker. The correct lamps were replaced and nothing said to the worker about the defects. The defects immediately ceased, and no further trouble was experienced. Computation revealed that the saving in electric current through the use of the smaller bulbs amounted to less than one cent per shift, and the resulting defects caused a loss of over two dollars. Many other similar cases could be cited to emphasize the effect of lighting upon quality.

In connection with a consideration of the economic effects of lighting it should be remembered that quantity of light is not the only factor that should be considered. The quality of the light is just as important. Glare and distribution are very important factors. These are especially significant in connection with eyestrain and fatigue. Their effect upon the workers' eyes should be considered carefully so as to prevent permanent damage to their eyes.

Air Conditioning. Air conditioning is similar to lighting in that many of the first industrial installations were made to improve or control quality. After the installations were in use it was found that output had also been improved.

The first important installations of air conditioning where economy of production was greatly affected were in the textile and perishable food industries. In some of these plants unsuitable weather conditions made production impossible during certain seasons. For example, the dipping of chocolates was extremely difficult in summer months. Air conditioning eliminated all of this trouble. Similar experiences were encountered in the textile, chewing gum and baking industries. One of the most recent uses of air conditioning to control and improve quality is in connection with blast furnaces for the production of pig iron. Experience thus far in this field indicates that more installations will soon be made.

The use of air conditioning in theaters, hotels, stores and office buildings is now becoming common. The economy of such installations is usually determined without difficulty.

A number of cases have shown that proper air conditioning may produce increases in productivity of workers as great as 20 to 25%. Increases of 10% are very common. It is quite probable that the future will see numerous factories built without windows so that artificial lighting and air conditioning may be employed with the greatest effect so that the workers may always have ideal working environment. One such factory is now in operation in this country with considerable success.

Drinking Water. Drinking water is another factor which has often been neglected but which may have a considerable effect upon output and contentment of workers. This is especially true where work must be done in very hot weather or in high temperatures. Not only should good, cool water be available but it should be located at places where the workers can obtain it readily without having to take too much time from their work. Considerable progress has been made recently in this respect. Much of this is due to the efforts of companies manufacturing water dispensing and cooling equipment. Water coolers of various types are available in compact units which are reasonable in first cost and will operate for as little as 2 cents per day.

A recent practice is to provide salt for workers who are working in hot places, either in the form of convenient salt tablets or by the addition of salt to the drinking water. This replaces the salt which is lost from the body in perspiration. Replacing this salt gives much greater worker comfort and increases efficiency to a considerable extent. This particular practice has been found to yield very great dividends, both in output and increased morale.

Washrooms. The economy resulting from the provision of clean and attractive washrooms is usually rather difficult to determine. However, there have been sufficient cases studied closely to leave no doubt that money invested in such facilities pays adequate dividends. It is unreasonable to expect workers to be neat and efficient in their work if they are forced to use filthy toilet facilities. Even where dirty tasks must be performed, they will usually be done more readily and better if the workers know that adequate washrooms are available where they may remove the evidences of their labor before going to their homes.

One cannot expect workers to take any pride in their appearance if they are forced to wash in dirty, germ-laden washrooms.

One of the direct results of good washrooms is a decrease in minor disease among the workers, resulting in less lost time due to illness. This alone should repay any investment made for such facilities. One foundry which installed very elaborate and beautifully tiled shower rooms for its workers stated that the result in increased efficiency and morale among the foundry workers was far beyond any expectation. It was noticed that the workers began to wear rather good street clothes to work, changing to their work clothes after arriving at the plant. Some foundry workers presented a better appearance when coming to the plant than some of the office workers. This example merely shows that most workers do desire to be clean and want to appear neat and respectable. Helping the worker to achieve this is bound to be reflected in his work. In addition it is a long step toward better employee relations.

Noise Reduction. There has probably been less attention given to noise reduction than to any other of the environmental factors. Yet it is a serious one. The extent to which noise may affect economy is illustrated by a judgment of $2,000 which was rendered against a company in Minneapolis in 1938.[6] A woman who lived across the street from this plant brought suit for damages, alleging that the noise from the plant caused her to lose sleep, made her nervous and inflicted mental anguish. While this is an extreme case, it illustrates what may result from uncontrolled noise.

The effect of noise upon the efficiency of workers has been shown by numerous experiments. In one of these, the Aetna Life Insurance Company of Hartford, Connecticut, reduced the noise level in certain offices 14.5%. The efficiency of the workers increased 8.8%. Errors of the typists decreased 29%. Errors of machine operators decreased 52%. Employee turnover dropped 47%. Absences decreased 37.5%.

When noise was reduced in the telephone receiving room of a telegraph station, the result was a decrease of 42% in the number of errors and a decrease of 5% in the cost per message. Other

[6] Business Week, November 19, 1938, has an account of this case.

tests have been conducted by comparing the number of errors made by typists using regular and noiseless typewriters. The results showed a large reduction in errors when noise was reduced by the use of noiseless machines.

What effect traffic and street noises have upon the economy of the nation is difficult to determine. Certainly it is not less than has been found to exist in factories and offices. One has only to try to sleep in many of the expensive hotel rooms while listening to the yelling of newsboys and the honking of automobile horns to become convinced that much remains to be done along the line of noise control.

Economy studies of the various environmental factors can be made in much the same manner as those of equipment. It is usually somewhat more difficult to determine the exact returns from such investments. However, in nearly all cases of this type the actual returns are considerably greater than those which may be determined directly.

REFERENCES

"A Symposium on Illumination," Instruments Publishing Co., Pittsburgh, 1935.
Luckiesh, M.: "Light and Work," D. Van Nostrand Company, Inc., New York, 1924.
Clark, J. H.: "Lighting in Relation to Public Health," The Williams and Wilkins Company, Baltimore, 1924.
American Engineering Council, "Safety and Production," Harper & Brothers, New York, 1928.

PROBLEMS

170. Adding a personnel department has reduced the labor turnover of a company 10%. The company has an average of 2,000 employees. An analysis indicates that the cost of hiring and training a new employee in this company is $15. The personnel department costs a total of $4,000 per year. Approximately one-half of this cost is chargeable to this part of the personnel program. Is the cost of this department justified?

171. A large company employing 15,000 workers believes that giving comprehensive aptitude tests to new employees, so as to fit them to the proper jobs, would reduce labor turnover at least 5%. The present turnover ratio is 30% and the company is adding 1,000 additional workers annually. The cost of hiring and training each new employee is computed to be $40.

   The proposed plan would cost $10,000 annually to administer plus $5 in wages for each employee who took the test. Would you advise adopting the plan?

172. The costs of producing a certain article are as follows:

Labor	$0.60
Material	0.92
Variable overhead	0.05
Fixed overhead	0.32
Total	$1.89

The average production per worker has been 12 units per day. It is estimated that each worker could produce two or three additional units per day if he applied himself properly. The company proposes to pay a bonus of 10 cents for the first unit over 12 produced each day, 20 cents for the second unit, 30 cents for the third, etc. At what output per day for each worker would the company just break even on this plan?

173. A proposed air conditioning system will cost $22,000. Annual operation expense will be $2,800. The equipment must be written off in five years. It is estimated that labor costs will be reduced 5% because of increased output which it is thought will result. Annual labor costs are now $150,000. Would you advise the installation on this basis?

174. What other factors might be considered in deciding upon the wisdom of installing the air conditioning system in Problem 173?

175. List the factors which might be included in an economy study of a proposed improved lighting system on a public highway.

Chapter XVIII

ELEMENTS OF STATISTICAL METHOD

Repetitive and Statistical Data. Every engineer has occasion to use numerical data. In the past, emphasis has been chiefly placed on repetitive data, the kind obtained for an input-output curve of a motor, a stress-strain diagram for a steel bar, or any other case in which one value of one quantity is recorded as corresponding to a definite value of another. For a given motor, for example, the performance curve implies that a repetition of the output values will give the input values shown on the curve. It is common experience that any operator attempting to duplicate the curve will have some variations from it. One usually ascribes these to errors of observation or technique, or considers the original curve to be in error. A little reflection will show the unwisdom of such conclusions in many cases. Consider the performance curve of the motor. The company which supplied the curve may have taken it from another motor, built to the same specifications. If so, deviations of manufacture are present. These cause slight changes in efficiency. Conductor sizes and spacing, clearances, ventilation characteristics, weather conditions and all other factors are not capable of exact duplication. Hence, no two motors are the same, neither will their performance curves be. More important still, the means of obtaining values of data for the input-output curve are, strictly speaking, averaging means. Input may be read from ammeter, voltmeter and other meters with swinging needles. These are built with dampers, so as to remain steady. Of course, the steadiness of the needle disguises small variations of the quantity to be read, so that one gets average values only — not the hop, skip and jump of the real quantity. Likewise, the output is taken by a dynamometer which must be loaded, or by a prony brake depending upon friction for its load. Every laboratory man knows how hard it is to get smooth operation of the brake. Damping is necessary to get anything like consistent values. Thus, the final curve represents the selection of pairs of values obtained by averaging the actual ones. The averaging occurs in the instruments, as noted, and also in the mind of the operator. Actually, the location of the curve is a compromise. The operator has tried to put it in the most probable location and, to a degree, he may have succeeded. But the method used is intuitive, and it becomes less and less dependable as greater accuracy is sought. If more delicate instruments are used, with less damping, and values are recorded for smaller and smaller intervals, the resulting points are less likely than before to give a smooth curve. The readings at each point may be taken a number of times to avoid arbitrary selection by the investigator. They will differ. Which one is to be used? Maybe the performance curve should be replaced by a band with variable shading.

For the cases just described, it is frequently found or assumed that mathematical expression of the natural laws involved is simple and that one can compute the value of the input, for example, from the output and the "natural-law" performance curve. It has already been indicated that such computation implies validity in all the averaging operations in the testing process.

Many phenomena which require analysis are not reducible to the characteristic curve form. In some cases, curves may be drawn, but they hide rather than reveal the kind of data at hand. For many of these statistical data are available. Records of stream flow, for example, are used as a basis for dam, channel and spillway design. Replacement records of telephone and telegraph poles, railway ties, telephone instruments and cable and automobiles are available, from which average life and probable life can be estimated. From these quantities, depreciation can be approximated. Mortality records of persons are to be had, more complete and accurate than any heretofore in use. Old age pension costs, life insurance premiums and population changes can be computed from them. Inspection and rejection data from automatic machines or assembly lines indicate the state of the things produced and, by suitable interpretation, furnish clues to improved processes and controls.

The physicist and the astronomer are often obliged to consider data from different sources but for the same quantity. For example, W. W. Campbell obtained a number of solar eclipse photographs in Australia in 1922. From each of the plates, measurements were taken to determine the apparent displacement of stars whose light paths came close to the solar mass. Measurements for a single star from different plates numbered as many as 75. From these, the most probable value was determined, and this value was checked with that to be expected from Einstein's law of universal gravitation. The fact that close agreement was found was an item of scientific importance.

Similar analysis has been used to establish the most probable value of the charge of an electron — a basic physical constant. R. A. Millikan has so examined his own values. The analyst may have the further problem of examining for agreement sets of values from several independent investigators. What can be inferred from significant differences among the sets?

In increasing numbers, engineers are engaged in solving problems of this type. The problems have two principal features:

1. A number of values of a quantity or property are available, instead of a single value.

2. How can the information presented by the available values be best presented and best used?

For example, an engineer is writing specifications for an airplane part where combination of strength and lightness is required. The low factor of safety, which is therefore necessary, is feasible only if the strength of the material is known, and the variability of that strength in different lots of the material. The engineer has data at hand showing ultimate tensile strength of current samples of the material. If he has 20 values, which one shall he use, if any, and what accuracy may he ascribe to the answer?

To obtain, analyze and interpret such data as have been mentioned above requires use of mathematical techniques or tools. Collectively, they may be called the statistical method. Before attempting the solution of engineering problems of this type, one needs to study the elements of statistical method.

The Frequency Distribution. To analyze numerical data, it is first necessary to arrange the values systematically. There are numerous ways to do this, but the most important for the engineer is the frequency distribution, where data are grouped according to magnitudes. Such a distribution is constructed in the following manner:

1. Using the range of the data (the interval between the highest and lowest magnitude) as a guide, divide the range into a number of equal intervals of convenient size, known as *class intervals* or *cells*.

2. Then place groups in a column in order of magnitude with the lowest class interval at the top.

3. Then score the data. Each value is checked at the class interval or cell into which it falls.

An example is given in Table 25.

TABLE 25. SEA WATER DENSITY READINGS IN CARIBBEAN [1]

Cell No.	Class interval	Frequency
0	26.85–26.89	1
1	26.90–26.94	2
2	26.95–26.99	4
3	27.00–27.04	7
4	27.05–27.09	18
5	27.10–27.14	30
6	27.15–27.19	30
7	27.20–27.24	21
8	27.25–27.29	12
9	27.30–27.34	13
10	27.35–27.39	7
11	27.40–27.44	2

The values tabulated are from a density surface where dissolved atmospheric oxygen attains its principal minimum concentration. They range from 1.02685 to 1.02744.

The frequency distribution can be presented pictorially on a chart with the class interval as abscissa and the frequency as ordinate. The frequencies are then plotted for each class interval. These plotted points, when connected, form a frequency polygon which can be smoothed into a curve. The data of Table 25 have been so plotted in Figure 51.

A distribution in which the frequencies are shown cumulatively

[1] From "Some Applications of Statistical Methods to Problems in Modern Physical Oceanography," by H. R. Seiwell, in *Proceedings of the Industrial Statistics Conference*, M.I.T., 1938.

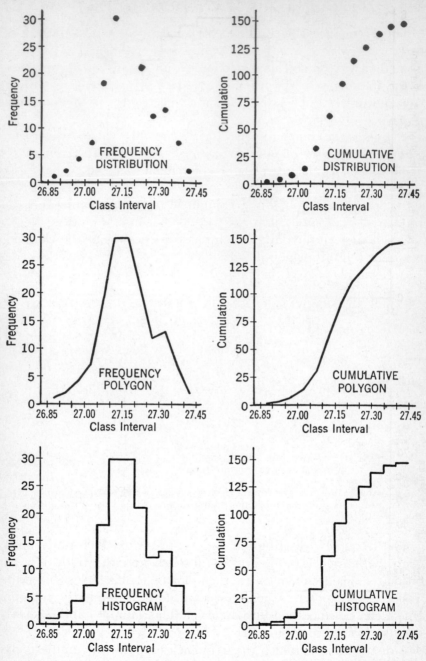

FIGURE 51. Graphical representation of statistical data regarding sea water density.

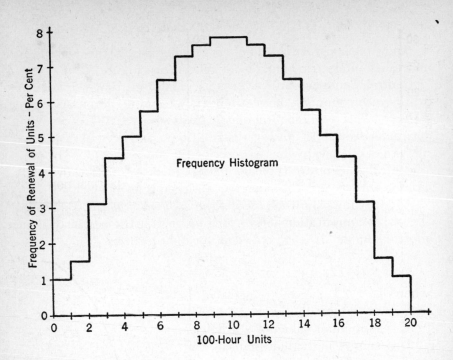

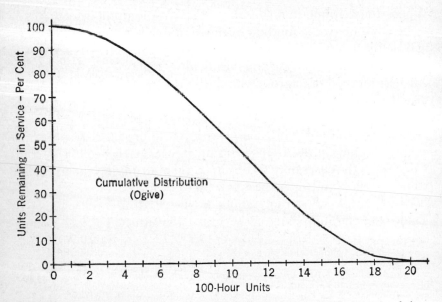

FIGURE 52. Frequency histogram and cumulative distribution curve of the mortality of electric lamps, in percentages.

is known as an *ogive*. The curve illustrating the cumulative mortality of electric lamps is an *ogive*. (See Figure 52.)

Central Tendency and Averages. The data that the engineer works with commonly have a tendency to group about a value or values. This grouping tendency gives rise to a peak which is characteristic of frequency distributions, and it makes possible the use of a typical value to describe the mass of data. The point of central tendency or typical value is called the *average*. Actually, however, there are three averages rather than one.

The first important average is the *arithmetic mean*. Because of its ease of computation and its long usage, it is the best known and most common. It is expressed in formula form as

$$\overline{X} = \frac{\Sigma(X)}{n}$$

where
  $\overline{X}$ = arithmetic mean
  X = individual value, or statistic
  Σ = sum of individual items
  n = number of items

Where the arithmetic mean of a considerable number of items is to be computed, the method outlined above is generally laborious and subject to error. With increasing numbers of items the problem of addition becomes difficult. A more convenient and efficient method is to group the data into the form of a frequency distribution, and then compute the arithmetic mean for the distribution.

Since the midpoint of each class interval or cell represents the average value of the items contained within the cell, the total value of all the cases may be obtained by multiplying the midpoint value by the number of cases for that group.

For example: For the frequency distribution table shown in Table 26,[2] the midpoint of the first class interval (49.5) is mul-

---

[2] The student will observe that this table is almost symmetrical. Apparently readings were taken to include one class beyond the peak frequency. Then the remaining values were assumed to duplicate in reverse order the initial frequency values of the table. This was probably due to (a) the difficulty and time required to obtain data on lamps of long life — they refuse to burn out, so to speak, and (b) the fact that customer satisfaction is lost with the lamps that "die" soon. Information about these is most desired. Such symmetry is rare in engineering practice. Although a less symmetrical curve is to be expected, these data are used as obtained.

TABLE 26. THE LIFE EXPERIENCE OF ELECTRIC LAMPS [3]

Cell No.	Class interval	Midpoint (M. P.)	Renewals of original units, or frequency	M. P. times frequency	Renewals of original units in per cent	Original units remaining (beginning of period)	Cumulative total of percentage remaining (beginning of period)
						75,614	100.0
0	0–99.5	49.5	755	37,373	1.0		
						74,859	99.0
1	99.5–199.5	149.5	1,142	170,729	1.5		
						73,717	97.5
2	199.5–299.5	249.5	2,340	583,830	3.1		
						71,377	94.4
3	299.5–399.5	349.5	3,322	1,161,040	4.4		
						68,055	90.0
4	399.5–499.5	449.5	3,775	1,696,860	5.0		
						64,280	85.0
5	499.5–599.5	549.5	4,303	2,364,500	5.7		
						59,977	79.3
6	599.5–699.5	649.5	4,983	3,236,460	6.6		
						54,994	72.7
7	699.5–799.5	749.5	5,511	4,130,490	7.3		
						49,483	65.4
8	799.5–899.5	849.5	5,738	4,874,430	7.6		
						43,745	57.8
9	899.5–999.5	949.5	5,888	5,590,660	7.8		
						37,857	50.0
10	999.5–1,099.5	1,049.5	5,888	6,179,460	7.8		
						31,969	42.2
11	1,099.5–1,199.5	1,149.5	5,838	6,710,780	7.6		
						26,131	34.6
12	1,199.5–1,299.5	1,249.5	5,511	6,885,990	7.3		
						20,620	27.3
13	1,299.5–1,399.5	1,349.5	4,983	6,724,560	6.6		
						15,637	20.7
14	1,399.5–1,499.5	1,449.5	4,303	6,237,200	5.7		
						11,334	15.0
15	1,499.5–1,599.5	1,549.5	3,775	5,849,360	5.0		
						7,559	10.0
16	1,599.5–1,699.5	1,649.5	3,322	5,479,640	4.4		
						4,237	5.6
17	1,699.5–1,799.5	1,749.5	2,340	4,093,830	3.1		
						1,897	2.5
18	1,799.5–1,899.5	1,849.5	1,142	2,112,130	1.5		
						755	1.0
19	1,899.5–1,999.5	1,949.5	755	1,471,870	1.0		
						0	0
			75,614	75,591,192			

$$\overline{X} = \frac{\Sigma(\text{M. P.} \times \text{Frequency})}{\text{Frequency}} = \frac{75,591,192}{75,614} = 999.70$$

[3] Taken from the mortality experience of electric lamps obtained from periodic inspections of lamps by the National Electric Lamp Association in 1915. The mortality is due entirely to use and therefore does not represent any replacements due to inadequacy, obsolescence or public requirements.

337

tiplied by the frequency indicated for that group (755) in order to obtain the total value for all the cases in that class interval. It is assumed that all the values included within the limits of a class interval will be distributed evenly in it, and therefore the average value of all the cases in each class interval coincides with the midpoint. If the class interval is not too large and if a sufficient number of cases are available, variations from that assumption are usually small and a sufficiently accurate result will be obtained. The products of each class interval midvalue and the number of units in that group (the frequency) are then added to obtain the total value of all the cases in the frequency distribution. The sum is divided by the number of cases (n) to obtain the arithmetic mean.

This method can be expressed in formula form as

$$\overline{X} = \frac{\Sigma(M.P. \times f.)}{n} = \frac{75,591,192}{75,614} = 999.70$$

This method is known as the "long method" because other shortcut methods give approximate answers. Such methods are valuable when the computation becomes heavy, owing to numerous data and large values.[4]

The arithmetic mean is the most generally recognized average. Its computation is relatively simple, but its value may be distorted by extreme values and therefore it may not be typical. For most problems in which the engineer is interested, however, it is the most significant and descriptive single number for a given set of data.

[4] The technique of computation is itself important. Many questions have been answered in practice, and the American Standards Association has become the recognized agency to harmonize and standardize procedures. As each engineering society develops new standards, it attempts to coordinate them with the A. S. A. standards. For the computations involved in handling of statistics the following procedure is recommended:

a. Computations should be carried two places beyond the original values. For example, if values are given to the nearest pound, computations should be to the nearest 0.01 pound. This is best accomplished by rounding off the values after computation. This applies to averages, measures of dispersion, control limits and similar computed functions.

b. Define class intervals so as to avoid ambiguities. If values are listed thus: 100 to 200, 200 to 300, etc., there is doubt as to which interval received the cases equal to 200. If the interval is 1, the class intervals can be 100 to 199, 200 to 299, etc., or 99.5 to 199.5, 199.5 to 299.5, etc.

c. From practice and experience, it is found desirable to divide the range into from 13 to 20 class intervals or cells. Too small a number gives too little information; too large a number increases the irregularities of the graphs.

d. Tables of squares and square roots are essential to computation.

For more detailed information on these questions, see "A. S. T. M. Manual on Presentation of Data," March, 1941, printing.

The *median* is the second important average. It is an average of position. It is the value of the middle datum when the data are arranged according to size. If the number of data is even, the median is the arithmetic mean of the central two items.

However, in the event that the data are grouped into class intervals and it is impossible to determine the value of each individual item (see Table 26), the median is computed from the grouped data by interpolation. The number of the desired datum is first determined by $n/2$ (where n equals the number of data). In Table 26 the median item will be the 37,807th item, 75,614/2. One must determine its value by interpolation (assuming, again, that the items are uniformly distributed in each class interval). It will be found by inspection that the 37,807th item falls in the 10th class interval which is 999.5–1,099.5 hours of life. The 37,757th item (75,614–37,857) is at the beginning of the group and the 43,645th item (75,614–31,969) marks the end. The value of the 37,807th or median item may be obtained through simple interpolation.

Value		Item number
Lower limit	999.5	No. 37,757
Median value	?	No. 37,807
Upper limit	1,099.5	No. 43,645

1. Determine the fraction of the distance necessary in the number column.

$$\frac{\text{Number of cases needed within group}}{\text{Total number of cases in group}} = \frac{50}{5,888} = \frac{i}{f}$$

2. Add that portion of the total difference on the other side to the lower limit. This difference in the value column will correspond to the size of the class interval. Thus $\frac{i}{f} C$ or in this instance $\frac{50}{5,888} 100$ is added to the lower limit of the group in which the median is contained. The formula form is

$$\text{Median} = L_{me} + \frac{i}{f} C = 999.5 + \frac{50}{5,888} 100 = 1,000.35$$

where

L_{mo} = the lower limit of the median class interval
i = the number of items needed within the group
f = total number of items in group (frequency)
C = class interval

This type of average or measure of central tendency is affected by the number of items rather than by the size of the items. It is easy to calculate and is not distorted in value by unusual items. This last advantage makes it more useful in some cases than the arithmetic mean.

But certain considerations make the median a difficult average to use. People in general, and this is important if the engineer is to attempt to explain results to the public, are not familiar with the median. Further, the items must be arranged according to size before the median can be determined, and the result cannot be manipulated algebraically to the same extent as the mean. Also, the median has larger standard deviation and probable error than the arithmetic mean, the importance of which will appear later.

The *mode* is the third of the important averages. It is merely the most frequent or most common value. This is significant only when a sufficiently large number of items and a suitable number of class intervals are available to give a smooth distribution. If that smooth distribution exists, the *mode* will be the value corresponding to the maximum point in the frequency distribution.

It is not possible to make an exact mathematical determination, but there are methods for obtaining reasonably accurate approximations to the mode. It is unnecessary to go into these extensively. A very simple and relatively accurate method of determining the value of the mode is based upon certain empirical relations that exist. For a moderately symmetrical distribution it has been found that the distance between the mean and the median is one-third of the distance between the mean and the mode. Since the value of the mean and the median can be determined accurately, the value of the mode may be approximately determined from the following relationship:

$$\text{mode} = \text{mean} - 3\,(\text{mean} - \text{median}) \tag{52}$$

The mode is an average of position and is therefore independent of the distorting influence of extreme items. However, the mode is not significant unless a large amount of data is available. It is possible with a limited number of items that the mode may not exist, because none of the values may be repeated or, if repeated, may occur but a few times.

Measures of Dispersion. Merely to determine the average or typical value is of limited use. The computer must be prepared to indicate the degree of variation about the average. It is in this way that the information contained in statistics can be revealed. The degree of variation about the average is called the dispersion, and it is possible to give it mathematical values.

The simplest measure of dispersion is the *range*. This is simply the difference between the maximum and minimum items in the series. It is easily calculated and readily understood. But since the range is dependent only upon the two extremes, it does not indicate the distribution of the items within the range. It is greatly affected by a few unusual values when these become the extremes. In the curve of physical mortality of electric lamps which has been used as an example, the range or dispersion of items would be from 49.5 hours of life to 1,949.5 hours of life for these items, if we use the midpoints of the first and last cells as extremes.

Since merely knowing the range does not fully indicate the manner of dispersion within the two extremes, it is important to develop other tests of deviation. A simple method for determining the variation of values about the arithmetic mean or median is to take the average distance of the items from either of these measures of central tendency. The value so obtained is known as the mean deviation. The formula for the computation of this measure of dispersion is

$$MD = \frac{\Sigma(X - \overline{X})}{n} \quad \text{or} \quad \frac{\Sigma(X - X_M)}{n} \tag{53}$$

where

MD is the mean deviation

$\Sigma(X - \overline{X})$ = the sum of the deviations of each value from the arithmetic mean, algebraic signs ignored

$\Sigma(X - X_M)$ = the sum of the deviations from another measure of central tendency such as the median, algebraic signs ignored

When the data are grouped in the form of a frequency distribution, the computation of the mean deviation becomes somewhat involved. It will not be undertaken here.[5]

The Standard Deviation. The *standard deviation* is the most important measure of dispersion. In practice, it is the most used. In theory, it is the most useful. The formula defining the standard deviation is

$$\sigma = \sqrt{\frac{\Sigma(X - \bar{X})^2}{n}} \tag{54}$$

where

$$\sigma = \text{standard deviation}$$
$$X - \bar{X} = \text{difference from arithmetic mean}$$
$$n = \text{total number of items}$$

It is often more convenient to use Equation (55), derived from (54), because of simpler computations.

$$\sigma = \sqrt{\frac{\Sigma X^2}{n} - \bar{X}^2} \tag{55}$$

Note that $\dfrac{\Sigma X \bar{X}}{n} = \bar{X}^2$, by definition of arithmetic mean.

In the tables regarding electric lamps, the procedure for determining the standard deviation is as follows (see Table 27).

1. The deviation of the midpoint of each group from the arithmetic mean is used as a measure of the average deviation from the mean of all items in that group.

2. The average deviation of each group is squared to obtain the necessary deviation squared.

3. The average deviation squared is multiplied by the frequency indicated for that group in order to obtain the total of the squared deviations for that group.

4. The totals are then added for the entire distribution.

5. The square root of the sum obtained after dividing by n is the standard deviation.

$$\sigma = \sqrt{\frac{\Sigma f(X - \bar{X})^2}{n}} \tag{56}$$

[5] For this computation, see Mills, *loc. cit.*, or other standard textbook on statistics.

TABLE 27. THE LIFE EXPERIENCE OF ELECTRIC LAMPS —
DERIVATION OF STANDARD DEVIATION

Hours (class interval)	Mid-point	Number of units (frequency)	Deviation from mean $(x = X - \overline{X})$ $\overline{X} = 999.70$	x^2	$f.x^2$
—0.5–99.5	49.5	755	950.2	902,880	681,674,000
99.5–199.5	149.5	1,142	850.2	722,840	825,483,000
199.5–299.5	249.5	2,340	750.2	562,400	1,316,952,000
299.5–399.5	349.5	3,322	650.2	422,760	1,404,408,000
399.5–499.5	449.5	3,775	550.2	302,720	1,142,768,000
499.5–599.5	599.5	4,303	450.2	202,680	872,132,000
599.5–699.5	649.5	4,983	350.2	122,640	611,115,000
699.5–799.5	749.5	5,511	250.2	62,600	344,989,000
799.5–899.5	849.5	5,738	150.2	22,560	129,449,000
899.5–999.5	949.5	5,888	50.2	2,520	14,837,700
999.5–1,099.5	1,049.5	5,888	49.8	2,480	14,602,200
1,099.5–1,199.5	1,149.5	5,838	149.8	22,400	131,004,000
1,199.5–1,299.5	1,249.5	5,511	249.8	62,400	343,886,000
1,299.5–1,399.5	1,349.5	4,983	349.8	122,360	609,719,000
1,399.5–1,499.5	1,449.5	4,303	449.8	202,320	870,583,000
1,499.5–1,599.5	1,549.5	3,775	549.8	302,280	1,141,107,000
1,599.5–1,699.5	1,649.5	3,322	649.8	422,240	1,402,681,000
1,699.5–1,799.5	1,749.5	2,340	749.8	562,200	1,315,548,000
1,799.5–1,899.5	1,849.5	1,142	849.8	722,160	824,707,000
1,899.5–1,999.5	1,949.5	755	949.8	902,120	681,101,000
		75,614			14,678,745,900

$$\sigma = \sqrt{\frac{14,678,745,900}{75,614}} = \sqrt{194,127.354142} = 440.60$$

The standard deviation can be interpreted by the engineer as "the radius of gyration of a set of n equal particles, with respect to a given centroidal axis." [6] It is a "root-mean-square" value and is, therefore, similarly analogous to the effective value of an alternating current.

The standard deviation, as a measure of central tendency, is sensitive. In a normal distribution, the distribution curve is symmetrical about an axis through the mean. For such a distribution, the range covered by one standard deviation on each side of the average (mean) will include 68.26% of the values, two standard deviations will include 95.46% of the values, and three deviations will include 99.73% of the values. These relations hold only for a "normal" distribution. The cases considered by the

[6] See H. L. Rietz, "Mathematical Statistics," p. 20.

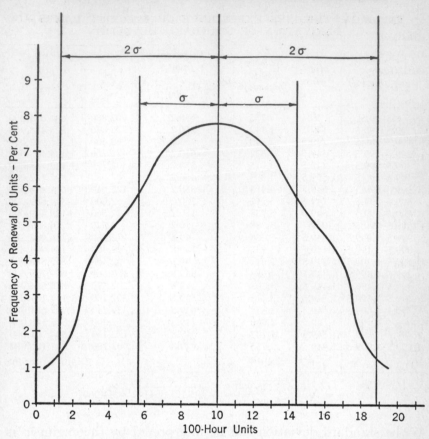

FIGURE 53. Mortality of electric lamps in per cent figures, showing standard deviation.

engineer are usually somewhat skewed. The distribution curve is not symmetrical about the average. There are mathematical measures of skewness, expressible as functions of the data available.[7] There are also mathematical measures of the effect of skewness on the percentage of values within the ranges: $\pm\ \sigma$,

---

[7] *Skewness.* The measure of skewness commonly used is designated by k. It is defined by the equation

$$k = \frac{\Sigma(X - \overline{X})^3}{n\sigma^3}$$

where the quantities listed have the meanings previously assigned. For symmetrical distribution curves, it is zero. For positive values the hump of the distribution curve is displaced to the left, for negative values to the right of the normal mid-position. For $k \neq 0$, the curve is not symmetrical; the converse is not necessarily true.

$\pm 2\,\sigma$, and $\pm 3\,\sigma$. Space will not permit presentation of this analysis. For a moderate degree of skewness, such as one finds in many engineering data subject to chance variations, the percentage values given are not greatly modified.

Obtaining and Handling of Data. It is apparent that the handling of data to get the most information from the values available can become a large task. The examples given in this chapter for determination of measures of central tendency and measures of dispersion involve considerable computation. If the program becomes more elaborate, questions are raised by the amount of labor involved and by the conclusions reached.

1. Could samples of the data be used with valid results, instead of the entire mass?

2. What measures, such as averages, deviations, and skewness, derived from masses of data, reveal most of the information contained in the data themselves?

3. What are good data and how are they obtained?

These questions are timely and appropriate. Much thought has been given to them, and one of the national societies has prepared an excellent manual on the subject.[8] The student who has statistical work to do will find this a valuable aid. Brief answers to the questions will be given.

1. *Samples and their use.* Samples can be used to represent data. In a very real sense, all data are themselves samples. When one runs a test on a motor or investigates the hardness of a given metal, he takes a number of readings or runs a number of tests. These are really samples of all that he might obtain. Quality control in mass manufacture is accomplished largely through inspection of samples. This is discussed in a later chapter. If samples are taken from a mass of data, too large to be handled as an entity, they may be subjected to the same techniques which would be used for the total data, and generalizations can be made from the results. In selecting samples from the total mass of data, we should attempt to meet these requirements:

a. The sample must be selected without bias or prejudice.

[8] See "A. S. T. M. Manual on Presentation of Data," including Supplement A, Supplement B, and Tables of Squares and Square Roots (1941 printing). This manual was sponsored by a committee of the society of which H. F. Dodge served as chairman. The work of Dodge in applying statistics to quality control is outstanding.

b. The components of the sample must be completely independent of one another.

c. There should be no underlying differences between conditions under which the data are selected.

d. Conditions must be the same for all items constituting the sample.

When one is attempting to isolate and eliminate assignable causes of variation, as in quality control, he may divide the data into subgroups. These may consist of data from the products of one machine as against another, the parts made from raw material from one source against those from others, or similar differentiations. In collecting data for each of the subgroups he will attempt to meet the requirements stated above. The purpose of using subgroups is to locate significant differences among the samples. Unless each subgroup is sampled according to the principles stated, differences in results may be due to sampling bias instead of differences in the subgroups themselves.

It is much easier to state these requirements to obtain good samples than to justify them. However, most of the stipulations are acceptable intuitively. Clearly, the size of a sample affects its value. One recognizes that when he insists on enough points to define a curve or enough data to give a frequency distribution. But sampling has become a science and should be studied as such.[9]

2. *The most information from given data.* Formulas and graphs are abbreviated methods of presenting data. If one is limited to two or three items to describe a mass of data, which shall he choose? In engineering testing, such as tensile strength of specimens, experience and theory are in accord as to the relative values of different combinations of characteristics to give the most information.

The two measures which convey the most information concerning a collection of data are a measure of central tendency and one of dispersion. For central tendency, the best characteristic is the arithmetic mean. Then come, in order, the median, the mode and the average of the maximum and minimum values. For degree of dispersion the best measure is the standard deviation. Then

[9] See Frederick C. Mills, "Statistical Methods Applied to Economics and Business," Chapter XVIII.

come, in order, the mean deviation and the range. The combination of the arithmetic mean and the standard deviation generally gives the most information possible with two characteristics.[10]

3. *Good data and how to obtain them.* It is not uncommon to hear criticisms of the quality of data on which conclusions are based. Such criticisms are directed either at the failure to follow the principles of sampling stated above or, more frequently, at vitiating factors which affect all the data or a material fraction of them. The vitiating factors require thoughtful study and analysis as aids to their elimination. In engineering work they are frequently designated as *assignable causes*. To present the question broadly Shewhart[11] subdivides errors in data into four types. These are:

A. Constant errors; theoretical, instrumental and personal.

B. Mistakes; manipulative, observational and numerical.

C. Effects of assignable causes.

D. Effect of constant chance system; methodological, instrumental and physiological.

Efforts are mainly directed at the reduction or elimination of types A, B and C. Constant errors are easy to understand. Failure to make the zero setting on an instrument, omission of a significant term from a formula used to reduce the data; these are typical. Mistakes also are easy to comprehend. Checking systems and repetition have done much to eliminate them. The effects of assignable causes here mentioned are those peculiar to the process investigated. For example, the mixing of readings obtained with different grades of raw materials in producing a given piece-part, the indiscriminate use of data from several machines producing the same product, are examples of assignable causes. Improvement through reduction of type D errors is a slow process. One is often satisfied with results if he believes that he has reduced the errors of the data to those of constant chance systems.

Methods of Collecting Data. It might be assumed from the discussion of errors that the engineer is interested only in the data

---

- For detailed discussion of this problem, see "A. S. T. M. Manual on Presentation of Data," p. 31.

[11] See Shewhart, *loc. cit.*, p. 378.

which he or his colleagues obtain through their own experiments and investigations. To some extent, this is the case. However, the increased use of statistical analysis lays emphasis on interpretation of data used, regardless of the source. When one seeks authoritative data in handbooks or in the studies of other investigators, he will still have the problems of evaluation and interpretation. In any case, collection and assembly of data must precede analysis. There are at least three ways to collect data.

1. The data can be obtained directly. In engineering fields this usually means by experiment. In problems of population, in market surveys and in other business, economic and social problems, this frequently involves interviews. A high degree of accuracy is attained in this manner through the acquisition of material direct from the source, and material that otherwise could not be obtained is often uncovered. There is the opportunity to check personally the information acquired. However, only small samples can be gathered because the time and expense involved permit work in only a limited field. Interviews involve a potential subjective source of bias that must not be overlooked.

2. Questionnaires may be used. These have the advantage of making the assembling of data relatively inexpensive, while allowing a large area to be covered easily and quickly. Often, however, the questions are difficult to state and must be correspondingly limited to forms easy to answer. Also, the questions may require a supplementary explanation; a large part of the sample sought will be lost through unanswered questionnaires; and so in many cases the results are unreliable. Also, the reasons for failure to reply may be significant for the data, and they are commonly unknown. Finally, most people dislike questionnaires. This affects the character and validity of their replies. Guesses take the place of recorded data, for example.

Experiment and interview are methods which supply *original* or *primary data*.

3. The most usual method of assembling data is to compile it from *secondary sources* (that is, information assembled by other individuals and agencies). Using such material makes for saving in time and cost, because the data are already compiled. With problems involving large masses of data, it is often the only fea-

sible method. This is true of census data, occupational data, and data which only governmental bureaus or semipublic agencies are in a position to obtain. This may be true of stream flow, rainfall and run-off data for streams. The great trouble with secondary data is the difficulty in verifying the accuracy of the material. It is quite possible that some of the rules for selecting statistical samples may have been violated, and that the violations may not be discovered. However, the investigator is often forced to make use of secondary data because of the technical and financial obstacles that make any other method impossible. The only guarantees he can have as to the quality of his material are the reputation of the group or individual who compiled the data and the evidence supplied by the material itself.

In the next chapter several engineering problems involving statistics will be discussed. These will serve to exemplify the statistical principles outlined in this chapter.

REFERENCES

"A. S. T. M. Manual on Presentation of Data," American Society of Testing Materials (printing of August, 1940, or later).

Barlow, Peter: "Tables of Squares, Cubes, Square Roots, Cube Roots, and Reciprocals," Spar and Chamberlain, New York, 1930.

Deming, W. Edwards, and Raymond T. Birge: "On the Statistical Theory of Errors," Graduate School, Department of Agriculture, Washington, 1937.

Fisher, R. A.: "Statistical Methods for Research Workers," Oliver and Boyd, Edinburgh, 1938.

Mills, Frederick C.: "Statistical Methods Applied to Economics and Business," Henry Holt and Company, Inc., New York, 1938.

Mills, F. C., and D. H. Davenport: "Manual of Problems and Tables in Statistics," Henry Holt and Company, Inc., New York, 1938.

Rietz, H. L.: "Mathematical Statistics," The Open Court Publishing Company, La Salle, Ill., 1927

Yule, G. U., and M. G. Kendall: "An Introduction to the Theory of Statistics," Charles Griffin & Company, Ltd., London, 1939.

Note: For additional references to applications of statistics, see lists following the next two chapters.

PROBLEMS

176. What is the difference between the mean deviation and the standard deviation of a set of statistical data?
177. Three measures of central tendency were discussed here. Can you suggest a possible fourth, based upon maximum and minimum values?

178. For the data on relative density of sea water, given in Table 25, compute the standard deviation. Use two methods: (a) the data as tabulated, (b) the actual values; e.g., 1.02685. What percentage of the values fall within $\pm \sigma$ from the mean?

179. Plot the cumulative survivor curve for radio tubes under certain service conditions, if the replacement experience is as follows:

Month	0–1	1–3	3–5	5–7	7–9	9–11	11–13
Number replaced	0	30	73	85	83	44	20

Total number in test, 335

180. Mention several laboratory experiments for college students in engineering in which you believe the values obtained for some quantity should be treated statistically. Explain.

181. If variations in data secured are solely those due to chance, then the distribution curve for sufficiently large numbers of readings approaches the "normal" distribution curve. For the normal curve, one-half of all values lie between $\pm 0.6740 \sigma$, measured from the mean. Check the values for radio tube replacements of Problem 179 to determine what percentage lie between these limits. Assume distribution within cells to be uniform.

182. In Table 27 of this chapter the standard deviation and mean value of the mortality statistics of electric lamps are given. Estimate from these values and the data what percentages of the values lie between $\pm \sigma$ and $\pm 2 \sigma$. Compare with the percentages to be expected from a normal distribution.

Chapter XIX

LIFE EXPECTANCY OF PHYSICAL PROPERTY

In the preceding chapter, the elements of statistical technique were discussed. Some examples were given to indicate how important this technique is to the engineer, as well as to the statistician and economist. Among the topics presented were: the measures of central tendency that are most commonly used, the measures of dispersion about the central tendency — such as the standard deviation — and a discussion of the collection and presentation of data.

One example to illustrate the technique is the life experience of electric lamps. This is an example of mortality of physical property. In depreciation studies it is important to determine the expected life of property in use.[1] This is particularly true when utility rates are to be set. Such rates are based upon the appraised value of a company's property. This value depends, in turn, on the cost and expected life of the different units of the property. Where the number and cost of the units are both small, estimated life based on experience and judgment will often meet the need. Out of these have come frequently used values for different units, such as 25 years for boilers, 20 years for generators, x years for refrigeration coils and the like. This is the prevailing custom. But to have experience and judgment, we require a firm foundation of fact. Cases in which large numbers of identical or closely similar pieces of equipment are in use call for better methods of determining the actual life of this equipment. The collective effect of error in appraisal may become serious. During recent years the methods of analysis of human mortality, used success-

---

[1] See Chapter VII, Valuation and Depreciation. The student is advised to review Chapter VII as a basis for the present discussion.

351

fully by life insurance and annuity companies, have been applied with similar success to a number of types of physical property. To understand the process, it is convenient to examine first the human mortality tables and curves and the methods used in interpreting them. This will be followed by application to examples of physical property.

Population Charts and Human Mortality Tables. The primary source of knowledge concerning human mortality has been the census. Over a century ago, interest in taxation, economics and industry caused the establishment of census offices in England and the assembly of population data. In the United States, the census is provided for in the Constitution. Mortality tables and curves followed in due course. But good tables for actuarial use are recent. Such use includes the establishment of insurance and retirement annuities rates by scientific use of available data.

Population Statistics. To interpret population statistics for technical use, we follow certain arrangements of the basic data and include some derived quantities. In Tables 28 and 29 will be found population statistics by single year of life for white males and white females in the United States. They were compiled and published by the National Resources Committee in 1937 from life tables prepared by the statistical bureau of the Metropolitan Life Insurance Company. Survivorship graphs for the same data are given in Figures 54 and 55.

The tables start with an arbitrary number of persons at birth (here the number is 100,000) and record the number living as each age is reached. Clearly, the table is a derived one, since the practical difficulties of obtaining the data on 100,000 specified persons during 100 years would be insurmountable. The number of persons alive as each age is reached is designated by l_x. The column headed q_x gives the ratio of the number dying during a year to the number alive at the beginning of the year. For example, in Table 28, $q_{25} = .00366$. This is $(l_{25} - l_{26}) \div l_{25} = (87,605 - 87,284) \div 87,605 = 0.00366$. It is the average probability of death for an individual during the year. The probability of death for any given individual may easily differ from this average because of environment, physical condition and prospects. The column headed e°_x gives the average (arithmetic mean) duration of

Age	q_x	l_x	e^0_x	Age	q_x	l_x	e^0_x
0	0.06086	100,000	59.31	50	0.01272	74,528	21.54
1	0.00988	93,914	62.12	51	1361	73,580	20.81
2	533	92,986	61.73	52	1460	72,579	20 09
3	373	92,490	61.06	53	1569	71,519	19.38
4	300	92,145	60.29	54	1689	70,397	18.68
5	251	91,869	59.47	55	1819	69,208	17.99
6	218	91,638	58.62	56	1960	67,949	17.32
7	192	91,438	57.74	57	2111	66,617	16.65
8	166	91,262	56.85	58	2272	65,211	16.00
9	151	91,111	55.95	59	2446	63,729	15.36
10	145	90,973	55.03	60	2635	62,170	14.73
11	147	90,841	54.11	61	2841	60,532	14.12
12	156	90,707	53.19	62	3065	58,812	13.52
13	171	90,565	52.27	63	3311	57,009	12.93
14	189	90,410	51.36	64	3579	55,121	12.35
15	210	90,239	50.46	65	3870	53,148	11.79
16	233	90,049	49.56	66	4186	51,091	11.25
17	255	89,839	48.68	67	4528	48,952	10.72
18	276	89,610	47.80	68	4897	46,735	10.20
19	295	89,363	46.93	69	5298	44,446	9.70
20	312	89,099	46.07	70	5733	42,091	9.22
21	327	88,821	45.21	71	6208	39,678	8.75
22	340	88,531	44.36	72	6725	37,215	8.29
23	350	88,230	43.51	73	7290	34,712	7.86
24	359	87,921	42.66	74	7905	32,181	7.43
25	366	87,605	41.81	75	8575	29,637	7.03
26	373	87,284	40.96	76	9304	27,096	6.64
27	381	86,958	40.12	77	0.10096	24,575	6.27
28	390	86,627	39.27	78	.10953	22,094	5.92
29	400	86,289	38.42	79	.11869	19,674	5.59
30	412	85,944	37.57	80	.12838	17,339	5.27
31	426	85,590	36.72	81	.13852	15,113	4.97
32	442	85,225	35.88	82	.14905	13,020	4.69
33	461	84,848	35.04	83	.15992	11,079	4.43
34	483	84,457	34.20	84	.17123	9,307	4.18
35	507	84,049	33.36	85	.18311	7,713	3.94
36	535	83,623	32.53	86	.19566	6,301	3.71
37	566	83,176	31.70	87	.20903	5,068	3.49
38	600	82,705	30.88	88	.22333	4,009	3.27
39	638	82,209	30.06	89	.23866	3,114	3.07
40	679	81,685	29.25	90	.25513	2,371	2.88
41	723	81,130	28.45	91	.27284	1,766	2.69
42	769	80,543	27.65	92	.29189	1,284	2.51
43	818	79,924	26.86	93	.31238	909	2.34
44	870	79,270	26.08	94	.33441	625	2.18
45	925	78,580	25.30	95	0.35809	416	2.03
46	985	77,853	24.53	96	.38350	267	1.88
47	0.01048	77,086	23.77	97	.41077	165	1.74
48	1117	76,278	23.02	98	.43998	97	1.60
49	1191	75,426	22.27	99	.47124	54	1.48
				100	.50465	29	1.33

TABLE 29. POPULATION STATISTICS COMPILED BY NATIONAL RESOURCES COMMITTEE, OCTOBER, 1937 WHITE FEMALES, UNITED STATES

Age	q_x	l_x	e^0_x	Age	q_x	l_x	e^0_x
0	0.04821	100,000	62.83	50	0.00955	78,795	23.41
1	0.00871	95,179	64.99	51	1023	78,043	22.63
2	465	94,350	64.55	52	1099	77,245	21.86
3	330	93,911	63.85	53	1184	76,396	21.09
4	255	93,601	63.06	54	1278	75,491	20.34
5	208	93,362	62.22	55	1382	74,526	19.60
6	178	93,168	61.35	56	1496	73,496	18.86
7	155	93,002	60.46	57	1620	72,396	18.14
8	130	92,858	59.55	58	1754	71,223	17.43
9	116	92,737	58.63	59	1902	69,974	16.74
10	109	92,629	57.70	60	2063	68,643	16.05
11	110	92,528	56.76	61	2239	67,227	15.38
12	117	92,426	55.82	62	2433	65,722	14.72
13	129	92,318	54.89	63	2645	64,123	14.07
14	144	92,199	53.96	64	2878	62,427	13.44
15	163	92,066	53.03	65	3134	60,630	12.83
16	183	91,916	52.12	66	3415	58,730	12.23
17	205	91,748	51.21	67	3723	56,724	11.64
18	227	91,560	50.32	68	4061	54,612	11.07
19	249	91,352	49.43	69	4430	52,394	10.52
20	270	91,125	48.55	70	4836	50,073	9.98
21	289	90,879	47.68	71	5282	47,651	9.46
22	305	90,616	46.82	72	5770	45,134	8.96
23	318	90,340	45.96	73	6304	42,530	8.48
24	328	90,053	45.11	74	6889	39,849	8.02
25	336	89,758	44.25	75	7527	37,104	7.58
26	343	89,456	43.40	76	8223	34,311	7.15
27	350	89,149	42.55	77	8979	31,490	6.75
28	358	88,837	41.70	78	9799	28,663	6.36
29	366	88,519	40.85	79	0.10676	25,854	6.00
30	374	88,195	39.99	80	.11606	23,094	5.66
31	383	87,865	39.14	81	.12583	20,414	5.34
32	394	87,528	38.29	82	.13599	17,845	5.03
33	405	87,183	37.44	83	.14652	15,418	4.75
34	417	86,830	36.59	84	.15747	13,159	4.48
35	431	86,468	35.74	85	.16093	11,087	4.22
36	447	86,095	34.89	86	.18097	9,214	3.97
37	464	85,710	34.05	87	.19369	7,547	3.74
38	485	85,312	33.21	88	.20716	6,085	3.52
39	507	84,898	32.36	89	.22145	4,824	3.31
40	532	84,468	31.53	90	.23662	3,756	3.11
41	560	84,019	30.69	91	.25275	2,867	2.92
42	590	83,548	29.86	92	.26990	2,142	2.74
43	624	83,055	29.04	93	.28813	1,564	2.56
44	660	82,537	28.22	94	.30752	1,113	2.40
45	699	81,992	27.40	95	0.32812	771	2.24
46	742	81,419	26.59	96	.35000	510	2.10
47	788	80,815	25.78	97	.37324	337	1.95
48	838	80,178	24.99	98	.39789	211	1.82
49	894	79,506	24.19	99	.42402	127	1.70
				100	.45171	73	1.51

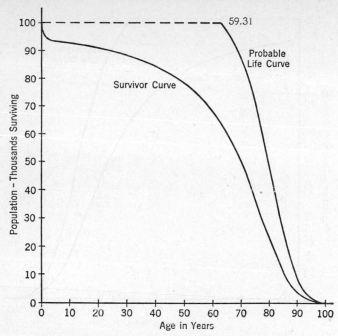

FIGURE 54. Population statistics — white males.

life beyond the given age of all persons alive at the given age. Thus $e°_{25} = 41.81$. This means that the average length of life of the 87,605 men living at age 25 will be $25 + 41.81 = 66.81$. Note the difference between this value and the median. The median is the age corresponding to $\frac{1}{2}(87,605) = 43,802$ living. This is 69 +, instead of 66.81. The value of $e°_x$ is called the *expectancy*.

The methods of determining charges for life insurance require special tables to simplify computations. If a variable annual charge were made, it would be q_x per dollar of insurance per person. This amount varies from year to year, increasing with age. Since most people favor equal annual premiums, as they are called, it is necessary:

1. To multiply the value of q_{x+k} by v^k to obtain its present value.

2. To sum the products, $v^k q_{x+k}$, from the age x to the end of the table (from $k = 0$ to $k = 100 - x$). The sum is the *net single premium* for insurance of 1.

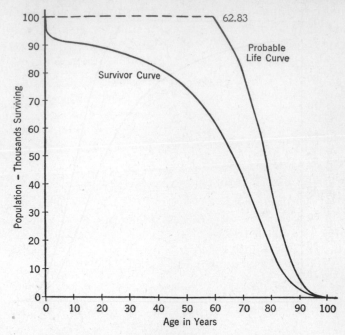

FIGURE 55. Population statistics — white females.

3. To determine the value of annual payments during the life of the insured to have the same present value as the net single premium.

For details of these computations the student is referred to texts on life insurance or the mathematical theory of investment.[2] Note also that costs as here determined allow no margin for error and no charge for cost of operation and management of the company.

It is not possible for the actuary to determine at what age an individual will die. The charts can only indicate that a definite proportion of a large population will die each year. The important thing about the curves is that they provide data from which it is possible to predict with fair accuracy the life and death rates of groups of people.

It is interesting to note that over the entire span of life women have a longer average life than men. Only a few years ago many

[2] See T. M. Putnam, "Mathematical Theory of Finance."

insurance companies did not issue life insurance policies to women, or issued them at increased premium charges over those for men. This was before adequate development and use of mortality tables for women were achieved. It was believed that the addition of childbirth to the other possibilities of death made a woman's life less secure than a man's. Since the development of the separate mortality tables for men and women, it appears that at equal rates women are better risks. Even during the child-bearing period, women have lower mortality rates than men.

The shape of this ogive curve (see Figures 54 and 55) is indicative of the rate of death: the steeper the curve, the greater the number of deaths per year. The curve is exceptionally steep during the first year. The death rate of infants during that year is especially high. For the first few days, weeks and months of life, the baby faces tremendous obstacles to continued life. After the first year, however, the curve drops less steeply until about the tenth year, when the rate of death is at its lowest. After the tenth year the deaths per year again increase and continue to do so up to about age 70.

For scientists a table of the probability of death at each age is interesting, but not informative as to its causes. What risks are especially great at each of those ages, what diseases are most deadly for a person at any special phase of life?

The diagram of Figure 56 was developed to aid in noting certain essential features from the curves showing causes of death. This line diagram indicates, for the year 1930 and for each of the principal causes of death, the range of ages about the median age of incidence within which fall two-thirds of all deaths from each disease shown. This is an interesting way of presenting data, using the median and the range. The intermediate numbers give the median age.

The chart shows at a glance a rather irregular staircase of diseases, beginning with the typical childhood disease, diphtheria. It ranges through the normal diseases and ends with the typical diseases of old age, those which affect the blood circulation.

If these population statistics are compared with those of earlier periods, a general trend for the average age at death to move higher and higher will be noted. Also, deaths now result from a

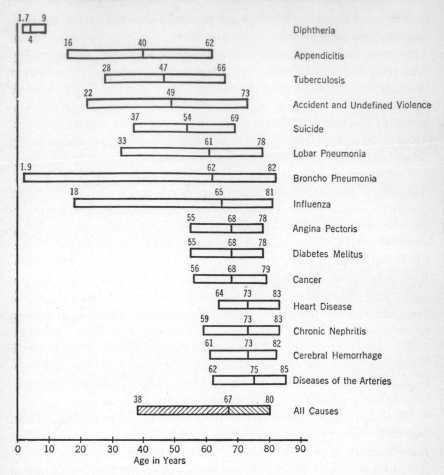

FIGURE 56. Age concentration of death from principal causes, United States exclusive of Texas, white males.

somewhat different order of causes. For example, fewer lives are being sacrificed to tuberculosis than formerly, but the losses from heart diseases are considerably increased. This is a significant shift, for heart diseases are generally afflictions of old age, whereas tuberculosis claims victims in the young and most productive ages. Further, the increase in the number of older people in proportion to total population, resulting from the increase in average length of life, leaves a greater proportion of the population open to attacks by such diseases.

The increase in the average age at death has created an interesting and perhaps serious problem for our nation. Our population increases have slowed down because of reduced immigration and the declining birth rate. However, on account of the longer average life of the individual, the number of persons of working age and their percentage of the total population have increased greatly. A memorandum of the National Resources Planning Board on "Population Growth and Unemployment" (issued March 1, 1940) is of interest:

... while the total population increased about nine million from 1930–1940, the number of persons in the working span of life, ages 20 to 64, increased nine and one-half million. Although the whole population gained only about 7 percent over 1930, the number of available workers increased by about 14 percent, approximately twice as fast . . . But since 1930, the volume and rate of population growth have declined rapidly, whereas the number of potential workers has continued to increase at about the same volume as in the last three decades. . . . Here is one of the contributing causes of continuing unemployment. In order to keep the number of unemployed from mounting each year, new jobs now have to be provided about twice as fast in comparison with population increase as in previous decades. . . . Forecasts of future population trends . . . show that the number of persons, ages 20 to 64, will probably increase more rapidly than the whole population for at least another decade.

So it can be seen readily that population statistics are significant. They set the rates of insurance policies, and they affect governmental policy in relation to industry and to unemployment. Yet it is only in recent years that the study of population statistics has been emphasized as fundamental to policy determinations.

Mortality of Physical Equipment. Human beings live, grow old and die. We record the statistics of human mortality and make many uses of the results. Physical property goes through life phases parallel to those of people. The wasting processes of obsolescence and decay are going on constantly in industry. The consideration of these processes is one of the most important problems facing economists, accountants, businessmen and engineers today. Until recently no method of determining, rather than guessing, these factors has been generally accepted. In fact, even now it is impossible to say that adequate work has been done in the field. Some attempts have been made to eliminate the subjective aspect of figuring life expectancy and rate of depreciation of physical property, but difficulties which seem almost insurmountable are the establishment of a criterion for obsolescence and means of measuring the productive life of an item of equipment.

Those who have considered the problem of life expectancy of physical property have set themselves three main objectives:

1. The establishment of mortality tables of physical property on an actuarial basis.

2. The development of accurate knowledge concerning the life characteristics of physical property.

3. The establishment of relations which permit effective use of the knowledge obtained and analyzed.

Before we can obtain accurate knowledge concerning life characteristics of physical property, and before we can establish relationships and laws for the various characteristics, we must have adequate statistical data concerning the actual life histories of the various types of industrial and engineering equipment. Yet, most manufacturing and industrial concerns have devoted little time to the collection of such material. It is only through the study of actual records of the service lives of large numbers of items of given types that we can obtain the information from which accurate and objective allowances for physical depreciation can be made.

So far the lack of necessary statistical life experience data has prevented the compilation of extensive mortality tables of physical property. It is incorrect to say, however, that engineers have not realized the importance of this problem. In 1903, John W. Alvord published tables of the life experience of 48 waterworks pumps and 32 waterworks boilers, although he did not develop a mortality table or utilize the data he had secured to calculate expectancies and probable life. In 1905 Mr. O. Christiani published an article on the life experience of 284,707 wooden poles, classifying them according to the type of preservative treatment they had received. From these data Mr. Christiani calculated the average life of the different types of poles and drew conclusions as to the economic value of the different methods of treatment. Because of the conclusions drawn from the data, the report has the honor to be one of the earliest examples of life statistics of physical property.

In 1913 Edwin Gruhl did some work with life statistics and called attention to the similarity between mortality curves of physical property and the theoretical normal probability curve and also the human mortality curve.

In 1916 the New York Telephone Company, in a rate case before the New Jersey Board of Public Utility Commissioners, presented the most complete and comprehensive mortality study of physical property developed to that time. Their computations showed only the average life of each type of physical item. They made no analysis of expectancy or probable life.

In 1928 the American Telephone and Telegraph Company presented testimony before the Interstate Commerce Commission on the depreciation charges of telephone companies. The testimony showed how many property units were placed in service during each calendar year, and how many of these were retired from service during the same and each subsequent calendar year.

For purposes of analysis the number of units in each was replaced by cost in dollars on a uniform cost level. It was stated that "there is a definite analogy between the types of data analyzed by the life insurance actuary and the type of data we [the telephone company] have." Further, definite mortality rates were determined and presented which enabled the company to figure depreciation on a definite basis. However, even such advance is only a beginning, and much further progress must be made before the actuarial basis of mortality tables of physical property can be considered established.

The Individual Unit Method. The simplest method for compiling life experience data of a given type of physical property is to record the age in years of each individual unit of property of that class as it goes out of service. This is known as the *individual unit method* of mortality table compilation. When a large number of such individual lives have thus been recorded, the data can be summarized and presented as shown in Table 26 of the last chapter concerning the mortality of electric lamps. The results are shown in Figure 52 of the same chapter.

Note the similarity of the survivor and probable life curves of electric lamps to those for men and women. The principal difference is the presence of the initial sharp drop in the human mortality curve, which does not occur in the physical property curve. This is a characteristic difference for physical property curves, although not a necessary one. Physical property, like electric lamps, might have a considerable percentage of units which would not last long. With modern methods of inspection, however, articles which need early replacement are being weeded out in advance of recorded use. Hence, the curve may be considered as analogous to the human mortality curve starting at age two or five, for example.

The data of the table reveal the inherent difficulties of the individual unit method. Note that data were apparently taken up to 1,199.5 hours of life only. When the number replaced in the 100-hour class interval, 1,099.5–1,199.5 was found to be less than the number in the preceding class interval, the mode was assumed passed. The remaining data were assumed to repeat in reverse order the experience of the first eight cells (or class intervals). This means that the cost and practical difficulties encountered in getting actual data until all lamps have burned out, been broken or thrown away were considered too great. Probably the results were needed at a given time and further delay was not feasible. Clearly, the value of the curve as a whole is reduced by the doubt concerning the last eight cell values.

From the discussion of distribution curves in the preceding chapter, please note the following practical points:

1. Readings are to the nearest hour. Hence, the class interval is chosen so as to leave no doubt where every entry goes.

2. The midpoint of the first interval is taken as 49.5, in spite of the arithmetical discrepancy. The readings it represents are those from 0 to 99.

3. In plotting the curve, the midpoint of the class interval is used to represent all the lamps that went out during the interval. This assumes uniform distribution of the lifetimes about the median time. Since such distribution does not usually exist, this assumption introduces a slight error. There are methods of making allowance for this, but they are seldom needed in engineering applications.

As has been implied, the greatest disadvantage of the individual unit method of establishing mortality tables is that many years of observation are required before any adequate results can be obtained. Theoretically, one should keep at the job until the last unit has been replaced. With railway ties, telephone poles, electric cable and similar physical units, this method would call for continuing the experiment until — in all probability — the need for the results had passed. Further, design practices change and the data, as finally obtained, would picture equipment no longer representative. On this account, it is customary to gather data on material of all ages at one time for a period of several years. The annual rates of replacement are used to derive the desired mortality tables and curves. Thus the *annual rate method* is obtained.

Mortality Curves by Annual Rate Method. There is no better illustration of this method than the compilation of human mortality curves. To wait 100 years for a human mortality curve by the individual unit method would supply no life insurance or old age pension rates now. Further, the conditions of life would probably change so much as to invalidate the results. The average age (expectancy at age 0) has increased 50% in about a century from approximately 40 to about 60 years.

Procedure is roughly as follows:

1. A period for obtaining the data is decided upon. From 1900–1915, for example, a cooperative study gave the American-Canadian mortality curves. The period should be long enough to give general instead of temporary characteristics.

2. Groups of satisfactory sample size at different ages are selected and the mortality of each recorded year by year for the period. The selection is important. It should be broadly representative. The principles of obtaining good data, as outlined in the last chapter, should be followed. This requires careful study.

3. From the data, the percentage of mortality at each age is computed. This is the percentage replaced during the year in terms of the number at the beginning of that year and is designated q_x.

4. Assuming 100% at the initial age — usually 0 — a survivor

curve is computed with percentages as ordinates, age as abscissas. This reads as follows:

Annual Rate Method

Age	Percentage	Method of obtaining
0	100	Starting values
1	$(100 - q_0)$	Subtract percentage dying
2	$(100 - q_0)(100 - q_1)$	Percentage surviving of percentage surviving previous, year
3	$(100 - q_0)(100 - q_1)(100 - q_2)$, etc.	Ditto

5. When this curve has been obtained, the vertical scale is changed to represent any arbitrary initial number of cases. In human mortality curves it is usually 100,000. The number should be justified to a degree by the volume of data assembled and the consistency of results.

The details of the process are laborious. They will not be examined here. In physical property curves there is the added complication that units have different dollar values. To take account of this, one can weight each unit with its cost. A unit costing five dollars can be considered as five one-dollar units. By applying this to all the units, one obtains a table of dollar entries, where each dollar needs to be assigned an age. It represents a dollar unit of the age indicated. Although the resulting computations are involved, the principle is clear.[3] Examples are cumbersome and none will be given here.

Average Life and Expectancy. To date, the most important use of physical mortality curves has been in the valuation of property. For this purpose it is desirable, as stated earlier, to know the probable remaining life of each unit of property, making due allowance for its present age. Let us return to the study of the electric lamps. What one obtains and desires is hours of service from each lamp. The result for the group is therefore measurable as lamp-hours of service, the product of the number of lamps by the average number of hours the group furnished.

[3] For an example of this, see Kurtz, "Mortality Curves of Physical Property," p. 62. The example treats the retirements of water stations in a large railroad system where the values of the stations differ. See also Grant, "Principles of Engineering Economy," p. 242.

In terms of the survivor curve, Figure 57, this is the area under the curve. For a given age, the area under the portion of the survivor curve to the right of the ordinate at that age gives the service in lamp-hours provided by the lamps surviving at the age selected. Hence, this gives a rule by which one may obtain the average life, beyond a given age, of all units reaching the age. This is the *expectancy* at the given life.

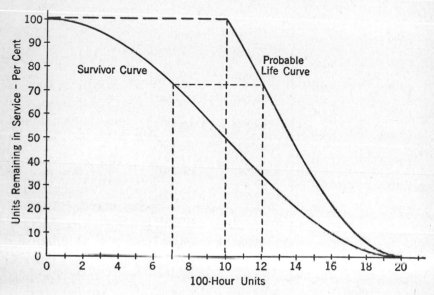

FIGURE 57. Survivor and probable life curves for electric lamps.

Expectancy at a Given Life. To obtain: Divide the area to the right of the ordinate at the given life by the value of that ordinate. The sum of this value, which is the expectancy, and the life at which it is obtained, is called the *probable life*. In Figure 57, the probable life curve is to the right of the survivor curve.

Examine the curves of Figure 57, and see Table 30. The computation of expectancy and probable life for the electric lamp mortality case is done by the area method. The survivor curve is treated as a broken line joining points at the class interval boundaries. Beginning at the right end of the curve, this gives the ordinate 0 at life 1,999.5 hours; the ordinate 755 or 1.0% at life 1,899.5 hours, etc., back to 75,614 or 100.0% at life −0.5 hours (zero life). (See Table 30.) These values are for the survivor curve. For the probable life curve, sum the areas beginning at the right, and divide the sum of the partial areas back to a given life by the value of the ordinate at that life. For life 699.5 hours,

TABLE 30. MORTALITY OF ELECTRIC LAMPS:
PROBABLE LIFE CURVE

Life in hours	Lamps in service	Partial areas	Sum of partial areas	Expectancy	Probable life
1,999.5	0			0	1,999.5
		37,750	37,750		
1,899.5	755			50.0	1,949.5
		132,600	170,350		
1,799.5	1,897			89.8	1,889.3
		306,700	477,050		
1,699.5	4,237			112.5	1,812.0
		589,800	1,066,850		
1,599.5	7,559			141.1	1,740.6
		944,650	2,011,500		
1,499.5	11,334			177.2	1,676.7
		1,348,550	3,360,050		
1,399.5	15,637			214.9	1,614.4
		1,812,850	5,172,900		
1,299.5	20,620			250.5	1,550.0
		2,337,550	7,510,450		
1,199.5	26,131			287.4	1,486.9
		2,905,000	10,415,450		
1,099.5	31,969			325.8	1,425.3
		3,491,300	13,906,750		
999.5	37,857			367.5	1,367.0
		4,080,100	17,986,850		
899.5	43,745			411.2	1,310.7
		4,661,400	22,648,250		
799.5	49,483			457.7	1,257.2
		5,223,850	27,872,100		
699.5	54,994			506.8	1,206.3
		5,748,550	33,620,650		
599.5	59,977			560.6	1,160.1
		6,212,850	39,833,500		
499.5	64,280			619.7	1,119.2
		6,616,750	46,450,250		
399.5	68,055			682.5	1,082.0
		6,971,600	53,421,850		
299.5	71,377			748.5	1,048.0
		7,254,700	60,676,550		
199.5	73,717			823.1	1,022.6
		7,428,800	68,105,350		
99.5	74,859			909.8	1,009.3
		7,523,650	75,629,000		
−9.5	75,614			1,000.2	999.7

divide the sum of the partial areas to the right by the number of lamps in service at 699.5 hours, 54,994, to obtain the expectancy, 506.8 hours. The average total life of lamps in service at 699.5 hours is therefore 699.5 + 506.8 = 1,206.3 hours.

The computation is easily verified, using the trapezoidal areas between ordinates.

Use of Mortality Curves for Valuation. For an example of the possible use of mortality curves for valuation, consider the equipment of a telephone company in a small city. It is desired to estimate the value of the plant. The cost of each item is determined, and its present value is computed by determining its life and subtracting depreciation for the period of service rendered. The straight-line or sinking fund method may be used. For practical purposes the straight-line method is often preferable, since it furnishes a "hedge" against unforeseen obsolescence. Court decisions generally have favored the sinking fund method. Choose one method and proceed. Apply it to buildings and other items that may occur in small numbers, using more or less arbitrary life values. Suppose that you find in the list of equipment the following items:

> Telephone instruments, 13,000 at $15.
> Telephone cable (50 pairs), 200 miles at $600 per 1,000 feet (in place).
> Aerial copper wire, #12, 650 circuit miles at $60 per mile (in place).
> Class A wooden poles, 15,000 at $25 per mile (in place).

For some of these, the cost of maintaining mortality data has been found too great to justify any possible gain in accuracy in estimating life. Assume, however, that mortality data have been kept on a sufficient number of wooden poles, properly selected to constitute a fair sample, to permit their use for life determination of all. Procedure for use of the mortality data for the wooden poles would then be:

1. Plot the survivor and probable life curves for the poles.
2. Determine the number of poles of each age.
3. From the curves determine the expectancy and probable life of each group.
4. Determine by the appropriate depreciation method the present value of each group.
5. Sum the values for the composite value.

Values and Limitations of the Method. The mortality curve method has several values, the chief of which is its logical soundness. The use of life data instead of conclusions based on a few isolated cases or general reasoning is sound engineering. It is also a direct and defensible method. The analogy with human mortality data and their use is strong justification. There are, however, several defects which have prevented its general use as advocates of the method foresaw a decade ago. First, the mortality data must be collected. This may prove more troublesome and expensive than the added accuracy of the results will justify. Further, methods and materials change and thereby affect the lives of the units. The telephone handset of today may be more or less rugged than that of 10 years ago. It may have a greater or a smaller rate of obsolescence. To build a table of data mixing several types of handsets may give misleading results. Next, the method has a sense of unreality to many who consider it too theoretical. Finally, to meet the objection of high cost, it is often necessary to resort to samples. For example, some railroads have kept records of the life of cross ties of certain sample miles of track, from which conclusions were drawn concerning the entire system. Such methods require justification of the sampling procedure. Much improvement in sampling methods and in the use of such methods has occurred during the past decade. The next chapter will deal with quality control of manufactured product, a subject in which sound sampling is of first importance. Perhaps wider understanding of sampling methods will advance the use of the method of mortality data of physical property — a method which is both ingenious and rational.

REFERENCES

Grant, Eugene L.: "Principles of Engineering Economy," The Ronald Press Company, New York, 1938.

Kurtz, Edwin B.: "Life Expectancy of Physical Property," The Ronald Press Company, New York, 1930.

Kurtz, Edwin B.: "Science of Valuation and Depreciation," The Ronald Press Company, New York, 1937.

Dodge, H. F., and H. G. Romig: "A Method of Sampling Inspection," Bell System Technical Journal, October. 1929.

Robertson, W. L.: "Quality Control by Sampling," Factory and Industrial Management, September, October, 1928.

Putnam, T. M.: "Mathematical Theory of Finance," John Wiley & Sons, Inc., New York, 1925.

National Resources Committee, Washington, "The Problems of a Changing Population," 1937. (This can be had with mortality tables.)

PROBLEMS

183. The following are human mortality data compiled during the period 1900–1915 for American and Canadian white males. The table starts at age 15 and terminates at age 100.

    a. Explain how the table may have been compiled.

    b. What method must be used?

    c. Plot the survivor curve, using five-year intervals.

    d. Plot the probable life curve, five-year intervals.

    e. Compare expectancy at ages 15, 25, 50, 65 and 80 with corresponding values of Table 28.

AMERICAN–CANADIAN MORTALITY, 1900–1915, WHITE MALES

Age	Number of living	Age	Number of living	Age	Number of living	Age	Number of living
15	100,000	36	91,554	58	72,943	79	20,408
16	99,654	37	91,102	59	71,301	80	17,843
17	99,302	38	90,636	60	69,555	81	15,421
18	98,942	39	90,154	61	67,699	82	13,163
19	98,575	40	89,653	62	65,734	83	11,085
20	98,199	41	89,129	63	63,658	84	9,200
21	97,814	42	88,580	64	61,470	85	7,515
22	97,421	43	88,001	65	59,172	86	6,034
23	97,020	44	87,390	66	56,766	87	4,756
24	96,614	45	86,742	67	54,258	88	3,675
25	96,203	46	86,053	68	51,652	89	2,778
26	95,788	47	85,320	69	48,958	90	2,051
27	95,371	48	84,537	70	46,185	91	1,476
28	94,952	49	83,701	71	43,346	92	1,034
29	94,533	50	82,805	72	40,455	93	702
30	94,114	51	81,846	73	37,529	94	462
31	93,694	52	80,820	74	34,587	95	294
32	93,274	53	79,719	75	31,650	96	180
33	92,853	54	78,541	76	28,740	97	106
34	92,427	55	77,278	77	25,880	98	59
35	91,994	56	75,928	78	23,094	99	32
		57	74,484			100	16

184. Discuss the problem of compiling mortality data for automobiles. What are the difficulties and limitations? What use can be made of "blue book" quotations?

185. In the illustrative example in the text, the valuation of certain telephone company property was discussed. Assume the mortality on telephone cable to be as follows:

Years in use	1	2	3	4	5	6	7	8	9	10	11	12	13
Per cent displaced each year	0.4	0.8	1.5	1.9	2.1	2.9	3.4	4.0	4.5	5.1	5.3	5.9	6.5
Years in use	14	15	16	17	18	19	20	21	22	23	24	25	26	27
Per cent displaced each year	7.0	7.3	7.1	6.5	5.4	5.0	4.1	3.4	2.6	2.4	1.9	1.4	1.1	0.5

Assume the installation to consist of 200 miles of 50-pair aerial cable, costing $600 per 1,000 feet in place.

a. Assume 12% of the installation to be 15 years old. Find its expectancy and present value, using both straight-line and sinking fund methods.

b. If life for all the cable is taken arbitrarily at 18 years, what is the present value of the 12% which is 15 years old? Use again both straight-line and sinking fund methods.

Chapter XX

STATISTICAL METHODS IN ENGINEERING QUALITY CONTROL

In the last chapter the statistical method of determining the life expectancy of physical property was presented. The use of the method in valuation and depreciation was indicated. It was shown that the statistical approach gave defensible values for expected life and that it furnished a rational basis for aiding in the valuation of property.

Now consider the problem of engineering quality control. This problem is even more dependent upon the use of statistical techniques than the determination of life expectancy of physical property. It is also a problem of more general importance. First, some of the characteristics and principles of mass production will be examined.

Mass Production and Quantity Production. In large scale production operations it is important to distinguish between those in which the quantity manufactured is increased by processes of enlargement and multiplication chiefly, and others in which the methods used for large quantities are specially devised to suit the quantity. For example, in manufacturing aircraft, the output of a factory could presumably be increased 10 times by simply enlarging the plant to 10 times its original size, using 10 times as many machines, 10 times as many men, and perhaps 10 times as much material. Where this is the principal method used, it gives *quantity production*. To obtain *mass production*, as now understood, the methods would be adjusted to the expected output. First, interchangeability of parts would probably be stressed so that parts manufacture would be specialized and, if desired, separated from assembly. Next, the machines and tools would be

371

selected to give economy of time, material and labor for the quantities needed. A zinc die may have met the smaller need; a more expensive cast iron or steel die may be much more economical for the larger. Operations may be rearranged to suit assembly convenience. This often requires introducing heat-treating and machining operations into an assembly order in such sequence that it is no longer best to have a machine shop, a press room, a heat-treating room in which all such operations are centralized.

Interchangeability. Generally speaking, the most important element in production in large quantities is interchangeability. This quality is a characteristic of large scale American manufacture. Its advantages are well discussed by several authors.[1] In the automobile world, the most striking demonstration was made some years ago when eight Cadillac engines were disassembled, the parts thrown into bins, reassembled at random, and the engines reused without special adjustment. The whole practice of spare parts distribution is based on interchangeability.

Even in the industries operating on a mass production basis there is a good deal of variation. These variations among the products create many problems. When a high standard of uniformity is required, the variations result in large percentages of rejections. In themselves, these rejections represent substantial costs. To locate defectives, there must be a large scale sampling and inspection system, and this too adds to the cost of the product. The great problem is the lack of conformity of the product to the design.

Another characteristic of mass production is the assembly line or its equivalent. This is the outgrowth of efforts to bring materials to the man, instead of the reverse. One investigator reported a few years ago that "eighty-five per cent of all manufacturing effort is devoted to picking up something in one place and putting it down in another at the right time." Time and motion study reveals the general prevalence of unnecessary motion. Many systems of supply have been devised to reduce loss of time and expenditure of human energy in reaching for things and picking

---

[1] See especially article on this development by J. W. Roe, "Interchangeable Manufacture," Mechanical Engineering, October, 1937, pp. 755–758.

them up. Present practice emphasizes (a) the reduction of the use of muscular and nervous energy by workers, (b) the use of machine power wherever possible in place of muscular energy and (c) the use of automatic operation and control.

It is striking to note the rapid increase in the amount of electric energy per worker used in a given industry. If energy only is needed, the difference in cost is amazing. One horsepower will cost about 35 cents per 24-hour day, whether supplied by electric motor or oil engine. If supplied by men, it will require approximately 10 men continuously. At $5 per man per eight-hour shift, the cost of one horsepower for 24 hours is about $150. For this reason and many others, all possible energy expenditure should be by machines. By raising the work to the workers' level, by using conveyors to supply parts and assemblies, by the development of power tools of all sizes and by automatic control, mass production has developed.

Quality Variation in Output. At least three factors may be conceived in determining the quality variation of output. The effect of stable or major causes inherent in producing the article is the first. Such causes include the heat-treating and alloying processes with steel. The changes caused by these processes are desired and may be essential to the satisfactory performance of the product. Harder and stronger steel may be required. If the process is controlled, so that the results are closely predictable, these major or stable causes, essential to the product, need only be checked for regularity. Variation due to "assignable" causes is the second. This variation, if essentially uniform, can be classified as stable. However, an assignable cause is usually one which causes irregularity and variations in the product. Discovery and elimination of these is a principal task in quality control. A remediable defect in one of several machines, a mixture of raw materials of different characteristics, a variation due to time of day, unsatisfactory light or noise environment of some workers; these and many others are the assignable causes which we seek to remove. The third factor is the chance variation. When processes have been stabilized and assignable causes eliminated or reduced, there remain a large number of small variations — sometimes plus, sometimes minus — that cannot be removed.

It is said that a process is brought to a state of quality control when the variations remaining appear to be predominantly of this type. One must then apply techniques based upon the study of what should happen if the remaining causes of variation are chance variations — in other words, if they obey the laws of chance. When this practice works it does not prove that the remaining causes are merely those due to chance. However, it gives a practical method of procedure, because the mathematics of chance is well advanced. Fortunately, the combined processes of sampling, computing averages and deviations of sample data, and making certain graphs from the results has commonly furnished clues to the presence of assignable causes. Further study has frequently led to the detection and removal of assignable causes and then to the desired condition of quality control.

Specification, Manufacture and Inspection. Mass production secures the necessary parts, subassemblies and complete units by three steps:

1. Specification.
2. Manufacture.
3. Inspection.

Steel rivets for a bridge are designed. Specifications are written and working drawings prepared. The rivets are manufactured, perhaps by the hundred thousand, and they are periodically inspected. Inspection includes checking dimensions, strength and uniformity. Some of the tests are nondestructive. They could be carried out on all the rivets, although to do so would usually be too expensive. But rivets tested directly for strength are destroyed. We thus find that, in general, destructive tests can be applied only to samples. The ones tested are not the ones finally used. Consequently, some means must be found to prophesy the performance of those not tested from the results of sample testing. To be scientific the forecast should be quantitative. Hence, both sampling and testing are organized so that the producer and the buyer can be assured, let us say, that the probability of any rivet accepted having a tensile strength less than a prescribed minimum is less than a given value, say 0.01. To obtain this result requires use of applications of statistical methods developed during the past 20 years. In brief, the methods may be used:

1. To keep the probability of defective parts below an assigned value, where complete inspection would destroy the product.

2. To keep the probability of defective parts below an assigned value, where complete inspection is unnecessary and uneconomical.

3. To coordinate the steps, specification, manufacture and inspection, so as to reduce costs, save material and improve uniformity.

The Statistical Method and the Control Chart. A full discussion of the statistical method as applied to quality control is impracticable and undesirable in an introductory text on engineering economy. An outline of the method, with application to an example or two, will be presented.

Tolerances. In the discussion of rivet manufacture above, it was tacitly assumed that the manufacturing process did not give a uniform product. In fact, all fabrication gives variable products. For interchangeability the variations must be controlled. When one buys new pistons for an automobile engine, they will differ in size from the old ones. If the cylinders have been rebored and oversize pistons are purchased, they will differ from the quoted specifications. The important question is, "how much?" To use them acceptably, a difference of a few thousandths of an inch in diameter causes no trouble. They neither bind nor "rattle." This fact of variation was not always understood. Many times in the past specifications called for "exact" diameters, lengths, weights, strengths and other properties. It was necessary to recognize tolerances at the specification stage, as well as in the shop, before the struggle for accuracy won battles. The best means of improving accuracy is a study of the causes of variation. This requires knowledge of the variations themselves, to be had by improved gauges, scales, testing machines and other instruments. When the knowledge is available, each step of the manufacturing process, from specification to inspection, can be examined for consistent and unnecessary causes of error. Tolerances can be established and variations of parts from specification can be studied. Up to this point progress is made without the use of special statistical methods. But the rate of progress changed when the control chart was introduced by Shewhart.[2]

The Control Chart; Purpose and Function. Both the purpose and the mode of functioning of a control chart can be understood by studying Figure 58.

The records of two producers are compared.[3] Producer A undertakes to obtain statistical control of the quality of his product. Producer B does not, although he may attempt to improve his product by attention to observable imperfections. In both cases successive samples are taken, consisting of five specimens each, which are presumably tested to destruction to obtain the tensile strength. These could be steel bolts, tension members for airplane construction or anything else produced in sufficient quantity to justify statistical examination. Such examination may be needed to reduce cost, to increase safety or to secure other benefits. Producer A uses his inspection by samples to guide an improvement process through four stages. Producer B probably desires to secure the improvement but fails to take the necessary steps to get it. The two cases are similar to two persons who plan to control their personal expenditures to secure better returns. Each records and plots what he spends. One analyzes, determines what expenditures fall on the fringe of his plan, and eliminates or reduces these. The other makes the records and simply files them. One brings his finances under control, the other does not.

Producer A starts manufacture of the given product on an experimental basis, using the best available suggestions from the shop and the research laboratory. He sets a minimum limit for individual specimens at 40,000 psi and a minimum limit — somewhat higher, say 44,000 psi — for averages of samples. The dots on the diagram each represent a sample average of five specimens. After a reasonable experimental fabrication period, production is started. From a study of the distribution of the sample averages from day to day for the experimental period, a trial level for average strength is selected and control limits set. These are

[2] W. A. Shewhart, "Economic Control of Quality of Manufactured Product," 1931. This is the standard work in this field. It is moderately difficult to read, but is really essential.

[3] This chart and elements of the discussion are by H. F. Dodge. See "Proceedings of the Industrial Statistics Conference at Massachusetts Institute of Technology," pp. cxi and cxxv.

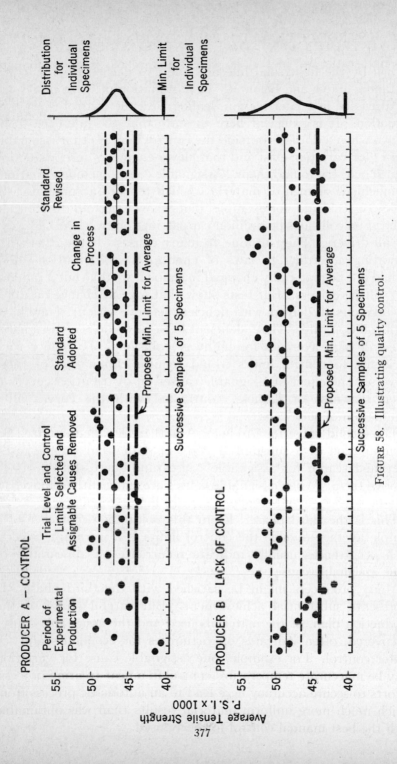

FIGURE 58. Illustrating quality control.

377

shown by the light solid line and the two dashed lines at equal distances above and below it. Determination of these limits will be discussed in a later section dealing with the control chart construction. It is sufficient here to state that the inference to be drawn when a dot falls outside the control limits is that assignable causes for variation exist and that clever engineers and production men should try to find them. Assignable causes include variations in machines or men or materials which tend to accumulate. In highway accidents, for example, plots show a certain distribution of head-on collisions per million car passings on two-lane highways for all drivers. They are due to many causes. If the causes are operating according to laws of chance, the distribution curve should not be materially changed in shape if we take out a random 10% of the drivers. But tests show that a great change occurs if we take out all drivers with deficient left-eye vision. They have high collision rates. Here, deficient left-eye vision is an assignable cause of high averages for highway collisions. To reduce such accidents to control limits would require elimination of these drivers. The effect of assignable causes on distribution curves is often skewness or flatness, contrasted with the curves after elimination of such causes.

The second stage for Producer A is therefore characterized by accumulation of a substantial body of data from sample tests, continual search for assignable causes and successful efforts to remove them. When assignable causes are sufficiently removed, a standard average and standard control limits are adopted.

This is the third phase. From this point the occurrence of a sample average outside the control limits is a warning. Several such occurrences usually indicate recurrence or appearance of some assignable cause.

Many producers might be satisfied with the third phase. It represents substantial achievement. But careful study of the production plan, of the materials used and the assignable causes discovered, often indicates opportunities for economies and for better control. For example, one assignable cause for variation may be inaccurate temperature control in a heat-treating process. Efforts to secure accuracy here lead to an automatic process from which much more uniform material results than was obtainable with the best manual control formerly used.

QUALITY CONTROL 379

Example from a Long-Established Process. At a recent conference an engineer from a shell-loading plant reported a study of shot-gun shell loading. Periodically, samples of loaded shells were taken from the production line and fired on a test range. At a certain range, it was required that 70% of all the shot strike within a 30-inch circle. This was set as an average standard. A plot of the results repeatedly showed that, while the 70% standard was maintained as the average, it represented a skew distribution. There were many values of 71%, 72%, 73%, up to 75% and few higher. There were occasional values of 60%, 61%, 62% but few between 62 and 70%. The low values fell outside the control lines and therefore suggested an assignable cause. By use of high-speed photography, the staff discovered that the cardboard wad that closed the front end of the shell was a major cause of trouble. Its resistance varied greatly with its attitude toward the air stream. Occasionally, it so blanketed the central portion of the charge as to cause the low percentages. By the cyclic principle, this information went to the design room. Specifications were changed so that the end of the paper shell was crimped and only a thin piece of paper used to aid in holding the shot in place. This represented a change of design after many years use of the former one. Results of sample tests changed at once. Normal distribution occurred about a higher average for the 30-inch circle. This incident also illustrates the skill required to isolate and remove assignable causes of variation.

Economies from Quality Control. Shewhart, the dean of writers and investigators in this subject, refers to the entire process of quality control as a "new tool of research-statistical method, plus mass production." He lists three economies which can be made through its use:

1. Reduction in the cost of inspection.
2. Reduction in the cost of rejection.
3. Savings through efficient use of material.

Each of these savings must be checked by the methods of engineering economy to see that quality control pays its way. The fact that a number of the large and most efficient corporations of the United States, England and Germany have adopted the new "tool" and employed staffs to ensure competent administration is evidence that it frequently does.

The fourth stage by Producer A follows a change in process. This can come as a result of treating the steps of production — specification, fabrication and inspection — as a cycle; thus S, F, I, S, F, etc. Shewhart calls the old method the straight-line method, the new method the circular or cyclic one. In the latter, the last step, inspection, supplies information to the first, specification. From results of sampling, suggestions for specification and actually for fabrication are continually obtained. Since there is a general trend to mass production, simplified design and automatic control, the process does not end with securing quality control.

Savings for Producer A. Producer A in the chart gained the benefits mentioned above. There was reduction in the cost of inspection. This follows from the theory of sampling.[4] Sampling methods are based on the theory of probability. They have improved rapidly within the past 20 years. Generally, the selection of specimens for sample testing is made so as to give a specified probability that not more than a given percentage of defectives will be allowed to pass inspection. Let the permissible percentage of defectives be 1%. It is often more economical to replace a small percentage of defectives than to devise a system to eliminate them. The amount of sampling required to achieve this result depends on the percentage of defectives identified by the sampling system. If, therefore, production is under quality control, the number of specimens that must be inspected is reduced, and a saving results. The saving is in both labor and parts if the specimen testing is destructive — as in ultimate strength tests, fuse-blowing times and shotgun shell accuracy. It is in labor at least if the specimen testing is nondestructive — as in condenser capacities, coil resistances and numerous accuracy requirements.

A second saving is in the cost of rejection. Products that do not pass tests are a problem. Not merely do they represent a loss in materials, they commonly represent a much greater loss in labor. In times of emergency operation, the loss of materials and labor expended means a loss of plant capacity which can be serious. Thus, munitions plants have much to gain from quality control.

---

[4] For a discussion of sampling see Shewhart, *loc. cit.*, Chap. XXIII, Sampling — Measurement. Also, see Mills, *loc. cit.*, Chap. XIV.

The third saving is through efficient use of material. Note that, for the first 10 samples, Producer A and Producer B had about the same average values and about the same number of samples below 43,000 psi strength. Examine conditions for the fourth stage of Producer A and the corresponding sample tests for Producer B. Producer A is securing a much more uniform product than Producer B and higher average and minimum values. Therefore, he has much more assurance in making shipments that there will be few rejections, especially if he is reasonably confident that he has maintained his customary standards. An empirical rule, advocated by Shewhart, calls for the last 25 sample sets to give results within the control limits. Producer A would be justified in shipping at once, whereas Producer B might have reason to doubt. Producer A is now in a position to accept a higher minimum strength limit, say 43,000 psi. Or, if this is not desired, he can achieve better combined quality. If the product is steel bolts, he might reduce brittleness and increase ductility without reducing average strength to the point of rejections. Consider the improvement in the condition of the industry if all producers achieved the quality control of Producer A. Design values could be readjusted, and fewer bolts would be required to give the same strength. Similar results could be secured in many other production items.

Note, finally, the difference in shape of distribution curves for individual specimens at the right end of the diagram. For Producer A, the curve is approximately symmetrical and tall rather than flat. In many cases of control, this shape of curve follows success in eliminating assignable causes. For Producer B, the curve is asymmetrical and flat. Also, it is irregular. These are symptoms of undetermined assignable causes.

The Control Chart: Construction. When test data concerning a particular quality are to be examined to see whether quality control may be assumed as established, we distinguish two cases. *Case A.* The standard value of the statistic (the quality or property to be controlled) is known from experience and is represented by an average value $\overline{X}$ and a standard deviation $\overline{\sigma}$. Statistically speaking, this assumes a normal universe and a complete sampling of it. Practically, it means that adequate past experience exists to consider $\overline{X}$ and $\overline{\sigma}$ as fully specifying the controlled quality.

The control chart is now to be constructed to check sets of currently observed values to see whether the property represented may be considered under control. The question as often phrased is, "Should these variations be left to chance?" The answer is taken from the control chart.

Summary: Case A. — The standard value of the statistic is defined by $\bar{X}$ and σ. Construct the control chart for checking samples of n values currently submitted.

Construction: Case A. See Figure 59.

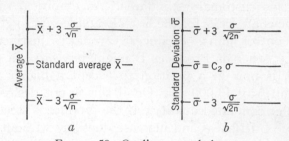

FIGURE 59. Quality control chart.

1. Construct a vertical scale of average $\bar{X}$ and locate the horizontal axis at the standard average $\bar{X}$.

2. Construct parallel control lines above and below for the values:

$$\bar{X} \pm 3 \frac{\sigma}{\sqrt{n}}$$

(Note that, as n increases indefinitely, the control lines approach the axis as a limit. The size n of the sample controls the spread.)

3. Compute the average $\bar{X}$ for each sample of n values and plot it on the chart.

4. Note points falling outside the control lines. The samples represented by such points are suspect.

The form of the control charts for both average $\bar{X}$ and standard deviation σ is shown. Figure 59a shows the construction for the average $\bar{X}$ chart. Points to be plotted on the chart are average values from samples of n. σ is the standard deviation for the property to be controlled. It assumes an infinite number of values as its base. Figure 59b shows the construction for the standard deviation chart. The standard deviation of a sample is designated $\bar{\sigma}$: for example, $\bar{\sigma}_A$ is the standard deviation for sample

A of n values. The coefficient C_2 is a multiplier dependent upon the sample size. A few values for much-used sample sizes are listed in Table 31. They are taken from a more complete table given by Shewhart and based upon statistical theory.[5]

TABLE 31. CORRECTION FACTOR C_2

n	C_2	n	C_2
3	0.7236	15	0.9490
4	0.7979	18	0.9576
5	0.8407	20	0.9619
6	0.8686	25	0.9696
7	0.8882	30	0.9748
8	0.9027	35	0.9784
9	0.9139	50	0.9849
10	0.9228	75	0.9900
11	0.9300	100	0.9925
12	0.9359		

n = size of sample. The correction factor is used in the equation:

$$\bar{\sigma} = C_2 \sigma$$

where σ is the standard deviation of the normal universe, and $\bar{\sigma}$ is the expected value for samples of size n.

Note: Values in this table are taken from Shewhart, "Economic Control of Quality of Manufactured Product," Table 29, p. 185.

Example. Use of Control Chart. Case A. The construction and interpretation of the charts in a practical case will fix and clarify the discussion.

In Table 32, three sets of 25 values each of tensile strength of steel bolts are given. Each set of 25 values is obtained by testing to destruction a random sample of 25 bolts of a given size. The three samples are taken successively from bolts supplied by three producers. For such steel bolts, past experience gives $\bar{X}$ = 9,430 and σ = 290. These values are based on large numbers previously produced under quality control conditions. The question to be asked of each producer is, "Should it be assumed that this sample represents a quantity of bolts produced under quality control conditions?"

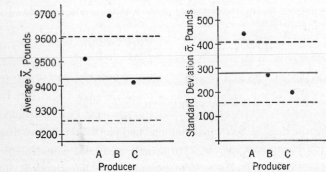

FIGURE 60. Control charts, Case A. Tensil strength of steel bolts.

[5] Shewhart, "Economic Control of Quality of Manufactured Product," Table 29 p. 185.

TABLE 32. TENSILE STRENGTH OF STEEL BOLTS
(Values in pounds)

Producer A	Producer B	Producer C
9,220	9,930	9,570
9,990	9,670	9,310
10,030	10,040	9,280
9,230	10,050	9,230
9,180	9,850	9,350
9,130	9,470	9,450
9,250	9,730	9,430
9,980	9,830	9,450
10,150	9,330	9,710
10,140	9,930	9,480
9,330	9,890	9,570
10,030	9,710	9,100
9,090	10,100	9,750
9,170	9,900	9,600
8,910	9,330	9,310
10,200	9,820	9,410
9,140	9,670	9,140
9,260	9,190	9,330
9,230	9,590	9,640
9,090	9,610	9,360
9,310	9,240	9,670
9,210	10,100	9,690
9,230	9,540	9,010
10,050	9,690	9,270
10,200	9,160	9,180

Standards for such steel bolts are given as:

$\overline{X} = 9,430 \qquad \sigma = 290 \qquad \overline{\sigma} = C_2\sigma = 281$

For these samples of 25, values are:

Producer A, $\overline{X}_A = 9,510 \; \overline{\sigma}_A = 442$

Producer B, $\overline{X}_B = 9,696 \; \overline{\sigma}_B = 276$

Producer C, $\overline{X}_C = 9,412 \; \overline{\sigma}_C = 200$

In Figure 60, the control charts for average $\overline{X}$ and standard deviation σ are shown. The axis of the first chart is at $\overline{X} = 9,430$ pounds. The control lines are at

$$9,430 \pm 3 \frac{290}{\sqrt{25}} = \begin{matrix} 9,604 \text{ pounds} \\ 9,256 \text{ pounds} \end{matrix}$$

For the second chart, the axis is at $\overline{\sigma} = C_2\sigma = 0.96965 \times 290 = 281$ pounds. The control lines are at

$$\overline{\sigma} \pm 3 \frac{\sigma}{\sqrt{2n}} = 281 \pm 3 \frac{290}{\sqrt{50}} = \begin{matrix} 404 \\ 158 \end{matrix}$$

The values for the three samples are computed and plotted on the two diagrams.

For Producer A, $\overline{X}_A = 9,510$ pounds, $\overline{\sigma}_A = 442$ pounds

For Producer B, $\overline{X}_B = 9,696$ pounds, $\overline{\sigma}_B = 276$ pounds

For Producer C, $\overline{X}_C = 9,412$ pounds, $\overline{\sigma}_C = 200$ pounds

For a sample to be satisfactory, both $\overline{X}$ and $\overline{\sigma}$ must fall between control lines. Hence, Producer A's sample is unsatisfactory. $\overline{\sigma}_A$ is too large. Since the average value falls between control lines, this means that the dispersion is too great. An assignable cause should be sought. Producer B's sample is unsatisfactory. The average $\overline{X}$ is too large. This may mean that heat-treating to higher strength has occurred. The standard values may call for this rejection because of the probability of excessive brittleness. Producer C's sample is acceptable. The chart values indicate a high probability that deviations in this sample are such as may reasonably be expected and be assigned to chance causes.

Construction of Control Chart: Case B. The most common problem in practice is to determine whether quality control has been achieved when no standards of quality are available. This is the case whenever a new product is introduced. It often occurs when changes in specifications are made, either as to material used or method of fabrication followed. We designate this as *Case B.*

Consider the data supplied in Case A concerning the strength of steel bolts. Assume that the values given represent tests of samples of five from 15 different lots produced on successive days under conditions that do not come under known standards. (See Table 33.) It is not known whether assignable causes for variation exist or whether these have been removed. Consequently, values based on statistical theory of a normal universe are not valid. It is generally found in practice that there are assignable causes of variation. The engineer discovers on checking statistical theory that progress is slow in furnishing mathematical answers to this problem. It has been proved, however, that the best value of average $\overline{X}$ which may represent the standard quality level is the grand average of all values used. In this case, it would be the average of the 75 test values. Using primes to indicate that standard quality values are not known, we find $\overline{X}' = 9,539$ pounds.

It has been found in practice that the presence of assignable causes is commonly discovered and that quality control may be achieved by applying the theory of statistics of a normal universe. From this theory, the best estimate for the standard deviation of the entire group is given approximately by

$$\overline{\sigma}' = \frac{\Sigma\sigma'}{m}$$

TABLE 33. TENSILE STRENGTH OF STEEL BOLTS
(Values in pounds)

Sample No.	Test specimen number					Average $\overline{X}_n$	Standard deviation σ_n
	1	2	3	4	5		
1	9,220	9,990	10,030	9,230	9,180	9,530	392.5
2	9,130	9,250	9,980	10,150	10,140	9,730	446.5
3	9,330	10,030	9,090	9,170	8,910	9,306	386.4
4	10,200	9,140	9,260	9,230	9,090	9,384	412.6
5	9,310	9,210	9,230	10,050	10,200	9,600	432.6
6	9,930	9,670	10,040	10,050	9,850	9,908	140.1
7	9,470	9,730	9,830	9,330	9,930	9,658	224.3
8	9,890	9,710	10,100	9,900	9,330	9,786	259.3
9	9,820	9,670	9,190	9,590	9,610	9,576	209.2
10	9,240	10,100	9,540	9,690	9,160	9,546	337.7
11	9,570	9,310	9,280	9,230	9,350	9,348	117.7
12	9,450	9,430	9,450	9,710	9,480	9,504	104.2
13	9,570	9,100	9,750	9,600	9,310	9,466	231.4
14	9,410	9,140	9,330	9,640	9,360	9,376	160.6
15	9,670	9,690	9,010	9,270	9,180	9,364	271.2
Sum						143,082	4,126.3
Average						9,539	275.1

$$\overline{X}' = \tfrac{1}{15}\Sigma\overline{X}_n = 9,539$$
$$\overline{\sigma}' = \frac{\Sigma\sigma'}{m} = \frac{4,126.3}{15} = 275.1$$

For Control Lines,

(a) $\overline{X}' = 9,539 \pm 3\dfrac{\overline{\sigma}'}{C_2\sqrt{n}} = 9,539 \pm 3\dfrac{275.1}{0.84069\sqrt{5}} = \begin{matrix}9,978\\9,100\end{matrix}$

(b) $\overline{\sigma}' \pm 3\dfrac{\overline{\sigma}'}{C_2\sqrt{2\,n}} = 275.1 + \dfrac{3\times275.1}{0.84069\sqrt{10}} = 275.1 \pm 309.1 = \begin{matrix}584\\0\end{matrix}$

n = number of specimens in sample
m = number of samples

For this case, σ' for each sample is computed in the usual way. This formula is valid only for equal subgroups, each numbering 25 or less. Hence, for the entire universe represented by all the samples here,

$$\overline{\sigma}' = \frac{4,126.3}{15} = 275.1$$

Control lines are obtained for the case of equal samples, each numbering less than 25, by the following formulas:

The central line for $\overline{X}'$ is the average of all test values, as just computed.

The central line for $\bar{\sigma}'$ is the average of the standard deviations of the several samples, computed in the usual way.

The control lines for averages are

$$\overline{X}' \pm 3 \frac{\bar{\sigma}'}{C_2\sqrt{n}}$$

where n is the number of specimens in the sample and C_2 is from Table 31. $\bar{\sigma}'$ is the average standard deviation of the samples.

The control lines for standard deviations are

$$\bar{\sigma}' \pm 3 \frac{\bar{\sigma}'}{C_2\sqrt{2n}}$$

For the example in Table 33, the values are:

Central lines: $\overline{X}' = 9,539$, $\bar{\sigma}' = 275.1$

Control lines: $\overline{X}' \pm 3 \dfrac{275.1}{0.84069\sqrt{5}} = \dfrac{9,978}{9,100}$

$\bar{\sigma}' \pm 3 \dfrac{275.1}{0.84069\sqrt{10}} = 275.1 \pm \dfrac{584}{0}$

Values are shown under Table 33.

It is noted that the values of $\overline{X}_n$ and σ'_n for all of the samples fall within the control lines of both averages and deviations. No figure is needed to check this result. This indicates that the lack of knowledge of standard values, which served as an aid in Case A, gives less ability to detect suspicious lots by sample tests. Experience has given the following rule. *Quality control may not be assumed unless at least 25 successive samples of not fewer than four specimens each fall within the control lines.* Of course, these should be the latest samples taken in the given production series, and the control lines should be based on all cumulative data available. In the practical case, a restudy of these data, divided into logical subgroups, might give the engineer valuable clues.

Knowledge of Statistics Necessary to Get Benefits. This chapter is not intended to provide adequate instruction for a quality control engineer. It is really a statement of the case for the use of this tool. The procedures to obtain quality control have been developed in small groups of workers and have spread slowly to larger groups. Colleges of engineering are just now taking note of them. To most members of engineering faculties and to most students, the subject is familiar by title only. Much progress is likely during the next several years. Enthusiasm will lead to some false applications and to some disappointments. These will occur chiefly when persons applying the method have made inadequate study of its statistical basis.

REFERENCES

Shewhart, W. A.: "Economic Control of Quality of Manufactured Product," D. Van Nostrand Company, Inc., New York, 1931. (This is the standard American work in the subject.)

Shewhart, W. A.: "Statistical Method from the Viewpoint of Quality Control," Graduate School, Department of Agriculture, Washington, 1939.

Pearson, E. S.: "The Application of Statistical Methods to Industrial Standardization and Quality Control," British Standards Institute, London, 1935.

Simon, Leslie E.: "Engineers' Manual of Statistical Methods," John Wiley and Sons, Inc., New York, 1941.

Freeman, H. A.: "Industrial Statistics," John Wiley and Sons, Inc., New York, 1942.

"A. S. T. M. Manual on Presentation of Data," American Society for Testing Materials, March, 1941, printing.

Dodge, H. F., and H. G. Romig: "Method of Sampling Inspection," Bell System Technical Journal, October, 1929.

Dodge, H. F.: "Statistical Control in Sampling Inspection," American Machinist, October 26, November 9, 1932.

Dodge, H. F.: "'Control Chart' Method of Analysis and Presentation of Data," A. S. T. M. Bulletin, 1937.

Rissik, H.: "Statistical Methods in Engineering Practice," The Engineer, London, November, December, 1940 (five parts).

PROBLEMS

186. What is a quality control chart? How is it used?

187. If samples of a product are examined and some important characteristic measured, such as ultimate strength resistance, would you expect the variations to be due wholly to chance?

188. What three important causes of variation in quality are discussed in this chapter?

189. Select some product for which you can conceive quality control charts as applicable and list several possible assignable causes of variation in some measured quality characteristic.

190. Quality control is attempted for certain structural parts in quantity production in a new plant. Experience in similar operations elsewhere appears

to justify setting 48,000 pounds per square inch as the standard average, $\overline{X}$, and 1,225 pounds per square inch as the standard deviation, σ.

During the first and third weeks of operation, 16 samples of six specimens each are tested to destruction. The average values for the samples are, in order:

First week: 47,620, 48,740, 49,470, 45,500, 46,600, 47,530, 48,320, 49,320, 46,660, 46,360, 47,170, 48,110, 48,970, 49,930, 45,330, 46,930.

Third week: 48,050, 49,320, 47,890, 46,460, 46,540, 49,010, 46,880, 48,900, 47,210, 47,040, 48,970, 47,420, 47,960, 48,370, 48,170, 47,630.

a. Construct the control chart for average $\overline{X}$ and show the values in order for the first week and for the third week.

b. Is the product under control during the first week? the third week?

c. Discuss the apparent changes between the first and third weeks.

TABLES

Table I. The Number of Each Day of the Year

Day of Month	Jan.	Feb.	Mar.	April	May	June	July	Aug.	Sept.	Oct.	Nov.	Dec.	Day of Month
1	1	32	60	91	121	152	182	213	244	274	305	335	1
2	2	33	61	92	122	153	183	214	245	275	306	336	2
3	3	34	62	93	123	154	184	215	246	276	307	337	3
4	4	35	63	94	124	155	185	216	247	277	308	338	4
5	5	36	64	95	125	156	186	217	248	278	309	339	5
6	6	37	65	96	126	157	187	218	249	279	310	340	6
7	7	38	66	97	127	158	188	219	250	280	311	341	7
8	8	39	67	98	128	159	189	220	251	281	312	342	8
9	9	40	68	99	129	160	190	221	252	282	313	343	9
10	10	41	69	100	130	161	191	222	253	283	314	344	10
11	11	42	70	101	131	162	192	223	254	284	315	345	11
12	12	43	71	102	132	163	193	224	255	285	316	346	12
13	13	44	72	103	133	164	194	225	256	286	317	347	13
14	14	45	73	104	134	165	195	226	257	287	318	348	14
15	15	46	74	105	135	166	196	227	258	288	319	349	15
16	16	47	75	106	136	167	197	228	259	289	320	350	16
17	17	48	76	107	137	168	198	229	260	290	321	351	17
18	18	49	77	108	138	169	199	230	261	291	322	352	18
19	19	50	78	109	139	170	200	231	262	292	323	353	19
20	20	51	79	110	140	171	201	232	263	293	324	354	20
21	21	52	80	111	141	172	202	233	264	294	325	355	21
22	22	53	81	112	142	173	203	234	265	295	326	356	22
23	23	54	82	113	143	174	204	235	266	296	327	357	23
24	24	55	83	114	144	175	205	236	267	297	328	358	24
25	25	56	84	115	145	176	206	237	268	298	329	359	25
26	26	57	85	116	146	177	207	238	269	299	330	360	26
27	27	58	86	117	147	178	208	239	270	300	331	361	27
28	28	59	87	118	148	179	209	240	271	301	332	362	28
29	29		88	119	149	180	210	241	272	302	333	363	29
30	30		89	120	150	181	211	242	273	303	334	364	30
31	31		90		151		212	243		304		365	31

Note. For leap years the number of the day is one greater than the number in the table after February 28.

Table II. ¼ %

Number of periods n	Amount of 1 at compound interest $s = (1+i)^n$	Present value of 1 $v^n = \dfrac{1}{(1+i)^n}$	Present value of an annuity of 1 $a_{\overline{n}\rceil} = \dfrac{1-v^n}{i}$	Amount of an annuity of 1 $s_{\overline{n}\rceil} = \dfrac{(1+i)^n-1}{i}$	Annuity whose present value is 1 $\dfrac{1}{a_{\overline{n}\rceil}} = \dfrac{1}{s_{\overline{n}\rceil}} + i$	Number of periods n
1	1.0025 0000	0.9975 0623	0.9975 0623	1.0000 0000	1.0025 0000	1
2	1.0050 0625	0.9950 1869	1.9925 2492	2.0025 0000	0.5018 7578	2
3	1.0075 1877	0.9925 3734	2.9850 6227	3.0075 0625	0.3350 0139	3
4	1.0100 3756	0.9900 6219	3.9751 2446	4.0150 2502	0.2515 6445	4
5	1.0125 6266	0.9875 9321	4.9627 1766	5.0250 6258	0.2015 0250	5
6	1.0150 9406	0.9851 3038	5.9478 4804	6.0376 2523	0.1681 2803	6
7	1.0176 3180	0.9826 7370	6.9305 2174	7.0527 1930	0.1442 8928	7
8	1.0201 7588	0.9802 2314	7.9107 4487	8.0703 5110	0.1264 1035	8
9	1.0227 2632	0.9777 7869	8.8885 2357	9.0905 2697	0.1125 0462	9
10	1.0252 8313	0.9753 4034	9.8638 6391	10.1132 5329	0.1013 8015	10
11	1.0278 4634	0.9729 0807	10.8367 7198	11.1385 3642	0.0922 7840	11
12	1.0304 1596	0.9704 8187	11.8072 5384	12.1663 8277	0.0846 9370	12
13	1.0329 9200	0.9680 6171	12.7753 1555	13.1967 9872	0.0782 7595	13
14	1.0355 7448	0.9656 4759	13.7409 6314	14.2297 9072	0.0727 7510	14
15	1.0381 6341	0.9632 3949	14.7042 0264	15.2653 6520	0.0680 0777	15
16	1.0407 5882	0.9608 3740	15.6650 4004	16.3035 2861	0.0638 3642	16
17	1.0433 6072	0.9584 4130	16.6234 8133	17.3442 8743	0.0601 5587	17
18	1.0459 6912	0.9560 5117	17.5795 3250	18.3876 4815	0.0568 8433	18
19	1.0485 8404	0.9536 6700	18.5331 9950	19.4336 1727	0.0539 5722	19
20	1.0512 0550	0.9512 8878	19.4844 8828	20.4822 0131	0.0513 2288	20
21	1.0538 3352	0.9489 1649	20.4334 0477	21.5334 0682	0.0489 3947	21
22	1.0564 6810	0.9465 5011	21.3799 5488	22.5872 4033	0.0467 7278	22
23	1.0591 0927	0.9441 8964	22.3241 4452	23.6437 0843	0.0447 9455	23
24	1.0617 5704	0.9418 3505	23.2659 7957	24.7028 1770	0.0429 8121	24
25	1.0644 1144	0.9394 8634	24.2054 6591	25.7645 7475	0.0413 1298	25
26	1.0670 7247	0.9371 4348	25.1426 0939	26.8289 8619	0.0397 7312	26
27	1.0697 4015	0.9348 0646	26.0774 1585	27.8960 5865	0.0383 4736	27
28	1.0724 1450	0.9324 7527	27.0098 9112	28.9657 9880	0.0370 2347	28
29	1.0750 9553	0.9301 4990	27.9400 4102	30.0382 1330	0.0357 9093	29
30	1.0777 8327	0.9278 3032	28.8678 7134	31.1133 0883	0.0346 4059	30
31	1.0804 7773	0.9255 1653	29.7933 8787	32.1910 9210	0.0335 6449	31
32	1.0831 7892	0.9232 0851	30.7165 9638	33.2715 6983	0.0325 5569	32
33	1.0858 8687	0.9209 0624	31.6375 0262	34.3547 4876	0.0316 0806	33
34	1.0886 0159	0.9186 0972	32.5561 1234	35.4406 3563	0.0307 1620	34
35	1.0913 2309	0.9163 1892	33.4724 3126	36.5292 3722	0.0298 7533	35
36	1.0940 5140	0.9140 3384	34.3864 6510	37.6205 6031	0.0290 8121	36
37	1.0967 8653	0.9117 5445	35.2982 1955	38.7146 1171	0.0283 3004	37
38	1.0995 2850	0.9094 8075	36.2077 0030	39.8113 9824	0.0276 1843	38
39	1.1022 7732	0.9072 1272	37.1149 1302	40.9109 2673	0.0269 4335	39
40	1.1050 3301	0.9049 5034	38.0198 6336	42.0132 0405	0.0263 0204	40
41	1.1077 9559	0.9026 9361	38.9225 5697	43.1182 3706	0.0256 9204	41
42	1.1105 6508	0.9004 4250	39.8229 9947	44.2260 3265	0.0251 1112	42
43	1.1133 4149	0.8981 9701	40.7211 9648	45.3365 9774	0.0245 5724	43
44	1.1161 2485	0.8959 5712	41.6171 5359	46.4499 3923	0.0240 2855	44
45	1.1189 1516	0.8937 2281	42.5108 7640	47.5660 6408	0.0235 2339	45
46	1.1217 1245	0.8914 9407	43.4023 7047	48.6849 7924	0.0230 4022	46
47	1.1245 1673	0.8892 7090	44.2916 4137	49.8066 9169	0.0225 7762	47
48	1.1273 2802	0.8870 5326	45.1786 9463	50.9312 0842	0.0221 3433	48
49	1.1301 4634	0.8848 4116	46.0635 3580	52.0585 3644	0.0217 0915	49
50	1.1329 7171	0.8826 3457	46.9461 7037	53.1886 8278	0.0213 0099	50

Table II (*continued*). ¼ %

Number of periods n	Amount of 1 at compound interest $s = (1+i)^n$	Present value of 1 $v^n = \dfrac{1}{(1+i)^n}$	Present value of an annuity of 1 $a_{\overline{n}\rvert} = \dfrac{1 - v^n}{i}$	Amount of an annuity of 1 $s_{\overline{n}\rvert} = \dfrac{(1+i)^n-1}{i}$	Annuity whose present value is 1 $\dfrac{1}{a_{\overline{n}\rvert}} = \dfrac{1}{s_{\overline{n}\rvert}} + i$	Number of periods n
51	1.1358 0414	0.8804 3349	47.8266 0386	54.3216 5449	0.0209 0886	51
52	1.1386 4365	0.8782 3790	48.7048 4176	55.4574 5862	0.0205 3184	52
53	1.1414 9026	0.8760 4778	49.5808 8953	56.5961 0227	0.0201 6906	53
54	1.1443 4398	0.8738 6312	50.4547 5265	57.7375 9252	0.0198 1974	54
55	1.1472 0484	0.8716 8391	51.3264 3656	58.8819 3650	0.0194 8314	55
56	1.1500 7285	0.8695 1013	52.1959 4669	60.0291 4135	0.0191 5858	56
57	1.1529 4804	0.8673 4178	53.0632 8847	61.1792 1420	0.0188 4542	57
58	1.1558 3041	0.8651 7883	53.9284 6730	62.3321 6223	0.0185 4308	58
59	1.1587 1998	0.8630 2128	54.7914 8858	63.4879 9264	0.0182 5101	59
60	1.1616 1678	0.8608 6911	55.6523 5769	64.6467 1262	0.0179 6869	60
61	1.1645 2082	0.8587 2230	56.5110 7999	65.8083 2940	0.0176 9564	61
62	1.1674 3213	0.8565 8085	57.3676 6083	66.9728 5023	0.0174 3142	62
63	1.1703 5071	0.8544 4474	58.2221 0557	68.1402 8235	0.0171 7561	63
64	1.1732 7658	0.8523 1395	59.0744 1952	69.3106 3306	0.0169 2780	64
65	1.1762 0977	0.8501 8848	59.9246 0800	70.4839 0964	0.0166 8764	65
66	1.1791 5030	0.8480 6831	60.7726 7631	71.6601 1942	0.0164 5476	66
67	1.1820 9817	0.8459 5343	61.6186 2974	72.8392 6971	0.0162 2886	67
68	1.1850 5342	0.8438 4382	62.4624 7355	74.0213 6789	0.0160 0961	68
69	1.1880 1605	0.8417 3947	63.3042 1302	75.2064 2131	0.0157 9674	69
70	1.1909 8609	0.8396 4037	64.1438 5339	76.3944 3736	0.0155 8996	70
71	1.1939 6356	0.8375 4650	64.9813 9989	77.5854 2345	0.0153 8902	71
72	1.1969 4847	0.8354 5786	65.8168 5774	78.7793 8701	0.0151 9368	72
73	1.1999 4084	0.8333 7412	66.6502 3216	79.9763 3548	0.0150 0370	73
74	1.2029 4069	0.8312 9618	67.4815 2834	81.1762 7632	0.0148 1887	74
75	1.2059 4804	0.8292 2312	68.3107 5146	82.3792 1701	0.0146 3898	75
76	1.2089 6291	0.8271 5523	69.1379 0670	83.5851 6505	0.0144 6385	76
77	1.2119 8532	0.8250 9250	69.9629 9920	84.7941 2797	0.0142 9327	77
78	1.2150 1528	0.8230 3491	70.7860 3411	86.0061 1329	0.0141 2708	78
79	1.2180 5282	0.8209 8246	71.6070 1657	87.2211 2857	0.0139 6511	79
80	1.2210 9795	0.8189 3512	72.4259 5169	88.4391 8139	0.0138 0721	80
81	1.2241 5070	0.8168 9289	73.2428 4458	89.6602 7934	0.0136 5321	81
82	1.2272 1108	0.8148 5575	74.0577 0033	90.8844 3004	0.0135 0298	82
83	1.2302 7910	0.8128 2369	74.8705 2402	92.1116 4112	0.0133 5639	83
84	1.2333 5480	0.8107 9670	75.6813 2072	93.3419 2022	0.0132 1330	84
85	1.2364 3819	0.8087 7476	76.4900 9548	94.5752 7502	0.0130 7359	85
86	1.2395 2928	0.8067 5787	77.2968 5335	95.8117 1321	0.0129 3714	86
87	1.2426 2811	0.8047 4600	78.1015 9935	97.0512 4249	0.0128 0384	87
88	1.2457 3468	0.8027 3915	78.9043 3850	98.2938 7060	0.0126 7357	88
89	1.2488 4901	0.8007 3731	79.7050 7581	99.5396 0527	0.0125 4625	89
90	1.2519 7114	0.7987 4046	80.5038 1627	100.7884 5429	0.0124 2177	90
91	1.2551 0106	0.7967 4859	81.3005 6486	102.0404 2542	0.0123 0004	91
92	1.2582 3882	0.7947 6168	82.0953 2654	103.2955 2649	0.0121 8096	92
93	1.2613 8441	0.7927 7973	82.8881 0628	104.5537 6530	0.0120 6446	93
94	1.2645 3787	0.7908 0273	83.6789 0900	105.8151 4972	0.0119 5044	94
95	1.2676 9922	0.7888 3065	84.4677 3966	107.0796 8759	0.0118 3884	95
96	1.2708 6847	0.7868 6349	85.2546 0315	108.3473 8681	0.0117 2957	96
97	1.2740 4564	0.7849 0124	86.0395 0439	109.6182 5528	0.0116 2257	97
98	1.2772 3075	0.7829 4388	86.8224 4827	110.8923 0091	0.0115 1776	98
99	1.2804 2383	0.7809 9140	87.6034 3967	112.1695 3167	0.0114 1508	99
100	1.2836 2489	0.7790 4379	88.3824 8346	113.4499 5550	0.0113 1446	100

Table III. ⅓ %

Number of periods n	Amount of 1 at compound interest $s = (1 + i)^n$	Present value of 1 $v^n = \dfrac{1}{(1 + i)^n}$	Present value of an annuity of 1 $a_{\overline{n}\rceil} = \dfrac{1 - v^n}{i}$	Amount of an annuity of 1 $s_{\overline{n}\rceil} = \dfrac{(1+i)^n - 1}{i}$	Annuity whose present value is 1 $\dfrac{1}{a_{\overline{n}\rceil}} = \dfrac{1}{s_{\overline{n}\rceil}} + i$	Number of periods n
1	1.0033 3333	0.9966 7774	0.9966 7774	1.0000 0000	1.0033 3333	1
2	1.0066 7778	0.9933 6652	1.9900 4426	2.0033 3333	0.5025 0139	2
3	1.0100 3337	0.9900 6630	2.9801 1056	3.0100 1111	0.3355 5802	3
4	1.0134 0015	0.9867 7704	3.9668 8760	4.0200 4448	0.2520 8680	4
5	1.0167 7815	0.9834 9871	4.9503 8631	5.0334 4463	0.2020 0444	5
6	1.0201 6741	0.9802 3127	5.9306 1759	6.0502 2278	0.1686 1650	6
7	1.0235 6797	0.9769 7469	6.9075 9228	7.0703 9019	0.1447 6824	7
8	1.0269 7986	0.9737 2893	7.8813 2121	8.0939 5816	0.1268 8228	8
9	1.0304 0313	0.9704 9395	8.8518 1516	9.1209 3802	0.1129 7118	9
10	1.0338 3780	0.9672 6972	9.8190 8487	10.1513 4114	0.1018 4248	10
11	1.0372 8393	0.9640 5620	10.7831 4107	11.1851 7895	0.0927 3736	11
12	1.0407 4154	0.9608 5335	11.7439 9442	12.2224 6288	0.0851 4990	12
13	1.0442 1068	0.9576 6115	12.7016 5557	13.2632 0442	0.0787 2989	13
14	1.0476 9138	0.9544 7955	13.6561 3512	14.3074 1510	0.0732 2716	14
15	1.0511 8369	0.9513 0852	14.6074 4364	15.3551 0648	0.0684 5825	15
16	1.0546 8763	0.9481 4803	15.5555 9167	16.4062 9017	0.0642 8557	16
17	1.0582 0326	0.9449 9803	16.5005 8970	17.4609 7781	0.0606 0389	17
18	1.0617 3060	0.9418 5851	17.4424 4821	18.5191 8107	0.0573 3140	18
19	1.0652 6971	0.9387 2941	18.3811 7762	19.5809 1167	0.0544 0348	19
20	1.0688 2060	0.9356 1071	19.3167 8832	20.6461 8137	0.0517 6844	20
21	1.0723 8334	0.9325 0236	20.2492 9069	21.7150 0198	0.0493 8445	21
22	1.0759 5795	0.9294 0435	21.1786 9504	22.7873 8532	0.0472 1726	22
23	1.0795 4448	0.9263 1663	22.1050 1167	23.8633 4327	0.0452 3861	23
24	1.0831 4296	0.9232 3916	23.0282 5083	24.9428 8775	0.0434 2492	24
25	1.0867 5344	0.9201 7192	23.9484 2275	26.0260 3071	0.0417 5640	25
26	1.0903 7595	0.9171 1487	24.8655 3763	27.1127 8414	0.0402 1630	26
27	1.0940 1053	0.9140 6798	25.7796 0561	28.2031 6009	0.0387 9035	27
28	1.0976 5724	0.9110 3121	26.6906 3682	29.2971 7062	0.0374 6632	28
29	1.1013 1609	0.9080 0453	27.5986 4135	30.3948 2786	0.0362 3367	29
30	1.1049 8715	0.9049 8790	28.5036 2925	31.4961 4395	0.0350 8325	30
31	1.1086 7044	0.9019 8130	29.4056 1055	32.6011 3110	0.0340 0712	31
32	1.1123 6601	0.8989 8468	30.3045 9523	33.7098 0154	0.0329 9830	32
33	1.1160 7389	0.8959 9802	31.2005 9325	34.8221 6754	0.0320 5067	33
34	1.1197 9414	0.8930 2128	32.0936 1454	35.9382 4143	0.0311 5885	34
35	1.1235 2679	0.8900 5444	32.9836 6898	37.0580 3557	0.0303 1803	35
36	1.1272 7187	0.8870 9745	33.8707 6642	38.1815 6236	0.0295 2399	36
37	1.1310 2945	0.8841 5028	34.7549 1670	39.3088 3423	0.0287 7291	37
38	1.1347 9955	0.8812 1290	35.6361 2960	40.4398 6368	0.0280 6141	38
39	1.1385 8221	0.8782 8528	36.5144 1488	41.5746 6322	0.0273 8644	39
40	1.1423 7748	0.8753 6739	37.3897 8228	42.7132 4543	0.0267 4527	40
41	1.1461 8541	0.8724 5920	38.2622 4147	43.8556 2292	0.0261 3543	41
42	1.1500 0603	0.8695 6066	39.1318 0213	45.0018 0833	0.0255 5466	42
43	1.1538 3938	0.8666 7175	39.9984 7388	46.1518 1436	0.0250 0095	43
44	1.1576 8551	0.8637 9245	40.8622 6633	47.3056 5374	0.0244 7246	44
45	1.1615 4446	0.8609 2270	41.7231 8903	48.4633 3925	0.0239 6749	45
46	1.1654 1628	0.8580 6249	42.5812 5153	49.5248 8371	0.0234 8451	46
47	1.1693 0100	0.8552 1179	43.4364 6332	50.7902 9999	0.0230 2213	47
48	1.1731 9867	0.8523 7055	44.2888 3387	51.9596 0099	0.0225 7905	48
49	1.1771 0933	0.8495 3876	45.1383 7263	53.1327 9966	0.0221 5410	49
50	1.1810 3303	0.8467 1637	45.9850 8900	54.3099 0899	0.0217 4618	50

Table III (*continued*). $\frac{1}{3}$ %

Number of periods n	Amount of 1 at compound interest $s = (1+i)^n$	Present value of 1 $v^n = \dfrac{1}{(1+i)^n}$	Present value of an annuity of 1 $a_{\overline{n}|} = \dfrac{1 - v^n}{i}$	Amount of an annuity of 1 $s_{\overline{n}|} = \dfrac{(1+i)^n - 1}{i}$	Annuity whose present value is 1 $\dfrac{1}{a_{\overline{n}|}} = \dfrac{1}{s_{\overline{n}|}} + i$	Number of periods n
51	1.1849 6981	0.8439 0336	46.8289 9236	55.4909 4202	0.0213 5429	51
52	1.1889 1971	0.8410 9969	47.6700 9205	56.6759 1183	0.0209 7751	52
53	1.1928 8277	0.8383 0534	48.5083 9739	57.8648 3154	0.0206 1499	53
54	1.1968 5905	0.8355 2027	49.3439 1767	59.0577 1431	0.0202 6592	54
55	1.2008 4858	0.8327 4446	50.1766 6213	60.2545 7336	0.0199 2958	55
56	1.2048 5141	0.8299 7787	51.0066 3999	61.4554 2194	0.0196 0529	56
57	1.2088 6758	0.8272 2047	51.8338 6046	62.6602 7334	0.0192 9241	57
58	1.2128 9714	0.8244 7222	52.6583 3268	63.8691 4092	0.0189 9035	58
59	1.2169 4013	0.8217 3311	53.4800 6580	65.0820 3806	0.0186 9856	59
60	1.2209 9659	0.8190 0310	54.2990 6890	66.2989 7818	0.0184 1652	60
61	1.2250 6658	0.8162 8216	55.1153 5106	67.5199 7478	0.0181 4377	61
62	1.2291 5014	0.8135 7026	55.9289 2133	68.7450 4136	0.0178 7984	62
63	1.2332 4730	0.8108 6737	56.7397 8870	69.9741 9150	0.0176 2432	63
64	1.2373 5813	0.8081 7346	57.5479 6216	71.2074 3880	0.0173 7681	64
65	1.2414 8266	0.8054 8850	58.3534 5065	72.4447 9693	0.0171 3695	65
66	1.2456 2093	0.8028 1246	59.1562 6311	73.6862 7959	0.0169 0438	66
67	1.2497 7300	0.8001 4531	59.9564 0842	74.9319 0052	0.0166 7878	67
68	1.2539 3891	0.7974 8702	60.7538 9543	76.1816 7352	0.0164 5985	68
69	1.2581 1871	0.7948 3756	61.5487 3299	77.4356 1243	0.0162 4729	69
70	1.2623 1244	0.7921 9690	62.3409 2989	78.6937 3114	0.0160 4083	70
71	1.2665 2015	0.7895 6502	63.1304 9490	79.9560 4358	0.0158 4021	71
72	1.2707 4188	0.7869 4188	63.9174 3678	81.2225 6372	0.0156 4518	72
73	1.2749 7769	0.7843 2745	64.7017 6423	82.4933 0560	0.0154 5553	73
74	1.2792 2761	0.7817 2171	65.4834 8595	83.7682 8329	0.0152 7103	74
75	1.2834 9170	0.7791 2463	66.2626 1058	85.0475 1090	0.0150 9147	75
76	1.2877 7001	0.7765 3618	67.0391 4676	86.3310 0260	0.0149 1666	76
77	1.2920 6258	0.7739 5632	67.8131 0308	87.6187 7261	0.0147 4641	77
78	1.2963 6945	0.7713 8504	68.5844 8812	88.9108 3519	0.0145 8056	78
79	1.3006 9068	0.7688 2230	69.3533 1042	90.2072 0464	0.0144 1892	79
80	1.3050 2632	0.7662 6807	70.1195 7849	91.5078 9532	0.0142 6135	80
81	1.3093 7641	0.7637 2233	70.8833 0082	92.8129 2164	0.0141 0770	81
82	1.3137 4099	0.7611 8505	71.6444 8587	94.1222 9804	0.0139 5781	82
83	1.3181 2013	0.7586 5619	72.4031 4206	95.4360 3904	0.0138 1156	83
84	1.3225 1386	0.7561 3574	73.1592 7780	96.7541 5917	0.0136 6881	84
85	1.3269 2224	0.7536 2366	73.9129 0146	98.0766 7303	0.0135 2944	85
86	1.3313 4532	0.7511 1993	74.6640 2139	99.4035 9527	0.0133 9333	86
87	1.3357 8314	0.7486 2451	75.4126 4591	100.7349 4059	0.0132 6038	87
88	1.3402 3575	0.7461 3739	76.1587 8329	102.0707 2373	0.0131 3046	88
89	1.3447 0320	0.7436 5853	76.9024 4182	103.4109 5947	0.0130 0349	89
90	1.3491 8554	0.7411 8790	77.6436 2972	104.7556 6267	0.0128 7936	90
91	1.3536 8283	0.7387 2548	78.3823 5520	106.1048 4821	0.0127 5797	91
92	1.3581 9510	0.7362 7125	79.1186 2645	107.4585 3104	0.0126 3925	92
93	1.3627 2242	0.7338 2516	79.8524 5161	108.8167 2614	0.0125 2310	93
94	1.3672 6483	0.7313 8720	80.5838 3882	110.1794 4856	0.0124 0944	94
95	1.3718 2238	0.7289 5735	81.3127 9616	111.5467 1339	0.0122 9819	95
96	1.3763 9512	0.7265 3556	82.0393 3172	112.9185 3577	0.0121 8928	96
97	1.3809 8310	0.7241 2182	82.7634 5354	114.2949 3089	0.0120 8263	97
98	1.3855 8638	0.7217 1610	83.4851 6964	115.6759 1399	0.0119 7818	98
99	1.3902 0500	0.7193 1837	84.2044 8802	117.0615 0037	0.0118 7585	99
100	1.3948 3902	0.7169 2861	84.9214 1663	118.4517 0537	0.0117 7559	100

Table IV. $\frac{5}{12}\%$

Number of periods n	Amount of 1 at compound interest $s = (1+i)^n$	Present value of 1 $v^n = \dfrac{1}{(1+i)^n}$	Present value of an annuity of 1 $a_{\overline{n}|} = \dfrac{1-v^n}{i}$	Amount of an annuity of 1 $s_{\overline{n}|} = \dfrac{(1+i)^n-1}{i}$	Annuity whose present value is 1 $\dfrac{1}{a_{\overline{n}|}} = \dfrac{1}{s_{\overline{n}|}} + i$	Number of periods n
1	1.0041 6667	0.9958 5062	0.9958 5062	1.0000 0000	1.0041 6667	1
2	1.0083 5069	0.9917 1846	1.9875 6908	2.0041 6667	0.5031 2717	2
3	1.0125 5216	0.9876 0345	2.9751 7253	3.0125 1736	0.3361 1496	3
4	1.0167 7112	0.9835 0551	3.9586 7804	4.0250 6952	0.2526 0958	4
5	1.0210 0767	0.9794 2457	4.9381 0261	5.0418 4064	0.2025 0693	5
6	1.0252 6187	0.9753 6057	5.9134 6318	6.0628 4831	0.1691 0564	6
7	1.0295 3379	0.9713 1343	6.8847 7661	7.0881 1018	0.1452 4800	7
8	1.0338 2352	0.9672 8308	7.8520 5969	8.1176 4397	0.1273 5512	8
9	1.0381 3111	0.9632 6946	8.8153 2915	9.1514 6749	0.1134 3876	9
10	1.0424 5666	0.9592 7249	9.7746 0164	10.1895 9860	0.1023 0596	10
11	1.0468 0023	0.9552 9211	10.7298 9374	11.2320 5526	0.0931 9757	11
12	1.0511 6190	0.9513 2824	11.6812 2198	12.2788 5549	0.0856 0748	12
13	1.0555 4174	0.9473 8082	12.6286 0280	13.3300 1739	0.0791 8532	13
14	1.0599 3983	0.9434 4978	13.5720 5257	14.3855 5913	0.0736 8082	14
15	1.0643 5625	0.9395 3505	14.5115 8762	15.4454 9896	0.0689 1045	15
16	1.0687 9106	0.9356 3656	15.4472 2418	16.5098 5520	0.0647 3655	16
17	1.0732 4436	0.9317 5425	16.3789 7843	17.5786 4627	0.0610 5387	17
18	1.0777 1621	0.9278 8805	17.3068 6648	18.6518 9063	0.0577 8053	18
19	1.0822 0670	0.9240 3789	18.2309 0438	19.7296 0684	0.0548 5191	19
20	1.0867 1589	0.9202 0371	19.1511 0809	20.8118 1353	0.0522 1630	20
21	1.0912 4387	0.9163 8544	20.0674 9352	21.8985 2942	0.0498 3183	21
22	1.0957 9072	0.9125 8301	20.9800 7653	22.9897 7330	0.0476 6427	22
23	1.1003 5652	0.9087 9636	21.8888 7289	24.0855 6402	0.0456 8531	23
24	1.1049 4134	0.9050 2542	22.7938 9831	25.1859 2054	0.0438 7139	24
25	1.1095 4526	0.9012 7012	23.6951 6843	26.2908 6187	0.0422 0270	25
26	1.1141 6836	0.8975 3041	24.5926 9884	27.4004 0713	0.0406 6247	26
27	1.1188 1073	0.8938 0622	25.4865 0506	28.5145 7549	0.0392 3645	27
28	1.1234 7244	0.8900 9748	26.3766 0254	29.6333 8622	0.0379 1239	28
29	1.1281 5358	0.8864 0413	27.2630 0668	30.7568 5867	0.0366 7974	29
30	1.1328 5422	0.8827 2610	28.1457 3278	31.8850 1224	0.0355 2936	30
31	1.1375 7444	0.8790 6334	29.0247 9612	33.0178 6646	0.0344 5330	31
32	1.1423 1434	0.8754 1577	29.9002 1189	34.1554 4090	0.0334 4458	32
33	1.1470 7398	0.8717 8334	30.7719 9524	35.2977 5524	0.0324 9708	33
34	1.1518 5346	0.8681 6599	31.6401 6122	36.4448 2922	0.0316 0540	34
35	1.1566 5284	0.8645 6364	32.5047 2486	37.5966 8268	0.0307 6476	35
36	1.1614 7223	0.8609 7624	33.3657 0109	38.7533 3552	0.0299 7090	36
37	1.1663 1170	0.8574 0372	34.2231 0481	39.9148 0775	0.0292 2003	37
38	1.1711 7133	0.8538 4603	35.0769 5084	41.0811 1945	0.0285 0875	38
39	1.1760 5121	0.8503 0310	35.9272 5394	42.2522 9078	0.0278 3402	39
40	1.1809 5142	0.8467 7487	36.7740 2881	43.4283 4199	0.0271 9310	40
41	1.1858 7206	0.8432 6128	37.6172 9009	44.6092 9342	0.0263 8352	41
42	1.1908 1319	0.8397 6227	38.4570 5236	45.7951 6548	0.0260 0303	42
43	1.1957 7491	0.8362 7778	39.2933 3013	46.9859 7866	0.0254 4961	43
44	1.2007 5731	0.8328 0775	40.1261 3788	48.1817 5358	0.0249 2141	44
45	1.2057 6046	0.8293 5211	40.9554 8999	49.3825 1088	0.0244 1675	45
46	1.2107 8446	0.8259 1082	41.7814 0081	50.5882 7134	0.0239 3409	46
47	1.2158 2940	0.8224 8380	42.6038 8461	51.7990 5581	0.0234 7204	47
48	1.2208 9536	0.8190 7100	43.4229 5562	53.0148 8521	0.0230 2929	48
49	1.2259 8242	0.8156 7237	44.2386 2799	54.2357 8056	0.0226 0468	49
50	1.2310 9068	0.8122 8784	45.0509 1582	55.4617 6298	0.0221 9711	50

Table IV (*continued*). 5½₂ %

Number of periods n	Amount of 1 at compound interest $s = (1+i)^n$	Present value of 1 $v^n = \dfrac{1}{(1+i)^n}$	Present value of an annuity of 1 $a_{\overline{n}|} = \dfrac{1-v^n}{i}$	Amount of an annuity of 1 $s_{\overline{n}|} = \dfrac{(1+i)^n-1}{i}$	Annuity whose present value is 1 $\dfrac{1}{a_{\overline{n}|}} = \dfrac{1}{s_{\overline{n}|}} + i$	Number of periods n
51	1.2362 2002	0.8089 1735	45.8598 3317	56.6928 5366	0.0218 0557	51
52	1.2413 7114	0.8055 6084	46.6653 9401	57.9290 7388	0.0214 2916	52
53	1.2465 4352	0.8022 1827	47.4676 1228	59.1704 4503	0.0210 6700	53
54	1.2517 3745	0.7988 8956	48.2665 0184	60.4169 8855	0.0207 1830	54
55	1.2569 5302	0.7955 7467	49.0620 7651	61.6687 2600	0.0203 8234	55
56	1.2621 9033	0.7922 7353	49.8543 5003	62.9256 7902	0.0200 5843	56
57	1.2674 4946	0.7889 8608	50.6433 3612	64.1878 6935	0.0197 4593	57
58	1.2727 3050	0.7857 1228	51.4290 4840	65.4553 1881	0.0194 4426	58
59	1.2780 3354	0.7824 5207	52.2115 0046	66.7280 4930	0.0191 5287	59
60	1.2833 5868	0.7792 0538	52.9907 0584	68.0060 8284	0.0188 7123	60
61	1.2887 0601	0.7759 7216	53.7666 7800	69.2894 4152	0.0185 9888	61
62	1.2940 7561	0.7727 5236	54.5394 3035	70.5781 4753	0.0183 3536	62
63	1.2994 6760	0.7695 4591	55.3089 7627	71.8722 2314	0.0180 8025	63
64	1.3048 8204	0.7663 5278	56.0753 2905	73.1716 9074	0.0178 3315	64
65	1.3103 1905	0.7631 7289	56.8385 0194	74.4765 7278	0.0175 9371	65
66	1.3157 7872	0.7600 0620	57.5985 0814	75.7868 9184	0.0173 6156	66
67	1.3212 6113	0.7568 5265	58.3553 6078	77.1026 7055	0.0171 3639	67
68	1.3267 6638	0.7537 1218	59.1090 7296	78.4239 3168	0.0169 1788	68
69	1.3322 9458	0.7505 8474	59.8596 5770	79.7506 9806	0.0167 0574	69
70	1.3378 4580	0.7474 7028	60.6071 2798	81.0829 9264	0.0164 9971	70
71	1.3434 2016	0.7443 6874	61.3514 9672	82.4208 3844	0.0162 9952	71
72	1.3490 1774	0.7412 8008	62.0927 7680	83.7642 5860	0.0161 0493	72
73	1.3546 3865	0.7382 0423	62.8309 8103	85.1132 7634	0.0159 1572	73
74	1.3602 8298	0.7351 4114	63.5661 2216	86.4679 1500	0.0157 3165	74
75	1.3659 5082	0.7320 9076	64.2982 1292	87.8281 9797	0.0155 5253	75
76	1.3716 4229	0.7290 5304	65.0272 6596	89.1941 4880	0.0153 7816	76
77	1.3773 5716	0.7260 2792	65.7532 9388	90.5657 9109	0.0152 0836	77
78	1.3830 9645	0.7230 1536	66.4763 0924	91.9431 4855	0.0150 4295	78
79	1.3888 5935	0.7200 1529	67.1963 2453	93.3262 4500	0.0148 8177	79
80	1.3946 4627	0.7170 2768	67.9133 5221	94.7151 0436	0.0147 2464	80
81	1.4004 5729	0.7140 5246	68.6274 0167	96.1097 5062	0.0145 7144	81
82	1.4062 9253	0.7110 8959	69.3384 9426	97.5102 0792	0.0144 2200	82
83	1.4121 5209	0.7081 3901	70.0466 3326	98.9165 0045	0.0142 7620	83
84	1.4180 3605	0.7052 0067	70.7518 3393	100.3286 5254	0.0141 3391	84
85	1.4239 4454	0.7022 7453	71.4541 0846	101.7466 8859	0.0139 9500	85
86	1.4298 7764	0.6993 6052	72.1534 6898	103.1706 3312	0.0138 5935	86
87	1.4358 3546	0.6964 5861	72.8499 2759	104.6005 1076	0.0137 2685	87
88	1.4418 1811	0.6935 6874	73.5434 9633	106.0363 4622	0.0135 9740	88
89	1.4478 2568	0.6906 9086	74.2341 8720	107.4781 6433	0.0134 7088	89
90	1.4538 5829	0.6878 2493	74.9220 1212	108.9259 9002	0.0133 4721	90
91	1.4599 1603	0.6849 7088	75.6069 8300	110.3798 4831	0.0132 2629	91
92	1.4659 9902	0.6821 2868	76.2891 1168	111.8397 6434	0.0131 0803	92
93	1.4721 0735	0.6792 9827	76.9604 0995	113.3057 6336	0.0129 9234	93
94	1.4782 4113	0.6764 7960	77.6448 8955	114.7778 7071	0.0128 7915	94
95	1.4844 0047	0.6736 7263	78.3185 6218	116.2561 1184	0.0127 6837	95
96	1.4905 8547	0.6708 7731	78.9894 3950	117.7405 1230	0.0126 5992	96
97	1.4967 9624	0.6680 9359	79.6575 3308	119.2310 9777	0.0125 5374	97
98	1.5030 3289	0.6653 2141	80.3228 5450	120.7278 9401	0.0124 4976	98
99	1.5092 9553	0.6625 6074	80.9854 1524	122.2309 2690	0.0123 4790	99
100	1.5155 8426	0.6598 1153	81.6452 2677	123.7402 2243	0.0122 4811	100

Table V. ½ %

Number of periods	Amount of 1 at compound interest	Present value of 1	Present value of an annuity of 1	Amount of an annuity of 1	Annuity whose present value is 1	Number of periods
n	$s = (1 + i)^n$	$v^n = \dfrac{1}{(1 + i)^n}$	$a_{\overline{n}\rvert} = \dfrac{1 - v^n}{i}$	$s_{\overline{n}\rvert} = \dfrac{(1+i)^n - 1}{i}$	$\dfrac{1}{a_{\overline{n}\rvert}} = \dfrac{1}{s_{\overline{n}\rvert}} + i$	n
1	1.0050 0000	0.9950 2488	0.9950 2488	1.0000 0000	1.0050 0000	1
2	1.0100 2500	0.9900 7450	1.9850 9938	2.0050 0000	0.5037 5312	2
3	1.0150 7513	0.9851 4876	2.9702 4814	3.0150 2500	0.3366 7221	3
4	1.0201 5050	0.9802 4752	3.9504 9566	4.0301 0013	0.2531 3279	4
5	1.0252 5125	0.9753 7067	4.9258 6633	5.0502 5063	0.2030 0997	5
6	1.0303 7751	0.9705 1808	5.8963 8441	6.0755 0188	0.1695 9546	6
7	1.0355 2940	0.9656 8963	6.8620 7404	7.1058 7939	0.1457 2854	7
8	1.0407 0704	0.9608 8520	7.8229 5924	8.1414 0879	0.1278 2886	8
9	1.0459 1058	0.9561 0468	8.7790 6392	9.1821 1583	0.1139 0736	9
10	1.0511 4013	0.9513 4794	9.7304 1186	10.2280 2641	0.1027 7057	10
11	1.0563 9583	0.9466 1489	10.6770 2673	11.2791 6654	0.0936 5903	11
12	1.0616 7781	0.9419 0534	11.6189 3207	12.3355 6237	0.0860 6643	12
13	1.0669 8620	0.9372 1924	12.5561 5131	13.3972 4018	0.0796 4224	13
14	1.0723 2113	0.9325 5646	13.4887 0777	14.4642 2639	0.0741 3609	14
15	1.0776 8274	0.9279 1688	14.4166 2465	15.5365 4752	0.0693 6436	15
16	1.0830 7115	0.9233 0037	15.3399 2502	16.6142 3026	0.0651 8937	16
17	1.0884 8651	0.9187 0684	16.2586 3186	17.6973 0141	0.0615 0579	17
18	1.0939 2894	0.9141 3616	17.1727 6802	18.7857 8791	0.0582 3173	18
19	1.0993 9858	0.9095 8822	18.0823 5624	19.8797 1685	0.0553 0253	19
20	1.1048 9558	0.9050 6290	18.9874 1915	20.9791 1544	0.0526 6645	20
21	1.1104 2006	0.9005 6010	19.8879 7925	22.0840 1101	0.0502 8163	21
22	1.1159 7216	0.8960 7971	20.7840 5896	23.1944 3107	0.0481 1380	22
23	1.1215 5202	0.8916 2160	21.6756 8055	24.3104 0322	0.0461 3465	23
24	1.1271 5978	0.8871 8567	22.5628 6622	25.4319 5524	0.0443 2061	24
25	1.1327 9558	0.8827 7181	23.4456 3803	26.5591 1502	0.0426 5186	25
26	1.1384 5955	0.8783 7991	24.3240 1794	27.6919 1059	0.0411 1163	26
27	1.1441 5185	0.8740 0986	25.1980 2780	28.8303 7015	0.0396 8565	27
28	1.1498 7261	0.8696 6155	26.0676 8936	29.9745 2200	0.0383 6167	28
29	1.1556 2197	0.8653 3488	26.9330 2423	31.1243 9461	0.0371 2914	29
30	1.1614 0008	0.8610 2973	27.7940 5397	32.2800 1658	0.0359 7892	30
31	1.1672 0708	0.8567 4600	28.6507 9997	33.4414 1666	0.0349 0304	31
32	1.1730 4312	0.8524 8358	29.5032 8355	34.6086 2375	0.0338 9453	32
33	1.1789 0833	0.8482 4237	30.3515 2592	35.7816 6686	0.0329 4727	33
34	1.1848 0288	0.8440 2226	31.1955 4818	36.9605 7520	0.0320 5586	34
35	1.1907 2689	0.8398 2314	32.0353 7132	38.1453 7807	0.0312 1550	35
36	1.1966 8052	0.8356 4492	32.8710 1624	39.3361 0496	0.0304 2194	36
37	1.2026 6393	0.8314 8748	33.7025 0372	40.5327 8549	0.0296 7139	37
38	1.2086 7725	0.8273 5073	34.5298 5445	41.7354 4942	0.0289 6045	38
39	1.2147 2063	0.8232 3455	35.3530 8900	42.9441 2666	0.0282 8607	39
40	1.2207 9424	0.8191 3886	36.1722 2786	44.1588 4730	0.0276 4552	40
41	1.2268 9821	0.8150 6354	36.9872 9141	45.3796 4153	0.0270 3631	41
42	1.2330 3270	0.8110 0850	37.7982 9991	46.6065 3974	0.0264 5622	42
43	1.2391 9786	0.8069 7363	38.6052 7354	47.8395 7244	0.0259 0320	43
44	1.2453 9385	0.8029 5884	39.4082 3238	49.0787 7030	0.0253 7541	44
45	1.2516 2082	0.7989 6402	40.2071 9640	50.3241 6415	0.0248 7117	45
46	1.2578 7892	0.7949 8907	41.0021 8547	51.5757 8497	0.0243 8894	46
47	1.2641 6832	0.7910 3390	41.7932 1937	52.8336 6390	0.0239 2733	47
48	1.2704 8916	0.7870 9841	42.5803 1778	54.0978 3222	0.0234 8503	48
49	1.2768 4161	0.7831 8250	43.3635 0028	55.3683 2138	0.0230 6087	49
50	1.2832 2581	0.7792 8607	44.1427 8635	56.6451 6299	0.0226 5376	50

Table V (*continued*). ½ %

Number of periods n	Amount of 1 at compound interest $s = (1 + i)^n$	Present value of 1 $v^n = \dfrac{1}{(1+i)^n}$	Present value of an annuity of 1 $a_{\overline{n}|} = \dfrac{1 - v^n}{i}$	Amount of an annuity of 1 $s_{\overline{n}|} = \dfrac{(1+i)^n-1}{i}$	Annuity whose present value is 1 $\dfrac{1}{a_{\overline{n}|}} = \dfrac{1}{s_{\overline{n}|}} + i$	Number of periods n
51	1.2896 4194	0.7754 0902	44.9181 9537	57.9283 8880	0.0222 6269	51
52	1.2960 9015	0.7715 5127	45.6897 4664	59.2180 3075	0.0218 8675	52
53	1.3025 7060	0.7677 1270	46.4574 5934	60.5141 2090	0.0215 2507	53
54	1.3090 8346	0.7638 9324	47.2213 5258	61.8166 9150	0.0211 7686	54
55	1.3156 2887	0.7600 9277	47.9814 4535	63.1257 7496	0.0208 4139	55
56	1.3222 0702	0.7563 1122	48.7377 5657	64.4414 0384	0.0205 1797	56
57	1.3288 1805	0.7525 4847	49.4903 0505	65.7636 1086	0.0202 0598	57
58	1.3354 6214	0.7488 0445	50.2391 0950	67.0924 2891	0.0199 0481	58
59	1.3421 3946	0.7450 7906	50.9841 8855	68.4278 9105	0.0196 1392	59
60	1.3488 5015	0.7413 7220	51.7255 6075	69.7700 3051	0.0193 3280	60
61	1.3555 9440	0.7376 8378	52.4632 4453	71.1188 8066	0.0190 6096	61
62	1.3623 7238	0.7340 1371	53.1972 5824	72.4744 7507	0.0187 9796	62
63	1.3691 8424	0.7303 6190	53.9276 2014	73.8368 4744	0.0185 4337	63
64	1.3760 3016	0.7267 2826	54.6543 4839	75.2060 3168	0.0182 9681	64
65	1.3829 1031	0.7231 1269	55.3774 6109	76.5820 6184	0.0180 5789	65
66	1.3898 2486	0.7195 1512	56.0969 7621	77.9649 7215	0.0178 2627	66
67	1.3967 7399	0.7159 3544	56.8129 1165	79.3547 9701	0.0176 0163	67
68	1.4037 5785	0.7123 7357	57.5252 8522	80.7515 7099	0.0173 8366	68
69	1.4107 7664	0.7088 2943	58.2341 1465	82.1553 2885	0.0171 7206	69
70	1.4178 3053	0.7053 0291	58.9394 1756	83.5661 0549	0.0169 6657	70
71	1.4249 1968	0.7017 9394	59.6412 1151	84.9839 3602	0.0167 6693	71
72	1.4320 4428	0.6983 0243	60.3395 1394	86.4088 5570	0.0165 7289	72
73	1.4392 0450	0.6948 2829	61.0343 4222	87.8408 9998	0.0163 8422	73
74	1.4464 0052	0.6913 7143	61.7257 1366	89.2801 0448	0.0162 0070	74
75	1.4536 3252	0.6879 3177	62.4136 4543	90.7265 0500	0.0160 2214	75
76	1.4609 0069	0.6845 0923	63.0981 5466	92.1801 3752	0.0158 4832	76
77	1.4682 0519	0.6811 0371	63.7792 5836	93.6410 3821	0.0156 7908	77
78	1.4755 4622	0.6777 1513	64.4569 7350	95.1092 4340	0.0155 1423	78
79	1.4829 2395	0.6743 4342	65.1313 1691	96.5847 8962	0.0153 5360	79
80	1.4903 3857	0.6709 8847	65.8023 0538	98.0677 1357	0.0151 9704	80
81	1.4977 9028	0.6676 5022	66.4699 5561	99.5580 5214	0.0150 4439	81
82	1.5052 7921	0.6643 2858	67.1342 8419	101.0558 4240	0.0148 9552	82
83	1.5128 0561	0.6610 2346	67.7953 0765	102.5611 2161	0.0147 5028	83
84	1.5203 6964	0.6577 3479	68.4530 4244	104.0739 2722	0.0146 0855	84
85	1.5279 7148	0.6544 6248	69.1075 0491	105.5942 9685	0.0144 7021	85
86	1.5356 1134	0.6512 0644	69.7587 1135	107.1222 6834	0.0143 3513	86
87	1.5432 8940	0.6479 6661	70.4066 7796	108.6578 7968	0.0142 0320	87
88	1.5510 0585	0.6447 4290	71.0514 2086	110.2011 6908	0.0140 7431	88
89	1.5587 6087	0.6415 3522	71.6929 5608	111.7521 7492	0.0139 4837	89
90	1.5665 5468	0.6383 4350	72.3312 9958	113.3109 3580	0.0138 2527	90
91	1.5743 8745	0.6351 6766	72.9664 6725	114.8774 9048	0.0137 0493	91
92	1.5822 5939	0.6320 0763	73.5984 7487	116.4518 7793	0.0135 8724	92
93	1.5901 7069	0.6288 6331	74.2273 3818	118.0341 3732	0.0134 7213	93
94	1.5981 2154	0.6257 3464	74.8530 7282	119.6243 0800	0.0133 5950	94
95	1.6061 1215	0.6226 2153	75.4756 9434	121.2224 2954	0.0132 4930	95
96	1.6141 4271	0.6195 2391	76.0952 1825	122.8285 4169	0.0131 4143	96
97	1.6222 1342	0.6164 4170	76.7116 5995	124.4426 8440	0.0130 3583	97
98	1.6303 2449	0.6133 7483	77.3250 3478	126.0648 9782	0.0129 3242	98
99	1.6384 7611	0.6103 2321	77.9353 5799	127.6952 2231	0.0128 3115	99
100	1.6466 6849	0.6072 8678	78.5426 4477	129.3336 9842	0.0127 3194	100

Table VI. $7/12 \%$

Number of periods n	Amount of 1 at compound interest $s = (1 + i)^n$	Present value of 1 $v^n = \dfrac{1}{(1+i)^n}$	Present value of an annuity of 1 $a_{\overline{n}|} = \dfrac{1 - v^n}{i}$	Amount of an annuity of 1 $s_{\overline{n}|} = \dfrac{(1+i)^n - 1}{i}$	Annuity whose present value is 1 $\dfrac{1}{a_{\overline{n}|}} = \dfrac{1}{s_{\overline{n}|}} + i$	Number of periods n
1	1.0058 3333	0.9942 0050	0.9942 0050	1.0000 0000	1.0058 3333	1
2	1.0117 0069	0.9884 3463	1.9826 3513	2.0058 3333	0.5043 7924	2
3	1.0176 0228	0.9827 0220	2.9653 3733	3.0175 3403	0.3372 2976	3
4	1.0235 3830	0.9770 0302	3.9423 4034	4.0351 3631	0.2536 5644	4
5	1.0295 0894	0.9713 3688	4.9136 7723	5.0586 7460	0.2035 1357	5
6	1.0355 1440	0.9657 0361	5.8793 8084	6.0881 8354	0.1700 8594	6
7	1.0415 5490	0.9601 0301	6.8394 8385	7.1236 9794	0.1462 0986	7
8	1.0476 3064	0.9545 3489	7.7940 1875	8.1652 5284	0.1283 0351	8
9	1.0537 4182	0.9489 9907	8.7430 1781	9.2128 8349	0.1143 7698	9
10	1.0598 8865	0.9434 9534	9.6865 1315	10.2666 2531	0.1032 3632	10
11	1.0660 7133	0.9380 2354	10.6245 3669	11.3265 1396	0.0941 2175	11
12	1.0722 9008	0.9325 8347	11.5571 2016	12.3925 8529	0.0865 2675	12
13	1.0785 4511	0.9271 7495	12.4842 9511	13.4648 7537	0.0801 0064	13
14	1.0848 3662	0.9217 9780	13.4060 9291	14.5434 2048	0.0745 9295	14
15	1.0911 6483	0.9164 5183	14.3225 4473	15.6282 5710	0.0698 1999	15
16	1.0975 2996	0.9111 3686	15.2336 8160	16.7194 2193	0.0656 4401	16
17	1.1039 3222	0.9058 5272	16.1395 3432	17.8169 5189	0.0619 5966	17
18	1.1103 7182	0.9005 9923	17.0401 3354	18.9208 8411	0.0586 8499	18
19	1.1168 4899	0.8953 7620	17.9355 0974	20.0312 5593	0.0557 5532	19
20	1.1233 6395	0.8901 8346	18.8256 9320	21.1481 0493	0.0531 1889	20
21	1.1299 1690	0.8850 2084	19.7107 1404	22.2714 6887	0.0507 3383	21
22	1.1365 0808	0.8798 8816	20.5906 0220	23.4013 8577	0.0485 6585	22
23	1.1431 3771	0.8747 8525	21.4653 8745	24.5378 9386	0.0465 8663	23
24	1.1498 0602	0.8697 1193	22.3350 9939	25.6810 3157	0.0447 7258	24
25	1.1565 1322	0.8646 6803	23.1997 6741	26.8308 3759	0.0431 0388	25
26	1.1632 5955	0.8596 5339	24.0594 2079	27.9873 5081	0.0415 6376	26
27	1.1700 4523	0.8546 6782	24.9140 8862	29.1506 1035	0.0401 3793	27
28	1.1768 7049	0.8497 1118	25.7637 9979	30.3206 5558	0.0388 1415	28
29	1.1837 3557	0.8447 8327	26.6085 8307	31.4975 2607	0.0375 8186	29
30	1.1906 4069	0.8398 8395	27.4484 6702	32.6812 6164	0.0364 3191	30
31	1.1975 8610	0.8350 1304	28.2834 8006	33.8719 0233	0.0353 5633	31
32	1.2045 7202	0.8301 7038	29.1136 5044	35.0694 8843	0.0343 4815	32
33	1.2115 9869	0.8253 5581	29.9390 0625	36.2740 6045	0.0334 0124	33
34	1.2186 6634	0.8205 6915	30.7595 7540	37.4856 5913	0.0325 1020	34
35	1.2257 7523	0.8158 1026	31.5753 8566	38.7043 2548	0.0316 7024	35
36	1.2329 2559	0.8110 7897	32.3864 6463	39.9301 0071	0.0308 7710	36
37	1.2401 1765	0.8063 7511	33.1928 3974	41.1630 2630	0.0301 2698	37
38	1.2473 5167	0.8016 9854	33.9945 3828	42.4031 4395	0.0294 1649	38
39	1.2546 2789	0.7970 4908	34.7915 8736	43.6504 9562	0.0287 4258	39
40	1.2619 4655	0.7924 2660	35.5840 1396	44.9051 2352	0.0281 0251	40
41	1.2693 0791	0.7878 3092	36.3718 4487	46.1670 7007	0.0274 9379	41
42	1.2767 1220	0.7832 6189	37.1551 0676	47.4363 7798	0.0269 1420	42
43	1.2841 5969	0.7787 1936	37.9338 2612	48.7130 9018	0.0263 6170	43
44	1.2916 5062	0.7742 0317	38.7080 2929	49.9972 4988	0.0258 3443	44
45	1.2991 8525	0.7697 1318	39.4777 4248	51.2889 0050	0.0253 3073	45
46	1.3067 6383	0.7652 4923	40.2429 9170	52.5880 8575	0.0248 4905	46
47	1.3143 8662	0.7608 1116	41.0038 0287	53.8948 4959	0.0243 8798	47
48	1.3220 5388	0.7563 9884	41.7602 0170	55.2092 3621	0.0239 4624	48
49	1.3297 6586	0.7520 1210	42.5122 1380	56.5312 9009	0.0235 2265	49
50	1.3375 2283	0.7476 5080	43.2598 6460	57.8610 5595	0.0231 1611	50

Table VI (*continued*). $7/12\%$

Number of periods n	Amount of 1 at compound interest $s = (1+i)^n$	Present value of 1 $v^n = \dfrac{1}{(1+i)^n}$	Present value of an annuity of 1 $a_{\overline{n}\rvert} = \dfrac{1-v^n}{i}$	Amount of an annuity of 1 $s_{\overline{n}\rvert} = \dfrac{(1+i)^n-1}{i}$	Annuity whose present value is 1 $\dfrac{1}{a_{\overline{n}\rvert}} = \dfrac{1}{s_{\overline{n}\rvert}} + i$	Number of periods n
51	1.3453 2504	0.7433 1480	44.0031 7940	59.1985 7877	0.0227 2563	51
52	1.3531 7277	0.7390 0394	44.7421 8335	60.5439 0381	0.0223 5027	52
53	1.3610 6628	0.7347 1809	45.4769 0144	61.8970 7659	0.0219 8919	53
54	1.3690 0583	0.7304 5709	46.2073 5853	63.2581 4287	0.0216 4157	54
55	1.3769 9170	0.7262 2080	46.9335 7933	64.6271 4870	0.0213 0671	55
56	1.3850 2415	0.7220 0908	47.6555 8841	66.0041 4040	0.0209 8390	56
57	1.3931 0346	0.7178 2179	48.3734 1020	67.3891 6455	0.0206 7251	57
58	1.4012 2990	0.7136 5878	49.0870 6898	68.7822 6801	0.0203 7196	58
59	1.4094 0374	0.7095 1991	49.7965 8889	70.1834 9791	0.0200 8170	59
60	1.4176 2526	0.7054 0505	50.5019 9394	71.5929 0165	0.0198 0120	60
61	1.4258 9474	0.7013 1405	51.2033 0800	73.0105 2691	0.0195 2999	61
62	1.4342 1246	0.6972 4678	51.9005 5478	74.4364 2165	0.0192 6762	62
63	1.4425 7870	0.6932 0310	52.5937 5787	75.8706 3411	0.0190 1366	63
64	1.4509 9374	0.6891 8286	53.2829 4073	77.3132 1281	0.0187 6773	64
65	1.4594 5787	0.6851 8594	53.9681 2668	78.7642 0655	0.0185 2946	65
66	1.4679 7138	0.6812 1221	54.6493 3888	80.2236 6442	0.0182 9848	66
67	1.4765 3454	0.6772 6151	55.3266 0040	81.6916 3579	0.0180 7449	67
68	1.4851 4766	0.6733 3373	55.9999 3413	83.1681 7034	0.0178 5716	68
69	1.4938 1102	0.6694 2873	56.6693 6287	84.6533 1800	0.0176 4622	69
70	1.5025 2492	0.6655 4638	57.3349 0925	86.1471 2902	0.0174 4138	70
71	1.5112 8965	0.6616 8654	57.9965 9579	87.6496 5394	0.0172 4239	71
72	1.5201 0550	0.6578 4909	58.6544 4488	89.1609 4359	0.0170 4901	72
73	1.5289 7279	0.6540 3389	59.3084 7877	90.6810 4909	0.0168 6100	73
74	1.5378 9179	0.6502 4082	59.9587 1959	92.2100 2188	0.0166 7814	74
75	1.5468 6283	0.6464 6975	60.6051 8934	93.7479 1367	0.0165 0024	75
76	1.5558 8620	0.6427 2054	61.2479 0988	95.2947 7650	0.0163 2709	76
77	1.5649 6220	0.6389 9308	61.8869 0297	96.8506 6270	0.0161 5851	77
78	1.5740 9115	0.6352 8724	62.5221 9021	98.4156 2490	0.0159 9432	78
79	1.5832 7334	0.6316 0289	63.1537 9310	99.9897 1604	0.0158 3436	79
80	1.5925 0910	0.6279 3991	63.7817 3301	101.5729 8938	0.0156 7847	80
81	1.6017 9874	0.6242 9817	64.4060 3118	103.1654 9849	0.0155 2650	81
82	1.6111 4257	0.6206 7755	65.0267 0874	104.7672 9723	0.0153 7830	82
83	1.6205 4090	0.6170 7793	65.6437 8667	106.3784 3980	0.0152 3373	83
84	1.6299 9405	0.6134 9919	66.2572 8585	107.9989 8070	0.0150 9268	84
85	1.6395 0235	0.6099 4120	66.8672 2705	109.6289 7475	0.0149 5501	85
86	1.6490 6613	0.6064 0384	67.4736 3089	111.2684 7710	0.0148 2060	86
87	1.6586 8567	0.6028 8700	68.0765 1789	112.9175 4322	0.0146 8935	87
88	1.6683 6134	0.5993 9056	68.6759 0843	114.3762 2889	0.0145 6115	88
89	1.6780 9344	0.5959 1439	69.2718 2283	116.2445 9022	0.0144 3588	89
90	1.6878 8232	0.5924 5838	69.8642 8121	117.9226 8367	0.0143 1347	90
91	1.6977 2830	0.5890 2242	70.4533 0363	119.6105 6599	0.0141 9380	91
92	1.7076 3172	0.5856 0638	71.0389 1001	121.3082 9429	0.0140 7679	92
93	1.7175 9290	0.5822 1015	71.6211 2017	123.0159 2601	0.0139 6236	93
94	1.7276 1219	0.5788 3363	72.1999 5379	124.7335 1891	0.0138 5042	94
95	1.7376 8993	0.5754 7668	72.7754 3047	126.4611 3110	0.0137 4090	95
96	1.7478 2646	0.5721 3920	73.3475 6967	128.1988 2103	0.0136 3372	96
97	1.7580 2211	0.5688 2108	73.9163 9075	129.9466 4749	0.0135 2880	97
98	1.7682 7724	0.5655 2220	74.4819 1294	131.7046 6960	0.0134 2608	98
99	1.7785 9219	0.5622 4245	75.0441 5539	133.4729 4684	0.0133 2549	99
100	1.7889 6731	0.5589 8172	75.6031 3712	135.2515 3903	0.0132 2696	100

Table VII. $\frac{2}{3}\%$

Number of periods n	Amount of 1 at compound interest $s = (1+i)^n$	Present value of 1 $v^n = \dfrac{1}{(1+i)^n}$	Present value of an annuity of 1 $a_{\overline{n}|} = \dfrac{1-v^n}{i}$	Amount of an annuity of 1 $s_{\overline{n}|} = \dfrac{(1+i)^n-1}{i}$	Annuity whose present value is 1 $\dfrac{1}{a_{\overline{n}|}} = \dfrac{1}{s_{\overline{n}|}} + i$	Number of periods n
1	1.0066 6667	0.9933 7748	0.9933 7748	1.0000 0000	1.0066 6667	1
2	1.0133 7778	0.9867 9882	1.9801 7631	2.0066 6667	0.5050 0554	2
3	1.0201 3363	0.9802 6373	2.9604 4004	3.0200 4444	0.3377 8762	3
4	1.0269 3452	0.9737 7192	3.9342 1196	4.0401 7807	0.2541 8051	4
5	1.0337 8075	0.9673 2310	4.9015 3506	5.0671 1259	0.2040 1772	5
6	1.0406 7262	0.9609 1699	5.8624 5205	6.1008 9335	0.1705 7709	6
7	1.0476 1044	0.9545 5330	6.8170 0535	7.1415 6597	0.1466 9198	7
8	1.0545 9451	0.9482 3175	7.7652 3710	8.1891 7641	0.1287 7907	8
9	1.0616 2514	0.9419 5207	8.7071 8917	9.2437 7092	0.1148 4763	9
10	1.0687 0264	0.9357 1398	9.6429 0315	10.3053 9606	0.1037 0321	10
11	1.0758 2732	0.9295 1720	10.5724 2035	11.3740 9870	0.0945 8572	11
12	1.0829 9951	0.9233 6145	11.4957 8180	12.4499 2602	0.0869 8843	12
13	1.0902 1950	0.9172 4648	12.4130 2828	13.5329 2553	0.0805 6052	13
14	1.0974 8763	0.9111 7200	13.3242 0028	14.6231 4503	0.0750 5141	14
15	1.1048 0422	0.9051 3775	14.2293 3802	15.7206 3266	0.0702 7734	15
16	1.1121 6958	0.8991 4346	15.1284 8148	16.8254 3688	0.0661 0049	16
17	1.1195 8404	0.8931 8886	16.0216 7035	17.9376 0646	0.0624 1546	17
18	1.1270 4794	0.8872 7371	16.9089 4405	19.0571 9051	0.0591 4030	18
19	1.1345 6159	0.8813 9772	17.7903 4177	20.1842 3844	0.0562 1027	19
20	1.1421 2533	0.8755 6065	18.6659 0242	21.3188 0003	0.0535 7362	20
21	1.1497 3950	0.8697 6224	19.5356 6466	22.4609 2536	0.0511 8843	21
22	1.1574 0443	0.8640 0222	20.3996 6688	23.6106 6487	0.0490 2041	22
23	1.1651 2046	0.8582 8035	21.2579 4723	24.7680 6930	0.0470 4123	23
24	1.1728 8793	0.8525 9638	22.1105 4361	25.9331 8976	0.0452 2729	24
25	1.1807 0718	0.8469 5004	22.9574 9365	27.1060 7769	0.0435 5876	25
26	1.1885 7857	0.8413 4110	23.7988 3475	28.2867 8488	0.0420 1886	26
27	1.1965 0242	0.8357 6931	24.6346 0406	29.4753 6344	0.0405 9331	27
28	1.2044 7911	0.8302 3441	25.4648 3847	30.6718 6586	0.0392 6983	28
29	1.2125 0897	0.8247 3617	26.2895 7464	31.8763 4497	0.0380 3789	29
30	1.2205 9236	0.8192 7434	27.1088 4898	33.0888 5394	0.0368 8832	30
31	1.2287 2964	0.8138 4868	27.9226 9766	34.3094 4630	0.0358 1316	31
32	1.2369 2117	0.8084 5896	28.7311 5662	35.5381 7594	0.0348 0542	32
33	1.2451 6731	0.8031 0492	29.5342 6154	36.7750 9711	0.0338 5898	33
34	1.2534 6843	0.7977 8635	30.3320 4789	38.0202 6443	0.0329 6843	34
35	1.2618 2489	0.7925 0299	31.1245 5088	39.2737 3286	0.0321 2898	35
36	1.2702 3705	0.7872 5463	31.9118 0551	40.5355 5774	0.0313 3637	36
37	1.2787 0530	0.7820 4102	32.6938 4653	41.8057 9479	0.0305 8680	37
38	1.2872 3000	0.7768 6194	33.4707 0848	43.0845 0009	0.0298 7687	38
39	1.2958 1153	0.7717 1716	34.2424 2564	44.3717 3009	0.0292 0354	39
40	1.3044 5028	0.7666 0645	35.0090 3209	45.6675 4163	0.0285 6406	40
41	1.3131 4661	0.7615 2959	35.7705 6168	46.9719 9191	0.0279 5595	41
42	1.3219 0092	0.7564 8635	36.5270 4803	48.2851 3852	0.0273 7697	42
43	1.3307 1360	0.7514 7650	37.2785 2453	49.6070 3944	0.0268 2509	43
44	1.3395 8502	0.7464 9984	38.0250 2437	50.9377 5304	0.0262 9847	44
45	1.3485 1559	0.7415 5613	38.7665 8050	52.2773 3806	0.0257 9541	45
46	1.3575 0569	0.7366 4516	39.5032 2566	53.6258 5365	0.0253 1439	46
47	1.3665 5573	0.7317 6672	40.2349 9238	54.9833 5934	0.0248 5399	47
48	1.3756 6610	0.7269 2058	40.9619 1296	56.3499 1507	0.0244 1292	48
49	1.3848 3721	0.7221 0654	41.6840 1949	57.7255 8117	0.0239 9001	49
50	1.3940 6946	0.7173 2437	42.4013 4387	59.1104 1837	0.0235 8416	50

Table VII (continued). $2/3\%$

Number of periods n	Amount of 1 at compound interest $s = (1+i)^n$	Present value of 1 $v^n = \dfrac{1}{(1+i)^n}$	Present value of an annuity of 1 $a_{\overline{n}|} = \dfrac{1-v^n}{i}$	Amount of an annuity of 1 $s_{\overline{n}|} = \dfrac{(1+i)^n-1}{i}$	Annuity whose present value is 1 $\dfrac{1}{a_{\overline{n}|}} = \dfrac{1}{s_{\overline{n}|}} + i$	Number of periods n
51	1.4033 6325	0.7125 7388	43.1139 1775	60.5044 8783	0.0231 9437	51
52	1.4127 1901	0.7078 5485	43.8217 7260	61.9078 5108	0.0228 1971	52
53	1.4221 3713	0.7031 6707	44.5249 3967	63.3205 7009	0.0224 5932	53
54	1.4316 1805	0.6985 1033	45.2234 5000	64.7427 0722	0.0221 1242	54
55	1.4411 6217	0.6938 8444	45.9173 3444	66.1743 2527	0.0217 7827	55
56	1.4507 6992	0.6892 8918	46.6066 2362	67.6154 8744	0.0214 5618	56
57	1.4604 4172	0.6847 2435	47.2913 4796	69.0662 5736	0.0211 4552	57
58	1.4701 7799	0.6801 8975	47.9715 3771	70.5266 9907	0.0208 4569	58
59	1.4799 7918	0.6756 8518	48.6472 2289	71.9968 7706	0.0205 5616	59
60	1.4898 4571	0.6712 1044	49.3184 3334	73.4768 5625	0.0202 7639	60
61	1.4997 7801	0.6667 6534	49.9851 9868	74.9667 0195	0.0200 0592	61
62	1.5097 7653	0.6623 4968	50.6475 4835	76.4664 7997	0.0197 4429	62
63	1.5198 4171	0.6579 6326	51.3055 1161	77.9762 5650	0.0194 9108	63
64	1.5299 7399	0.6536 0588	51.9591 1749	79.4960 9821	0.0192 4590	64
65	1.5401 7381	0.6492 7737	52.6083 9486	81.0260 7220	0.0190 0837	65
66	1.5504 4164	0.6449 7752	53.2533 7238	82.5662 4601	0.0187 7815	66
67	1.5607 7792	0.6407 0614	53.8940 7852	84.1166 8765	0.0185 5491	67
68	1.5711 8310	0.6364 6306	54.5305 4158	85.6774 6557	0.0183 3835	68
69	1.5816 5766	0.6322 4807	55.1627 8965	87.2486 4867	0.0181 2816	69
70	1.5922 0204	0.6280 6100	55.7908 5064	88.8303 0633	0.0179 2409	70
71	1.6028 1672	0.6239 0165	56.4147 5229	90.4225 0837	0.0177 2586	71
72	1.6135 0217	0.6197 6985	57.0345 2215	92.0253 2510	0.0175 3324	72
73	1.6242 5885	0.6156 6541	57.6501 8756	93.6388 2726	0.0173 4600	73
74	1.6350 8724	0.6115 8816	58.2617 7572	95.2630 8611	0.0171 6391	74
75	1.6459 8782	0.6075 3791	58.8693 1363	96.8981 7335	0.0169 8678	75
76	1.6569 6107	0.6035 1448	59.4728 2811	98.5441 6118	0.0168 1440	76
77	1.6680 0748	0.5995 1769	60.0723 4581	100.2011 2225	0.0166 4659	77
78	1.6791 2753	0.5955 4738	60.6678 9319	101.8691 2973	0.0164 8318	78
79	1.6903 2172	0.5916 0336	61.2594 9654	103.5482 5726	0.0163 2400	79
80	1.7015 9053	0.5876 8545	61.8471 8200	105.2385 7898	0.0161 6889	80
81	1.7129 3116	0.5837 9350	62.4309 7549	106.9401 6950	0.0160 1769	81
82	1.7243 5403	0.5799 2732	63.0109 0281	108.6531 0397	0.0158 7027	82
83	1.7358 4972	0.5760 8674	63.5869 8954	110.3774 5799	0.0157 2649	83
84	1.7474 2205	0.5722 7159	64.1592 6114	112.1133 0771	0.0155 8621	84
85	1.7590 7153	0.5684 8171	64.7277 4285	113.8607 2977	0.0154 4933	85
86	1.7707 9868	0.5647 1693	65.2924 5979	115.6198 0130	0.0153 1570	86
87	1.7826 0400	0.5609 7709	65.8534 3687	117.3905 9997	0.0151 8524	87
88	1.7944 8803	0.5572 6201	66.4106 9888	119.1732 0397	0.0150 5781	88
89	1.8064 5128	0.5535 7153	66.9642 7041	120.9676 9200	0.0149 3334	89
90	1.8184 9429	0.5499 0549	67.5141 7590	122.7741 4328	0.0148 1170	90
91	1.8306 1758	0.5462 6374	68.0604 3964	124.5926 3757	0.0146 9282	91
92	1.8428 2170	0.5426 4610	68.6030 8574	126.4232 5515	0.0145 7660	92
93	1.8551 0718	0.5390 5241	69.1421 3815	128.2660 7685	0.0144 6296	93
94	1.8674 7456	0.5354 8253	69.6776 2068	130.1211 8403	0.0143 5181	94
95	1.8799 2439	0.5319 3629	70.2095 5696	131.9886 5859	0.0142 4308	95
96	1.8924 5722	0.5284 1353	70.7379 7049	133.8685 8298	0.0141 3668	96
97	1.9050 7360	0.5249 1410	71.2628 8460	135.7610 4020	0.0140 3255	97
98	1.9177 7409	0.5214 3785	71.7843 2245	137.6661 1380	0.0139 3062	98
99	1.9305 5925	0.5179 8462	72.3023 0707	139.5838 8790	0.0138 3082	99
100	1.9434 2965	0.5145 5426	72.8168 6132	141.5144 4715	0.0137 3308	100

Table VIII. $\frac{3}{4}\%$

Number of periods n	Amount of 1 at compound interest $s = (1+i)^n$	Present value of 1 $v^n = \dfrac{1}{(1+i)^n}$	Present value of an annuity of 1 $a_{\overline{n}|} = \dfrac{1-v^n}{i}$	Amount of an annuity of 1 $s_{\overline{n}|} = \dfrac{(1+i)^n-1}{i}$	Annuity whose present value is 1 $\dfrac{1}{a_{\overline{n}|}} = \dfrac{1}{s_{\overline{n}|}} + i$	Number of periods n
1	1.0075 0000	0.9925 5583	0.9925 5583	1.0000 0000	1.0075 0000	1
2	1.0150 5625	0.9851 6708	1.9777 2291	2.0075 0000	0.5056 3200	2
3	1.0226 6917	0.9778 3333	2.9555 5624	3.0225 5625	0.3383 4579	3
4	1.0303 3919	0.9705 5417	3.9261 1041	4.0452 2542	0.2547 0501	4
5	1.0380 6673	0.9633 2920	4.8894 3961	5.0755 6461	0.2045 2242	5
6	1.0458 5224	0.9561 5802	5.8455 9763	6.1136 3135	0.1710 6891	6
7	1.0536 9613	0.9490 4022	6.7946 3785	7.1594 8358	0.1471 7488	7
8	1.0615 9885	0.9419 7540	7.7366 1325	8.2131 7971	0.1292 5552	8
9	1.0695 6084	0.9349 6318	8.6715 7642	9.2747 7856	0.1153 1929	9
10	1.0775 8255	0.9280 0315	9.5995 7958	10.3443 3940	0.1041 7123	10
11	1.0856 6441	0.9210 9494	10.5206 7452	11.4219 2194	0.0950 5094	11
12	1.0938 0690	0.9142 3815	11.4349 1267	12.5075 8636	0.0874 5148	12
13	1.1020 1045	0.9074 3241	12.3423 4508	13.6013 9325	0.0810 2188	13
14	1.1102 7553	0.9006 7733	13.2430 2242	14.7034 0370	0.0755 1146	14
15	1.1186 0259	0.8939 7254	14.1369 9495	15.8136 7923	0.0707 3639	15
16	1.1269 9211	0.8873 1766	15.0243 1261	16.9322 8183	0.0665 5879	16
17	1.1354 4455	0.8807 1231	15.9050 2492	18.0592 7394	0.0628 7321	17
18	1.1439 6039	0.8741 5614	16.7791 8107	19.1947 1849	0.0595 9766	18
19	1.1525 4009	0.8676 4878	17.6468 2984	20.3386 7888	0.0566 6740	19
20	1.1611 8414	0.8611 8985	18.5080 1969	21.4912 1897	0.0540 3063	20
21	1.1698 9302	0.8547 7901	19.3627 9870	22.6524 0312	0.0516 4543	21
22	1.1786 6722	0.8484 1589	20.2112 1459	23.8222 9614	0.0494 7748	22
23	1.1875 0723	0.8421 0014	21.0533 1473	25.0009 6336	0.0474 9846	23
24	1.1964 1353	0.8358 3140	21.8891 4614	26.1884 7059	0.0456 8474	24
25	1.2053 8663	0.8296 0933	22.7187 5547	27.3848 8412	0.0440 1650	25
26	1.2144 2703	0.8234 3358	23.5421 8905	28.5902 7075	0.0424 7693	26
27	1.2235 3523	0.8173 0380	24.3594 9286	29.8046 9778	0.0410 5176	27
28	1.2327 1175	0.8112 1966	25.1707 1251	31.0282 3301	0.0397 2871	28
29	1.2419 5709	0.8051 8080	25.9758 9331	32.2609 4476	0.0384 9723	29
30	1.2512 7176	0.7991 8690	26.7750 8021	33.5029 0184	0.0373 4816	30
31	1.2606 5630	0.7932 3762	27.5683 1783	34.7541 7361	0.0362 7352	31
32	1.2701 1122	0.7873 3262	28.3556 5045	36.0148 2991	0.0352 6634	32
33	1.2796 3706	0.7814 7158	29.1371 2203	37.2849 4113	0.0343 2048	33
34	1.2892 3434	0.7756 5418	29.9127 7621	38.5645 7819	0.0334 3053	34
35	1.2989 0359	0.7698 8008	30.6826 5629	39.8538 1253	0.0325 9170	35
36	1.3086 4537	0.7641 4896	31.4468 0525	41.1527 1612	0.0317 9973	36
37	1.3184 6021	0.7584 6051	32.2052 6576	42.4613 6149	0.0310 5082	37
38	1.3283 4866	0.7528 1440	32.9580 8016	43.7798 2170	0.0303 4157	38
39	1.3383 1128	0.7472 1032	33.7052 9048	45.1081 7037	0.0296 6893	39
40	1.3483 4861	0.7416 4796	34.4469 3844	46.4464 8164	0.0290 3016	40
41	1.3584 6123	0.7361 2701	35.1830 6545	47.7948 3026	0.0284 2276	41
42	1.3686 4969	0.7306 4716	35.9137 1260	49.1532 9148	0.0278 4452	42
43	1.3789 1456	0.7252 0809	36.6389 2070	50.5219 4117	0.0272 9338	43
44	1.3892 5642	0.7198 0952	37.3587 3022	51.9008 5573	0.0267 6751	44
45	1.3996 7584	0.7144 5114	38.0731 8136	53.2901 1215	0.0262 6521	45
46	1.4101 7341	0.7091 3264	38.7823 1401	54.6897 8799	0.0257 8495	46
47	1.4207 4971	0.7038 5374	39.4861 6774	56.0999 6140	0.0253 2532	47
48	1.4314 0533	0.6986 1414	40.1847 8189	57.5207 1111	0.0248 8504	48
49	1.4421 4087	0.6934 1353	40.8781 9542	58.9521 1644	0.0244 6292	49
50	1.4529 5693	0.6882 5165	41.5664 4707	60.3942 5732	0.0240 5787	50

406

Table VIII (continued). ¾ %

Number of periods n	Amount of 1 at compound interest $s = (1+i)^n$	Present value of 1 $v^n = \dfrac{1}{(1+i)^n}$	Present value of an annuity of 1 $a_{\overline{n}\rceil} = \dfrac{1-v^n}{i}$	Amount of an annuity of 1 $s_{\overline{n}\rceil} = \dfrac{(1+i)^n-1}{i}$	Annuity whose present value is 1 $\dfrac{1}{a_{\overline{n}\rceil}} = \dfrac{1}{s_{\overline{n}\rceil}} + i$	Number of periods n
51	1.4638 5411	0.6831 2819	42.2495 7525	61.8472 1424	0.0236 6888	51
52	1.4748 3301	0.6780 4286	42.9276 1812	63.3110 6835	0.0232 9503	52
53	1.4858 9426	0.6729 9540	43.6006 1351	64.7859 0136	0.0229 3546	53
54	1.4970 3847	0.6679 8551	44.2685 9902	66.2717 9562	0.0225 8938	54
55	1.5082 6626	0.6630 1291	44.9316 1193	67.7688 3409	0.0222 5605	55
56	1.5195 7825	0.6580 7733	45.5896 8926	69.2771 0035	0.0219 3478	56
57	1.5309 7509	0.6531 7849	46.2428 6776	70.7966 7860	0.0216 2496	57
58	1.5424 5740	0.6483 1612	46.8911 8388	72.3276 5369	0.0213 2597	58
59	1.5540 2583	0.6434 8995	47.5346 7382	73.8701 1109	0.0210 3727	59
60	1.5656 8103	0.6386 9970	48.1733 7352	75.4241 3693	0.0207 5836	60
61	1.5774 2363	0.6339 4511	48.8073 1863	76.9898 1795	0.0204 8873	61
62	1.5892 5431	0.6292 2592	49.4365 4455	78.5672 4159	0.0202 2795	62
63	1.6011 7372	0.6245 4185	50.0610 8640	80.1564 9590	0.0199 7560	63
64	1.6131 8252	0.6198 9266	50.6809 7906	81.7576 6962	0.0197 3127	64
65	1.6252 8139	0.6152 7807	51.2962 5713	83.3708 5214	0.0194 9460	65
66	1.6374 7100	0.6106 9784	51.9069 5497	84.9961 3353	0.0192 6524	66
67	1.6497 5203	0.6061 5170	52.5131 0667	86.6336 0453	0.0190 4286	67
68	1.6621 2517	0.6016 3940	53.1147 4607	88.2833 5657	0.0188 2716	68
69	1.6745 9111	0.5971 6070	53.7119 0677	89.9454 8174	0.0186 1785	69
70	1.6871 5055	0.5927 1533	54.3046 2210	91.6200 7285	0.0184 1464	70
71	1.6998 0418	0.5883 0306	54.8929 2516	93.3072 2340	0.0182 1728	71
72	1.7125 5271	0.5839 2363	55.4768 4880	95.0070 2758	0.0180 2554	72
73	1.7253 9685	0.5795 7681	56.0564 2561	96.7195 8028	0.0178 3917	73
74	1.7383 3733	0.5752 6234	56.6316 8795	98.4449 7714	0.0176 5796	74
75	1.7513 7486	0.5709 7999	57.2026 6794	100.1833 1446	0.0174 8170	75
76	1.7645 1017	0.5667 2952	57.7693 9746	101.9346 8932	0.0173 1020	76
77	1.7777 4400	0.5625 1069	58.3319 0815	103.6991 9949	0.0171 4328	77
78	1.7910 7708	0.5583 2326	58.8902 3141	105.4769 4349	0.0169 8074	78
79	1.8045 1015	0.5541 6701	59.4443 9842	107.2680 2056	0.0168 2244	79
80	1.8180 4398	0.5500 4170	59.9944 4012	109.0725 3072	0.0166 6821	80
81	1.8316 7931	0.5459 4710	60.5403 8722	110.0905 7470	0.0165 1790	81
82	1.8454 1691	0.5418 8297	61.0822 7019	112.7222 5401	0.0163 7136	82
83	1.8592 5753	0.5378 4911	61.6201 1930	114.5676 7091	0.0162 2847	83
84	1.8732 0196	0.5338 4527	62.1539 6456	116.4269 2845	0.0160 8908	84
85	1.8872 5098	0.5298 7123	62.6838 3579	118.3001 3041	0.0159 5308	85
86	1.9014 0536	0.5259 2678	63.2097 6257	120.1873 8139	0.0158 2034	86
87	1.9156 6590	0.5220 1169	63.7317 7427	122.0887 8675	0.0156 9076	87
88	1.9300 3339	0.5181 2575	64.2499 0002	124.0044 5265	0.0155 6423	88
89	1.9445 0865	0.5142 6873	64.7641 6875	125.9344 8604	0.0154 4064	89
90	1.9590 9246	0.5104 4043	65.2746 0918	127.8789 9469	0.0153 1989	90
91	1.9737 8565	0.5066 4063	65.7812 4981	129.8380 8715	0.0152 0190	91
92	1.9885 8905	0.5028 6911	66.2841 1892	131.8118 7280	0.0150 8657	92
93	2.0035 0346	0.4991 2567	66.7832 4458	133.8004 6185	0.0149 7382	93
94	2.0185 2974	0.4954 1009	67.2786 5467	135.8039 6531	0.0148 6356	94
95	2.0336 6871	0.4917 2217	67.7703 7685	137.8224 9505	0.0147 5571	95
96	2.0489 2123	0.4880 6171	68.2584 3856	139.8561 6377	0.0146 5020	96
97	2.0642 8814	0.4844 2850	68.7428 6705	141.9050 8499	0.0145 4696	97
98	2.0797 7030	0.4808 2233	69.2236 8938	143.9693 7313	0.0144 4592	98
99	2.0953 6858	0.4772 4301	69.7009 3239	146.0491 4343	0.0143 4701	99
100	2.1110 8384	0.4736 9033	70.1746 2272	148.1445 1201	0.0142 5017	100

Table IX. 1 %

Number of periods n	Amount of 1 at compound interest $s = (1+i)^n$	Present value of 1 $v^n = \dfrac{1}{(1+i)^n}$	Present value of an annuity of 1 $a_{\overline{n}|} = \dfrac{1-v^n}{i}$	Amount of an annuity of 1 $s_{\overline{n}|}= \dfrac{(1+i)^n-1}{i}$	Annuity whose present value is 1 $\dfrac{1}{a_{\overline{n}|}} = \dfrac{1}{s_{\overline{n}|}} + i$	Number of periods n
1	1.0100 0000	0.9900 9901	0.9900 9901	1.0000 0000	1.0100 0000	1
2	1.0201 0000	0.9802 9605	1.9703 9506	2.0100 0000	0.5075 1244	2
3	1.0303 0100	0.9705 9015	2.9409 8521	3.0301 0000	0.3400 2211	3
4	1.0406 0401	0.9609 8034	3.9019 6555	4.0604 0100	0.2562 8109	4
5	1.0510 1005	0.9514 6569	4.8534 3124	5.1010 0501	0.2060 3980	5
6	1.0615 2015	0.9420 4524	5.7954 7647	6.1520 1506	0.1725 4837	6
7	1.0721 3535	0.9327 1805	6.7281 9453	7.2135 3521	0.1486 2828	7
8	1.0828 5671	0.9234 8322	7.6516 7775	8.2856 7056	0.1306 9029	8
9	1.0936 8527	0.9143 3982	8.5660 1758	9.3685 2727	0.1167 4037	9
10	1.1046 2213	0.9052 8695	9.4713 0453	10.4622 1254	0.1055 8208	10
11	1.1156 6835	0.8963 2372	10.3676 2825	11.5668 3467	0.0964 5408	11
12	1.1268 2503	0.8874 4923	11.2550 7747	12.6825 0301	0.0888 4879	12
13	1.1380 9328	0.8786 6260	12.1337 4007	13.8093 2804	0.0824 1482	13
14	1.1494 7421	0.8699 6297	13.0037 0304	14.9474 2132	0.0769 0117	14
15	1.1609 6896	0.8613 4947	13.8650 5252	16.0968 9554	0.0721 2378	15
16	1.1725 7864	0.8528 2126	14.7178 7378	17.2578 6449	0.0679 4460	16
17	1.1843 0443	0.8443 7749	15.5622 5127	18.4304 4314	0.0642 5806	17
18	1.1961 4748	0.8360 1731	16.3982 6858	19.6147 4757	0.0609 8205	18
19	1.2081 0895	0.8277 3992	17.2260 0850	20.8108 9504	0.0580 5175	19
20	1.2201 9004	0.8195 4447	18.0455 5297	22.0190 0399	0.0554 1532	20
21	1.2323 9194	0.8114 3017	18.8569 8313	23.2391 9403	0.0530 3075	21
22	1.2447 1586	0.8033 9621	19.6603 7934	24.4715 8598	0.0508 6371	22
23	1.2571 6302	0.7954 4179	20.4558 2113	25.7163 0183	0.0488 8584	23
24	1.2697 3465	0.7875 6613	21.2433 8726	26.9734 6485	0.0470 7347	24
25	1.2824 3200	0.7797 6844	22.0231 5570	28.2431 9950	0.0454 0675	25
26	1.2952 5631	0.7720 4796	22.7952 0366	29.5256 3150	0.0438 6888	26
27	1.3082 0888	0.7644 0392	23.5596 0759	30.8208 8781	0.0424 4553	27
28	1.3212 9097	0.7568 3557	24.3164 4316	32.1290 9669	0.0411 2444	28
29	1.3345 0388	0.7493 4215	25.0657 8530	33.4503 8766	0.0398 9502	29
30	1.3478 4892	0.7419 2292	25.8077 0822	34.7848 9153	0.0387 4811	30
31	1.3613 2740	0.7345 7715	26.5422 8537	36.1327 4045	0.0376 7573	31
32	1.3749 4068	0.7273 0411	27.2695 8947	37.4940 6785	0.0366 7089	32
33	1.3886 9009	0.7201 0307	27.9896 9255	38.8690 0853	0.0357 2744	33
34	1.4025 7699	0.7129 7334	28.7026 6589	40.2576 9862	0.0348 3997	34
35	1.4166 0276	0.7059 1420	29.4085 8009	41.6602 7560	0.0340 0368	35
36	1.4307 6878	0.6989 2495	30.1075 0504	43.0768 7836	0.0332 1431	36
37	1.4450 7647	0.6920 0490	30.7995 0994	44.5076 4714	0.0324 6805	37
38	1.4595 2724	0.6851 5337	31.4846 6330	45.9527 2361	0.0317 6150	38
39	1.4741 2251	0.6783 6967	32.1630 3298	47.4122 5085	0.0310 9160	39
40	1.4888 6373	0.6716 5314	32.8346 8611	48.8863 7336	0.0304 5560	40
41	1.5037 5237	0.6650 0311	33.4996 8922	50.3752 3709	0.0298 5102	41
42	1.5187 8989	0.6584 1892	34.1581 0814	51.8789 8946	0.0292 7563	42
43	1.5339 7779	0.6518 9992	34.8100 0806	53.3977 7936	0.0287 2737	43
44	1.5493 1757	0.6454 4546	35.4554 5352	54.9317 5715	0.0282 0441	44
45	1.5648 1075	0.6390 5492	36.0945 0844	56.4810 7472	0.0277 0505	45
46	1.5804 5885	0.6327 2764	36.7272 3608	58.0458 8547	0.0272 2775	46
47	1.5962 6344	0.6264 6301	37.3536 9909	59.6263 4432	0.0267 7111	47
48	1.6122 2608	0.6202 6041	37.9739 5949	61.2226 0777	0.0263 3384	48
49	1.6283 4834	0.6141 1921	38.5880 7871	62.8348 3385	0.0259 1474	49
50	1.6446 3182	0.6080 3882	39.1961 1753	64.4631 8218	0.0255 1273	50

Table IX (*continued*). 1%

Number of periods n	Amount of 1 at compound interest $s = (1 + i)^n$	Present value of 1 $v^n = \dfrac{1}{(1+i)^n}$	Present value of an annuity of 1 $a_{\overline{n}|} = \dfrac{1 - v^n}{i}$	Amount of an annuity of 1 $s_{\overline{n}|} = \dfrac{(1+i)^n - 1}{i}$	Annuity whose present value is 1 $\dfrac{1}{a_{\overline{n}|}} = \dfrac{1}{s_{\overline{n}|}} + i$	Number of periods n
51	1.6610 7814	0.6020 1864	39.7981 3617	66.1078 1401	0.0251 2680	51
52	1.6776 8892	0.5960 5806	40.3941 9423	67.7688 9215	0.0247 5603	52
53	1.6944 6581	0.5901 5649	40.9843 5072	69.4465 8107	0.0243 9956	53
54	1.7114 1047	0.5843 1336	41.5686 6408	71.1410 4688	0.0240 5658	54
55	1.7285 2457	0.5785 2808	42.1471 9216	72.8524 5735	0.0237 2637	55
56	1.7458 0982	0.5728 0008	42.7199 9224	74.5809 8192	0.0234 0823	56
57	1.7632 6792	0.5671 2879	43.2871 2102	76.3267 9174	0.0231 0156	57
58	1.7809 0060	0.5615 1365	43.8486 3468	78.0900 5966	0.0228 0573	58
59	1.7987 0960	0.5559 5411	44.4045 8879	79.8709 6025	0.0225 2020	59
60	1.8166 9670	0.5504 4962	44.9550 3841	81.6696 6986	0.0222 4445	60
61	1.8348 6367	0.5449 9962	45.5000 3803	83.4863 6655	0.0219 7800	61
62	1.8532 1230	0.5396 0358	46.0396 4161	85.3212 3022	0.0217 2041	62
63	1.8717 4443	0.5342 6097	46.5739 0258	87.1744 4252	0.0214 7125	63
64	1.8904 6187	0.5289 7126	47.1028 7385	89.0461 8695	0.0212 3013	64
65	1.9093 6649	0.5237 3392	47.6266 0777	90.9366 4882	0.0209 9667	65
66	1.9284 6015	0.5185 4844	48.1451 5621	92.8460 1531	0.0207 7052	66
67	1.9477 4475	0.5134 1429	48.6585 7050	94.7744 7546	0.0205 5136	67
68	1.9672 2220	0.5083 3099	49.1669 0149	96.7222 2021	0.0203 3888	68
69	1.9868 9442	0.5032 9801	49.6701 9949	98.6894 4242	0.0201 3280	69
70	2.0067 6337	0.4983 1486	50.1685 1435	100.6763 3684	0.0199 3282	70
71	2.0268 3100	0.4933 8105	50.6618 9539	102.6831 0021	0.0197 3870	71
72	2.0470 9931	0.4884 9609	51.1503 9148	104.7099 3121	0.0195 5019	72
73	2.0675 7031	0.4836 5949	51.6340 5097	106.7570 3052	0.0193 6706	73
74	2.0882 4601	0.4788 7078	52.1129 2175	108.8246 0083	0.0191 8910	74
75	2.1091 2847	0.4741 2949	52.5870 5124	110.9128 4684	0.0190 1609	75
76	2.1302 1975	0.4694 3514	53.0564 8637	113.0219 7530	0.0188 4784	76
77	2.1515 2195	0.4647 8726	53.5212 7364	115.1521 9506	0.0186 8416	77
78	2.1730 3717	0.4601 8541	53.9814 5905	117.3037 1701	0.0185 2488	78
79	2.1947 6754	0.4556 2912	54.4370 8817	119.4767 5418	0.0183 6984	79
80	2.2167 1522	0.4511 1794	54.8882 0611	121.6715 2172	0.0182 1885	80
81	2.2388 8237	0.4466 514⅄	55.3348 5753	123.8882 3694	0.0180 7180	81
82	2.2612 7119	0.4422 2913	55.7770 8666	126.1271 1931	0.0179 2851	82
83	2.2838 8390	0.4378 5063	56.2149 3729	128.3883 9050	0.0177 8886	83
84	2.3067 2274	0.4335 1547	56.6484 5276	130.6722 7440	0.0176 5273	84
85	2.3297 8997	0.4292 2324	57.0776 7600	132.9789 9715	0.0175 1998	85
86	2.3530 8787	0.4249 7350	57.5026 4951	135.3087 8712	0.0173 9050	86
87	2.3766 1875	0.4207 6585	57.9234 1535	137.6618 7499	0.0172 6417	87
88	2.4003 8494	0.4165 9985	58.3400 1520	140.0384 9374	0.0171 4089	88
89	2.4243 8879	0.4124 7510	58.7524 9030	142.4388 7868	0.0170 2056	89
90	2.4486 3267	0.4083 9119	59.1608 8148	144.8632 6746	0.0169 0306	90
91	2.4731 1900	0.4043 4771	59.5652 2919	147.3119 0014	0.0167 8832	91
92	2.4978 5019	0.4003 4427	59.9655 7346	149.7850 1914	0.0166 7624	92
93	2.5228 2869	0.3963 8046	60.3619 5392	152.2828 6933	0.0165 6673	93
94	2.5480 5698	0.3924 5590	60.7544 0982	154.8056 9803	0.0164 5971	94
95	2.5735 3755	0.3885 7020	61.1429 8002	157.3537 5501	0.0163 5511	95
96	2.5992 7293	0.3847 2297	61.5277 0299	159.9272 9256	0.0162 5284	96
97	2.6252 6565	0.3809 1383	61.9086 1682	162.5265 6548	0.0161 5284	97
98	2.6515 1831	0.3771 4241	62.2857 5923	165.1518 3114	0.0160 5503	98
99	2.6780 3349	0.3734 0832	62.6591 6755	167.8033 4945	0.0159 5936	99
100	2.7048 1383	0.3697 1121	63.0288 7877	170.4813 8294	0.0158 6574	100

Table X. $1\frac{1}{4}\%$

Number of periods n	Amount of 1 at compound interest $s = (1+i)^n$	Present value of 1 $v^n = \dfrac{1}{(1+i)^n}$	Present value of an annuity of 1 $a_{\overline{n}|} = \dfrac{1-v^n}{i}$	Amount of an annuity of 1 $s_{\overline{n}|} = \dfrac{(1+i)^n-1}{i}$	Annuity whose present value is 1 $\dfrac{1}{a_{\overline{n}|}} = \dfrac{1}{s_{\overline{n}|}} + i$	Number of periods n
1	1.0125 0000	0.9876 5432	0.9876 5432	1.0000 0000	1.0125 0000	1
2	1.0251 5625	0.9754 6106	1.9631 1538	2.0125 0000	0.5093 9441	2
3	1.0379 7070	0.9634 1833	2.9265 3371	3.0376 5625	0.3417 0117	3
4	1.0509 4534	0.9515 2428	3.8780 5798	4.0756 2695	0.2578 6102	4
5	1.0640 8215	0.9397 7706	4.8178 3504	5.1265 7229	0.2075 6211	5
6	1.0773 8318	0.9281 7488	5.7460 0992	6.1906 5444	0.1740 3381	6
7	1.0908 5047	0.9167 1593	6.6627 2585	7.2680 3762	0.1500 8872	7
8	1.1044 8610	0.9053 9845	7.5681 2429	8.3588 8809	0.1321 3314	8
9	1.1182 9218	0.8942 2069	8.4623 4498	9.4633 7420	0.1181 7055	9
10	1.1322 7083	0.8831 8093	9.3455 2591	10.5816 6637	0.1070 0307	10
11	1.1464 2422	0.8722 7746	10.2178 0337	11.7139 3720	0.0978 6839	11
12	1.1607 5452	0.8615 0860	11.0793 1197	12.8603 6142	0.0902 5831	12
13	1.1752 6395	0.8508 7269	11.9301 8466	14.0211 1594	0.0838 2100	13
14	1.1899 5475	0.8403 6809	12.7705 5275	15.1963 7988	0.0783 0515	14
15	1.2048 2918	0.8299 9318	13.6005 4592	16.3863 3463	0.0735 2646	15
16	1.2198 8955	0.8197 4635	14.4202 9227	17.5911 6382	0.0693 4672	16
17	1.2351 3817	0.8096 2602	15.2299 1829	18.8110 5336	0.0656 6023	17
18	1.2505 7739	0.7996 3064	16.0295 4893	20.0461 9153	0.0623 8479	18
19	1.2662 0961	0.7897 5866	16.8193 0759	21.2967 6893	0.0594 5548	19
20	1.2820 3723	0.7800 0855	17.5993 1613	22.5629 7854	0.0568 2039	20
21	1.2980 6270	0.7703 7881	18.3696 9495	23.8450 1577	0.0544 3748	21
22	1.3142 8848	0.7608 6796	19.1305 6291	25.1430 7847	0.0522 7238	22
23	1.3307 1709	0.7514 7453	19.8820 3744	26.4573 6695	0.0502 9666	23
24	1.3473 5105	0.7421 9707	20.6242 3451	27.7880 8403	0.0484 8665	24
25	1.3641 9294	0.7330 3414	21.3572 6865	29.1354 3508	0.0468 2247	25
26	1.3812 4535	0.7239 8434	22.0812 5299	30.4996 2802	0.0452 8729	26
27	1.3985 1092	0.7150 4626	22.7962 9925	31.8808 7337	0.0438 6677	27
28	1.4159 9230	0.7062 1853	23.5025 1778	33.2793 8429	0.0425 4863	28
29	1.4336 9221	0.6974 9978	24.2000 1756	34.6953 7659	0.0413 2228	29
30	1.4516 1336	0.6888 8867	24.8889 0623	36.1290 6880	0.0401 7854	30
31	1.4697 5853	0.6803 8387	25.5692 9010	37.5806 8216	0.0391 0942	31
32	1.4881 3051	0.6719 8407	26.2412 7418	39.0504 4069	0.0381 0791	32
33	1.5067 3214	0.6636 8797	26.9049 6215	40.5385 7120	0.0371 6786	33
34	1.5255 6629	0.6554 9449	27.5604 5644	42.0453 0334	0.0362 8387	34
35	1.5446 3587	0.6474 0177	28.2078 5822	43.5708 6963	0.0354 5111	35
36	1.5639 4382	0.6394 0916	28.8472 6737	45.1155 0550	0.0346 6533	36
37	1.5834 9312	0.6315 1522	29.4787 8259	46.6794 4932	0.0339 2270	37
38	1.6032 8678	0.6237 1873	30.1025 0133	48.2926 4243	0.0332 1983	38
39	1.6233 2787	0.6160 1850	30.7185 1983	49.8862 2921	0.0325 5365	39
40	1.6436 1946	0.6084 1334	31.3269 3316	51.4895 5708	0.0319 2141	40
41	1.6641 6471	0.6009 0206	31.9278 3522	53.1331 7654	0.0313 2063	41
42	1.6849 6677	0.5934 8352	32.5213 1874	54.7973 4125	0.0307 4906	42
43	1.7060 2885	0.5861 5656	33.1074 7530	56.4823 0801	0.0302 0466	43
44	1.7273 5421	0.5789 2006	33.6863 9536	58.1883 3687	0.0296 8557	44
45	1.7489 4614	0.5717 7290	34.2581 6825	59.9156 9108	0.0291 9012	45
46	1.7708 0797	0.5647 1397	34.8228 8222	61.6646 3721	0.0287 1675	46
47	1.7929 4306	0.5577 4219	35.3806 2442	63.4354 4518	0.0282 6406	47
48	1.8153 5485	0.5508 5649	35.9314 8091	65.2283 8824	0.0278 3075	48
49	1.8380 4679	0.5440 5579	36.4755 3670	67.0437 4310	0.0274 1563	49
50	1.8610 2237	0.5373 3905	37.0128 7574	68.8817 8989	0.0270 1763	50

Table X (continued). 1¼%

Number of periods n	Amount of 1 at compound interest $s = (1+i)^n$	Present value of 1 $v^n = \dfrac{1}{(1+i)^n}$	Present value of an annuity of 1 $a_{\overline{n}|} = \dfrac{1-v^n}{i}$	Amount of an annuity of 1 $s_{\overline{n}|} = \dfrac{(1+i)^n-1}{i}$	Annuity whose present value is 1 $\dfrac{1}{a_{\overline{n}|}} = \dfrac{1}{s_{\overline{n}|}} + i$	Number of periods n
51	1.8842 8515	0.5307 0524	37.5435 8099	70.7428 1226	0.0266 3571	51
52	1.9078 3872	0.5241 5332	38.0677 3431	72.6270 9741	0.0262 6897	52
53	1.9316 8670	0.5176 8229	38.5854 1660	74.5349 3613	0.0259 1653	53
54	1.9558 3279	0.5112 9115	39.0967 0776	76.4666 2283	0.0255 7760	54
55	1.9802 8070	0.5049 7892	39.6016 8667	78.4224 5562	0.0252 5145	55
56	2.0050 3420	0.4987 4461	40.1004 3128	80.4027 3631	0.0249 3739	56
57	2.0300 9713	0.4925 8727	40.5930 1855	82.4077 7052	0.0246 3478	57
58	2.0554 7335	0.4865 0594	41.0795 2449	84.4378 6765	0.0243 4303	58
59	2.0811 6676	0.4804 9970	41.5600 2419	86.4933 4099	0.0240 6158	59
60	2.1071 8135	0.4745 6760	42.0345 9179	88.5745 0776	0.0237 8993	60
61	2.1335 2111	0.4687 0874	42.5033 0054	90.6816 8910	0.0235 2758	61
62	2.1601 9013	0.4629 2222	42.9662 2275	92.8152 1022	0.0232 7410	62
63	2.1871 9250	0.4572 0713	43.4234 2988	94.9754 0034	0.0230 2904	63
64	2.2145 3241	0.4515 6259	43.8749 9247	97.1625 9285	0.0227 9203	64
65	2.2422 1407	0.4459 8775	44.3209 8022	99.3771 2526	0.0225 6268	65
66	2.2702 4174	0.4404 8173	44.7614 6195	101.6193 3933	0.0223 4065	66
67	2.2986 1976	0.4350 4368	45.1965 0563	103.8895 8107	0.0221 2560	67
68	2.3273 5251	0.4296 7277	45.6261 7840	106.1882 0083	0.0219 1724	68
69	2.3564 4442	0.4243 6817	46.0505 4656	108.5155 5334	0.0217 1527	69
70	2.3858 9997	0.4191 2905	46.4696 7562	110.8719 9776	0.0215 1941	70
71	2.4157 2372	0.4139 5462	46.8836 3024	113.2578 9773	0.0213 2941	71
72	2.4459 2027	0.4088 4407	47.2924 7431	115.6736 2145	0.0211 4501	72
73	2.4764 9427	0.4037 9661	47.6962 7093	118.1195 4172	0.0209 6600	73
74	2.5074 5045	0.3988 1147	48.0950 8240	120.5960 3599	0.0207 9215	74
75	2.5387 9358	0.3938 8787	48.4889 7027	123.1034 8644	0.0206 2325	75
76	2.5705 2850	0.3890 2506	48.8779 9533	125.6422 8002	0.0204 5910	76
77	2.6026 6011	0.3842 2228	49.2622 1761	128.2128 0852	0.0202 9953	77
78	2.6351 9336	0.3794 7879	49.6416 9640	130.8154 6863	0.0201 4435	78
79	2.6681 3327	0.3747 9387	50.0164 9027	133.4506 6199	0.0199 9341	79
80	2.7014 8494	0.3701 6679	50.3866 5706	136.1187 9526	0.0198 4652	80
81	2.7352 5350	0.3655 9683	50.7522 5389	138.8202 8020	0.0197 0356	81
82	2.7694 4417	0.3610 8329	51.1133 3717	141.5555 3370	0.0195 6437	82
83	2.8040 6222	0.3566 2547	51.4699 6264	144.3249 7787	0.0194 2881	83
84	2.8391 1300	0.3522 2268	51.8221 8532	147.1290 4010	0.0192 9675	84
85	2.8746 0191	0.3478 7426	52.1700 5958	149.9681 5310	0.0191 6808	85
86	2.9105 3444	0.3435 7951	52.5136 3909	152.8427 5501	0.0190 4267	86
87	2.9469 1612	0.3393 3779	52.8529 7688	155.7532 8945	0.0189 2041	87
88	2.9837 5257	0.3351 4843	53.1881 2531	158.7002 0557	0.0188 0119	88
89	3.0210 4948	0.3310 1080	53.5191 3611	161.6839 5814	0.0186 8490	89
90	3.0588 1260	0.3269 2425	53.8460 6035	164.7050 0762	0.0185 7146	90
91	3.0970 4775	0.3228 8814	54.1689 4850	167.7638 2021	0.0184 6076	91
92	3.1357 6085	0.3189 0187	54.4878 5037	170.8608 6796	0.0183 5271	92
93	3.1749 5786	0.3149 6481	54.8028 1518	173.9966 2881	0.0182 4774	93
94	3.2146 4483	0.3110 7636	55.1138 9154	177.1715 8667	0.0181 4425	94
95	3.2548 2789	0.3072 3591	55.4211 2744	180.3862 3151	0.0180 4366	95
96	3.2955 1324	0.3034 4287	55.7245 7031	183.6410 5940	0.0179 4540	96
97	3.3367 0716	0.2996 9666	56.0242 6698	186.9365 7264	0.0178 4941	97
98	3.3784 1600	0.2959 9670	56.3202 6368	190.2732 7980	0.0177 5560	98
99	3.4206 4620	0.2923 4242	56.6126 0610	193.6516 9580	0.0176 6391	99
100	3.4634 0427	0.2887 3326	56.9013 3936	197.0723 4200	0.0175 7428	100

411

Table XI. 1½ %

Number of periods	Amount of 1 at compound interest	Present value of 1	Present value of an annuity of 1	Amount of an annuity of 1	Annuity whose present value is 1	Number of periods
n	$s = (1+i)^n$	$v^n = \dfrac{1}{(1+i)^n}$	$a_{\overline{n}|} = \dfrac{1-v^n}{i}$	$s_{\overline{n}|} = \dfrac{(1+i)^n-1}{i}$	$\dfrac{1}{a_{\overline{n}|}} = \dfrac{1}{s_{\overline{n}|}} + i$	n
1	1.0150 0000	0.9852 2167	0.9852 2167	1.0000 0000	1.0150 0000	1
2	1.0302 2500	0.9706 6175	1.9558 8342	2.0150 0000	0.5112 7792	2
3	1.0456 7838	0.9563 1699	2.9122 0042	3.0452 2500	0.3433 8296	3
4	1.0613 6355	0.9421 8423	3.8543 8465	4.0909 0338	0.2594 4478	4
5	1.0772 8400	0.9282 6033	4.7826 4497	5.1522 6693	0.2090 8932	5
6	1.0934 4326	0.9145 4219	5.6971 8717	6.2295 5093	0.1755 2521	6
7	1.1098 4491	0.9010 2679	6.5982 1396	7.3229 9419	0.1515 5616	7
8	1.1264 9259	0.8877 1112	7.4859 2508	8.4328 3911	0.1335 8402	8
9	1.1433 8998	0.8745 9224	8.3605 1732	9.5593 3169	0.1196 0982	9
10	1.1605 4083	0.8616 6723	9.2221 8455	10.7027 2167	0.1084 3418	10
11	1.1779 4894	0.8489 3323	10.0711 1779	11.8632 6249	0.0992 9384	11
12	1.1956 1817	0.8363 8742	10.9075 0521	13.0412 1143	0.0916 7999	12
13	1.2135 5244	0.8240 2702	11.7315 3222	14.2368 2960	0.0852 4036	13
14	1.2317 5573	0.8118 4928	12.5433 8150	15.4503 8205	0.0797 2332	14
15	1.2502 3207	0.7998 5150	13.3432 3301	16.6821 3778	0.0749 4436	15
16	1.2689 8555	0.7880 3104	14.1312 6405	17.9323 6984	0.0707 6508	16
17	1.2880 2033	0.7763 8526	14.9076 4931	19.2013 5539	0.0670 7966	17
18	1.3073 4064	0.7649 1159	15.6725 6089	20.4893 7572	0.0638 0578	18
19	1.3269 5075	0.7536 0747	16.4261 6837	21.7967 1636	0.0608 7847	19
20	1.3468 5501	0.7424 7042	17.1686 3879	23.1236 6710	0.0582 4574	20
21	1.3670 5783	0.7314 9795	17.9001 3673	24.4705 2211	0.0558 6550	21
22	1.3875 6370	0.7206 8763	18.6208 2437	25.8375 7994	0.0537 0331	22
23	1.4083 7715	0.7100 3708	19.3308 6145	27.2251 4364	0.0517 3075	23
24	1.4295 0281	0.6995 4392	20.0304 0537	28.6335 2080	0.0499 2410	24
25	1.4509 4535	0.6892 0583	20.7196 1120	30.0630 2361	0.0482 6345	25
26	1.4727 0953	0.6790 2052	21.3986 3172	31.5139 6896	0.0467 3196	26
27	1.4948 0018	0.6689 8574	22.0676 1746	32.9866 7850	0.0453 1527	27
28	1.5172 2218	0.6590 9925	22.7267 1671	34.4814 7867	0.0440 0108	28
29	1.5399 8051	0.6493 5887	23.3760 7558	35.9987 0085	0.0427 7878	29
30	1.5630 8022	0.6397 6243	24.0158 3801	37.5386 8137	0.0416 3919	30
31	1.5865 2642	0.6303 0781	24.6461 4582	39.1017 6159	0.0405 7430	31
32	1.6103 2432	0.6209 9292	25.2671 3874	40.6882 8801	0.0395 7710	32
33	1.6344 7918	0.6118 1568	25.8789 5442	42.2986 1233	0.0386 4144	33
34	1.6589 9637	0.6027 7407	26.4817 2849	43.9330 9152	0.0377 6189	34
35	1.6838 8132	0.5938 6608	27.0755 9458	45.5920 8789	0.0369 3363	35
36	1.7091 3954	0.5850 8974	27.6606 8431	47.2759 6921	0.0361 5240	36
37	1.7347 7663	0.5764 4309	28.2371 2740	48.9851 0874	0.0354 1437	37
38	1.7607 9828	0.5679 2423	28.8050 5163	50.7198 8538	0.0347 1613	38
39	1.7872 1025	0.5595 3126	29.3645 8288	52.4806 8366	0.0340 5463	39
40	1.8140 1841	0.5512 6232	29.9158 4520	54.2678 9391	0.0334 2710	40
41	1.8412 2868	0.5431 1559	30.4589 6079	56.0819 1232	0.0328 3106	41
42	1.8688 4712	0.5350 8925	30.9940 5004	57.9231 4100	0.0322 6426	42
43	1.8968 7982	0.5271 8153	31.5212 3157	59.7919 8812	0.0317 2465	43
44	1.9253 3302	0.5193 9067	32.0406 2223	61.6888 6794	0.0312 1038	44
45	1.9542 1301	0.5117 1494	32.5523 3718	63.6142 0096	0.0307 1976	45
46	1.9835 2621	0.5041 5265	33.0564 8983	65.5684 1398	0.0302 5125	46
47	2.0132 7910	0.4967 0212	33.5531 9195	67.5519 4018	0.0298 0342	47
48	2.0434 7829	0.4893 6170	34.0425 5365	69.5652 1929	0.0293 7500	48
49	2.0741 3046	0.4821 2975	34.5246 8339	71.6086 9758	0.0289 6478	49
50	2.1052 4242	0.4750 0468	34.9996 8807	73.6828 2804	0.0285 7168	50

Table XI (*continued*). 1½ %

Number of periods n	Amount of 1 at compound interest $s = (1 + i)^n$	Present value of 1 $v^n = \dfrac{1}{(1 + i)^n}$	Present value of an annuity of 1 $a_{\overline{n}\mid} = \dfrac{1 - v^n}{i}$	Amount of an annuity of 1 $s_{\overline{n}\mid} = \dfrac{(1+i)^n - 1}{i}$	Annuity whose present value is 1 $\dfrac{1}{a_{\overline{n}\mid}} = \dfrac{1}{s_{\overline{n}\mid}} + i$	Number of periods n
51	2.1368 2106	0.4679 8491	35.4676 7298	75.7880 7046	0.0281 9469	51
52	2.1688 7337	0.4610 6887	35.9287 4185	77.9248 9152	0.0278 3287	52
53	2.2014 0647	0.4542 5505	36.3829 9690	80.0937 6489	0.0274 8537	53
54	2.2344 2757	0.4475 4192	36.8305 3882	82.2951 7136	0.0271 5138	54
55	2.2679 4398	0.4409 2800	37.2714 6681	84.5295 9893	0.0268 3018	55
56	2.3019 6314	0.4344 1182	37.7058 7863	86.7975 4292	0.0265 2106	56
57	2.3364 9259	0.4279 9194	38.1338 7058	89.0995 0606	0.0262 2341	57
58	2.3715 3998	0.4216 6694	38.5555 3751	91.4359 9865	0.0259 3661	58
59	2.4071 1308	0.4154 3541	38.9709 7292	93.8075 3863	0.0256 6012	59
60	2.4432 1978	0.4092 9597	39.3802 6889	96.2146 5171	0.0253 9343	60
61	2.4798 6807	0.4032 4726	39.7835 1614	98.6578 7149	0.0251 3604	61
62	2.5170 6609	0.3972 8794	40.1808 0408	101.1377 3956	0.0248 8751	62
63	2.5548 2208	0.3914 1669	40.5722 2077	103.6548 0565	0.0246 4741	63
64	2.5931 4442	0.3856 3221	40.9578 5298	106.2096 2774	0.0244 1534	64
65	2.6320 4158	0.3799 3321	41.3377 8618	108.8027 7215	0.0241 9094	65
66	2.6715 2221	0.3743 1843	41.7121 0461	111.4348 1374	0.0239 7386	66
67	2.7115 9504	0.3687 8663	42.0808 9125	114.1063 3594	0.0237 6376	67
68	2.7522 6896	0.3633 3658	42.4442 2783	116.8179 3098	0.0235 6033	68
69	2.7935 5300	0.3579 6708	42.8021 9490	119.5701 9995	0.0233 6329	69
70	2.8354 5629	0.3526 7692	43.1548 7183	122.3637 5295	0.0231 7235	70
71	2.8779 8814	0.3474 6495	43.5023 3678	125.1992 0924	0.0229 8727	71
72	2.9211 5796	0.3423 3000	43.8446 6677	128.0771 9738	0.0228 0779	72
73	2.9649 7533	0.3372 7093	44.1819 3771	130.9983 5534	0.0226 3368	73
74	3.0094 4996	0.3322 8663	44.5142 2434	133.9633 3067	0.0224 6473	74
75	3.0545 9171	0.3273 7599	44.8416 0034	136.9727 8063	0.0223 0072	75
76	3.1004 1059	0.3225 3793	45.1641 3826	140.0273 7234	0.0221 4146	76
77	3.1469 1674	0.3177 7136	45.4819 0962	143.1277 8292	0.0219 8676	77
78	3.1941 2050	0.3130 7523	45.7949 8485	146.2746 9967	0.0218 3645	78
79	3.2420 3230	0.3084 4850	46.1034 3335	149.4688 2016	0.0216 9036	79
80	3.2906 6279	0.3038 9015	46.4073 2349	152.7108 5247	0.0215 4832	80
81	3.3400 2273	0.2993 9916	46.7067 2265	156.0015 1525	0.0214 1019	81
82	3.3901 2307	0.2949 7454	47.0016 9720	159.3415 3798	0.0212 7583	82
83	3.4409 7492	0.2906 1531	47.2923 1251	162.7316 6105	0.0211 4509	83
84	3.4925 8954	0.2863 2050	47.5786 3301	166.1726 3597	0.0210 1784	84
85	3.5449 7838	0.2820 8917	47.8607 2218	169.6652 2551	0.0208 9396	85
86	3.5981 5306	0.2779 2036	48.1386 4254	173.2102 0389	0.0207 7333	86
87	3.6521 2535	0.2738 1316	48.4124 5571	176.8083 5695	0.0206 5584	87
88	3.7069 0723	0.2697 6666	48.6822 2237	180.4604 8230	0.0205 4138	88
89	3.7625 1084	0.2657 7997	48.9480 0234	184.1673 8954	0.0204 2984	89
90	3.8189 4851	0.2618 5218	49.2098 5452	187.9299 0038	0.0203 2113	90
91	3.8762 3273	0.2579 8245	49.4678 3696	191.7488 4889	0.0202 1516	91
92	3.9343 7622	0.2541 6990	49.7220 0686	195.6250 8162	0.0201 1182	92
93	3.9933 9187	0.2504 1369	49.9724 2055	199.5594 5784	0.0200 1104	93
94	4.0532 9275	0.2467 1300	50.2191 3355	203.5528 4971	0.0199 1273	94
95	4.1140 9214	0.2430 6699	50.4622 0054	207.6061 4246	0.0198 1681	95
96	4.1758 0352	0.2394 7487	50.7016 7541	211.7202 3459	0.0197 2321	96
97	4.2384 4057	0.2359 3583	50.9376 1124	215.8960 3811	0.0196 3186	97
98	4.3020 1718	0.2324 4909	51.1700 6034	220.1344 7868	0.0195 4268	98
99	4.3665 4744	0.2290 1389	51.3990 7422	224.4364 9586	0.0194 5560	99
100	4.4320 4565	0.2256 2944	51.6247 0367	228.8030 4330	0.0193 7057	100

Table XII. $1\frac{3}{4}\%$

Number of periods n	Amount of 1 at compound interest $s = (1+i)^n$	Present value of 1 $v^n = \dfrac{1}{(1+i)^n}$	Present value of an annuity of 1 $a_{\overline{n}|} = \dfrac{1-v^n}{i}$	Amount of an annuity of 1 $s_{\overline{n}|} = \dfrac{(1+i)^n-1}{i}$	Annuity whose present value is 1 $\dfrac{1}{a_{\overline{n}|}} = \dfrac{1}{s_{\overline{n}|}} + i$	Number of periods n
1	1.0175 0000	0.9828 0098	0.9828 0098	1.0000 0000	1.0175 0000	1
2	1.0353 0625	0.9658 9777	1.9486 9875	2.0175 0000	0.5131 6295	2
3	1.0534 2411	0.9492 8528	2.8979 8403	3.0528 0625	0.3450 6746	3
4	1.0718 5903	0.9329 5851	3.8309 4254	4.1062 3036	0.2610 3237	4
5	1.0906 1656	0.9169 1254	4.7478 5508	5.1780 8938	0.2106 2142	5
6	1.1097 0235	0.9011 4254	5.6489 9762	6.2687 0596	0.1770 2256	6
7	1.1291 2215	0.8856 4378	6.5346 4139	7.3784 0831	0.1530 3059	7
8	1.1488 8178	0.8704 1157	7.4050 5297	8.5075 3045	0.1350 4292	8
9	1.1689 8721	0.8554 4135	8.2604 9432	9.6564 1224	0.1210 5813	9
10	1.1894 4449	0.8407 2860	9.1012 2291	10.8253 9945	0.1098 7534	10
11	1.2102 5977	0.8262 6889	9.9274 9181	12.0148 4394	0.1007 3038	11
12	1.2314 3931	0.8120 5788	10.7395 4969	13.2251 0371	0.0931 1377	12
13	1.2529 8950	0.7980 9128	11.5376 4097	14.4565 4303	0.0866 7283	13
14	1.2749 1682	0.7843 6490	12.3220 0587	15.7095 3253	0.0811 5562	14
15	1.2972 2786	0.7708 7459	13.0928 8046	16.9844 4935	0.0763 7739	15
16	1.3199 2935	0.7576 1631	13.8504 9677	18.2816 7721	0.0721 9958	16
17	1.3430 2811	0.7445 8605	14.5950 8282	19.6016 0656	0.0685 1623	17
18	1.3665 3111	0.7317 7990	15.3268 6272	20.9446 3468	0.0652 4492	18
19	1.3904 4540	0.7191 9401	16.0460 5673	22.3111 6578	0.0623 2061	19
20	1.4147 7820	0.7068 2458	16.7528 8130	23.7016 1119	0.0596 9122	20
21	1.4395 3681	0.6946 6789	17.4475 4919	25.1163 8938	0.0573 1464	21
22	1.4647 2871	0.6827 2028	18.1302 6948	26.5559 2620	0.0551 5638	22
23	1.4903 6146	0.6709 7817	18.8012 4764	28.0206 5490	0.0531 8796	23
24	1.5164 4279	0.6594 3800	19.4606 8565	29.5110 1637	0.0513 8565	24
25	1.5429 8054	0.6480 9632	20.1087 8196	31.0274 5915	0.0497 2952	25
26	1.5699 8269	0.6369 4970	20.7457 3166	32.5704 3969	0.0482 0269	26
27	1.5974 5739	0.6259 9479	21.3717 2644	34.1404 2238	0.0467 9079	27
28	1.6254 1290	0.6152 2829	21.9869 5473	35.7378 7977	0.0454 8151	28
29	1.6538 5762	0.6046 4697	22.5916 0171	37.3632 9267	0.0442 6424	29
30	1.6828 0013	0.5942 4764	23.1858 4934	39.0171 5029	0.0431 2975	30
31	1.7122 4913	0.5840 2716	23.7698 7650	40.6999 5042	0.0420 7005	31
32	1.7422 1349	0.5739 8247	24.3438 5897	42.4121 9955	0.0410 7812	32
33	1.7727 0223	0.5641 1053	24.9079 6951	44.1544 1305	0.0401 4779	33
34	1.8037 2452	0.5544 0839	25.4623 7789	45.9271 1527	0.0392 7363	34
35	1.8352 8970	0.5448 7311	26.0072 5100	47.7308 3979	0.0384 5082	35
36	1.8674 0727	0.5355 0183	26.5427 5283	49.5661 2949	0.0376 7507	36
37	1.9000 8689	0.5262 9172	27.0690 4455	51.4335 3675	0.0369 4257	37
38	1.9333 3841	0.5172 4002	27.5862 8457	53.3336 2365	0.0362 4990	38
39	1.9671 7184	0.5083 4400	28.0946 2857	55.2669 6206	0.0355 9399	39
40	2.0015 9734	0.4996 0098	28.5942 2955	57.2341 3390	0.0349 7209	40
41	2.0366 2530	0.4910 0834	29.0852 3789	59.2357 3124	0.0343 8170	41
42	2.0722 6624	0.4825 6348	29.5678 0135	61.2723 5654	0.0338 2057	42
43	2.1085 3090	0.4742 6386	30.0420 6522	63.3446 2278	0.0332 8666	43
44	2.1454 3019	0.4661 0699	30.5081 7221	65.4531 5367	0.0327 7810	44
45	2.1829 7522	0.4580 9040	30.9662 6261	67.5985 8386	0.0322 9321	45
46	2.2211 7728	0.4502 1170	31.4164 7431	69.7815 5908	0.0318 3043	46
47	2.2600 4789	0.4424 6850	31.8589 4281	72.0027 3637	0.0313 8836	47
48	2.2995 9872	0.4348 5848	32.2938 0129	74.2627 8425	0.0309 6569	48
49	2.3398 4170	0.4273 7934	32.7211 8063	76.5623 8298	0.0305 6124	49
50	2.3807 8893	0.4200 2883	33.1412 0946	78.9022 2468	0.0301 7391	50

Table XII (continued). 1¾ %

Number of periods n	Amount of 1 at compound interest $s = (1 + i)^n$	Present value of 1 $v^n = \dfrac{1}{(1 + i)^n}$	Present value of an annuity of 1 $a_{\overline{n}|} = \dfrac{1 - v^n}{i}$	Amount of an annuity of 1 $s_{\overline{n}|} = \dfrac{(1+i)^n - 1}{i}$	Annuity whose present value is 1 $\dfrac{1}{a_{\overline{n}|}} = \dfrac{1}{s_{\overline{n}|}} + i$	Number of periods n
51	2.4224 5274	0.4128 0475	33.5540 1421	81.2830 1361	0.0298 0269	51
52	2.4648 4566	0.4057 0492	33.9597 1913	83.7054 6635	0.0294 4665	52
53	2.5070 8046	0.3987 2719	34.3584 4633	86.1703 1201	0.0291 0492	53
54	2.5518 7012	0.3918 6947	34.7503 1579	88.6782 9247	0.0287 7672	54
55	2.5965 2785	0.3851 2970	35.1354 4550	91.2301 6259	0.0284 6129	55
56	2.6419 6708	0.3785 0585	35.5139 5135	93.8266 9043	0.0281 5795	56
57	2.6882 0151	0.3719 9592	35.8859 4727	96.4686 5752	0.0278 6606	57
58	2.7352 4503	0.3655 9796	36.2515 4523	99.1568 5902	0.0275 8503	58
59	2.7831 1182	0.3593 1003	36.6108 5526	101.8921 0405	0.0273 1430	59
60	2.8318 1628	0.3531 3025	36.9639 8552	104.6752 1588	0.0270 5336	60
61	2.8813 7306	0.3470 5676	37.3110 4228	107.5070 3215	0.0268 0172	61
62	2.9317 9709	0.3410 8772	37.6521 3000	110.3884 0522	0.0265 5892	62
63	2.9831 0354	0.3352 2135	37.9873 5135	113.3202 0231	0.0263 2455	63
64	3.0343 0785	0.3294 5587	38.3168 0723	116.3033 0585	0.0260 9821	64
65	3.0884 2574	0.3237 8956	38.6405 9678	119.3386 1370	0.0258 7952	65
66	3.1424 7319	0.3182 2069	38.9588 1748	122.4270 3944	0.0256 6813	66
67	3.1974 6647	0.3127 4761	39.2715 6509	125.5695 1263	0.0254 6372	67
68	3.2534 2213	0.3073 6866	39.5789 3375	128.7669 7910	0.0252 6596	68
69	3.3103 5702	0.3020 8222	39.8810 1597	132.0204 0124	0.0250 7459	69
70	3.3682 8827	0.2968 8670	40.1779 0267	135.3307 5826	0.0248 8930	70
71	3.4272 3331	0.2917 8054	40.4696 8321	138.6990 4653	0.0247 0985	71
72	3.4872 0990	0.2867 6221	40.7564 4542	142.1262 7984	0.0245 3600	72
73	3.5482 3607	0.2818 3018	41.0382 7560	145.6134 8974	0.0243 6750	73
74	3.6103 3020	0.2769 8298	41.3152 5857	149.1617 2581	0.0242 0113	74
75	3.6735 1098	0.2722 1914	41.5874 7771	152.7720 5601	0.0240 4570	75
76	3.7377 9742	0.2675 3724	41.8550 1495	156.4455 6699	0.0238 9200	76
77	3.8032 0888	0.2629 3586	42.1179 5081	160.1833 6441	0.0237 4284	77
78	3.8697 6503	0.2584 1362	42.3763 6443	163.9865 7329	0.0235 9806	78
79	3.9374 8592	0.2539 6916	42.6303 3359	167.8563 3832	0.0234 5748	79
80	4.0063 9192	0.2496 0114	42.8799 3474	171.7938 2424	0.0233 2093	80
81	4.0765 0378	0.2453 0825	43.1252 4298	175.8002 1617	0.0231 8828	81
82	4.1478 1260	0.2410 8919	43.3663 3217	179.8767 1995	0.0230 5936	82
83	4.2204 2984	0.2369 4269	43.6032 7486	184.0245 6255	0.0229 3406	83
84	4.2942 8737	0.2328 6751	43.8361 4237	188.2449 9239	0.0228 1223	84
85	4.3694 3740	0.2288 6242	44.0650 0479	192.5392 7976	0.0226 9375	85
86	4.4459 0255	0.2249 2621	44.2899 3099	196.9087 1716	0.0225 7850	86
87	4.5237 0584	0.2210 5770	44.5109 8869	201.3546 1971	0.0224 6636	87
88	4.6028 7070	0.2172 5572	44.7282 4441	205.8783 2555	0.0223 5724	88
89	4.6834 2093	0.2135 1914	44.9417 6355	210.4811 9625	0.0222 5102	89
90	4.7653 8080	0.2098 4682	45.1516 1037	215.1646 1718	0.0221 4760	90
91	4.8487 7496	0.2062 3766	45.3578 4803	219.9299 9798	0.0220 4690	91
92	4.9336 2853	0.2026 9057	45.5605 3860	224.7787 7295	0.0219 4882	92
93	5.0199 6703	0.1992 0450	45.7597 4310	229.7124 0148	0.0218 5327	93
94	5.1078 1645	0.1957 7837	45.9555 2147	234.7323 6850	0.0217 6017	94
95	5.1972 0324	0.1924 1118	46.1479 3265	239.8401 8495	0.0216 6944	95
96	5.2881 5429	0.1891 0190	46.3370 3455	245.0373 8819	0.0215 8101	96
97	5.3806 9699	0.1858 4953	46.5228 8408	250.3255 4248	0.0214 9480	97
98	5.4748 5919	0.1826 5310	46.7055 3718	255.7062 3947	0.0214 1074	98
99	5.5706 6923	0.1795 1165	46.8850 4882	261.1810 9866	0.0213 2876	99
100	5.6681 5594	0.1764 2422	47.0614 7304	266.7517 6789	0.0212 4880	100

Table XIII. 2%

Number of periods n	Amount of 1 at compound interest $s = (1 + i)^n$	Present value of 1 $v^n = \dfrac{1}{(1 + i)^n}$	Present value of an annuity of 1 $a_{\overline{n}|} = \dfrac{1 - v^n}{i}$	Amount of an annuity of 1 $s_{\overline{n}|} = \dfrac{(1+i)^n - 1}{i}$	Annuity whose present value is 1 $\dfrac{1}{a_{\overline{n}|}} = \dfrac{1}{s_{\overline{n}|}} + i$	Number of periods n
1	1.0200 0000	0.9803 9216	0.9803 9216	1.0000 0000	1.0200 0000	1
2	1.0404 0000	0.9611 6878	1.9415 6094	2.0200 0000	0.5150 4950	2
3	1.0612 0800	0.9423 2233	2.8838 8327	3.0604 0000	0.3467 5467	3
4	1.0824 3216	0.9238 4543	3.8077 2870	4.1216 0800	0.2626 2375	4
5	1.1040 8080	0.9057 3081	4.7134 5951	5.2040 4016	0.2121 5839	5
6	1.1261 6242	0.8879 7138	5.6014 3089	6.3081 2096	0.1785 2581	6
7	1.1486 8567	0.8705 6018	6.4719 9107	7.4342 8338	0.1545 1196	7
8	1.1716 5938	0.8534 9037	7.3254 8144	8.5829 6905	0.1365 0980	8
9	1.1950 9257	0.8367 5527	8.1622 3671	9.7546 2843	0.1225 1544	9
10	1.2189 9442	0.8203 4830	8.9825 8501	10.9497 2100	0.1113 2653	10
11	1.2433 7431	0.8042 6304	9.7868 4805	12.1687 1542	0.1021 7794	11
12	1.2682 4179	0.7884 9318	10.5753 4122	13.4120 8973	0.0945 5960	12
13	1.2936 0663	0.7730 3253	11.3483 7375	14.6803 3152	0.0881 1835	13
14	1.3194 7876	0.7578 7502	12.1062 4877	15.9739 3815	0.0826 0197	14
15	1.3458 6834	0.7430 1473	12.8492 6350	17.2934 1692	0.0778 2547	15
16	1.3727 8571	0.7284 4581	13.5777 0931	18.6392 8525	0.0736 5013	16
17	1.4002 4142	0.7141 6256	14.2918 7188	20.0120 7096	0.0699 6984	17
18	1.4282 4625	0.7001 5937	14.9920 3125	21.4123 1238	0.0667 0210	18
19	1.4568 1117	0.6864 3076	15.6784 6201	22.8405 5863	0.0637 8177	19
20	1.4859 4740	0.6729 7133	16.3514 3334	24.2973 6980	0.0611 5672	20
21	1.5156 6634	0.6597 7582	17.0112 0916	25.7833 1719	0.0587 8477	21
22	1.5459 7967	0.6468 3904	17.6580 4820	27.2989 8354	0.0566 3140	22
23	1.5768 9926	0.6341 5592	18.2922 0412	28.8449 6321	0.0546 6810	23
24	1.6084 3725	0.6217 2149	18.9139 2560	30.4218 6247	0.0528 7110	24
25	1.6406 0599	0.6095 3087	19.5234 5647	32.0302 9972	0.0512 2044	25
26	1.6734 1811	0.5975 7928	20.1210 3576	33.6709 0572	0.0496 9923	26
27	1.7068 8648	0.5858 6204	20.7068 9780	35.3443 2383	0.0482 9309	27
28	1.7410 2421	0.5743 7455	21.2812 7236	37.0512 1031	0.0469 8967	28
29	1.7758 4469	0.5631 1231	21.8443 8466	38.7922 3451	0.0457 7836	29
30	1.8113 6158	0.5520 7089	22.3964 5555	40.5680 7921	0.0446 4992	30
31	1.8475 8882	0.5412 4597	22.9377 0152	42.3794 4079	0.0435 9635	31
32	1.8845 4059	0.5306 3330	23.4683 3482	44.2270 2961	0.0426 1061	32
33	1.9222 3140	0.5202 2873	23.9885 6355	46.1115 7020	0.0416 8653	33
34	1.9606 7603	0.5100 2817	24.4985 9172	48.0338 0160	0.0408 1867	34
35	1.9998 8955	0.5000 2761	24.9986 1933	49.9944 7763	0.0400 0221	35
36	2.0398 8734	0.4902 2315	25.4888 4248	51.9943 6719	0.0392 3285	36
37	2.0806 8509	0.4806 1093	25.9694 5341	54.0342 5453	0.0385 0678	37
38	2.1222 9879	0.4711 8719	26.4406 4060	56.1149 3962	0.0378 2057	38
39	2.1647 4477	0.4619 4822	26.9025 8883	58.2372 3841	0.0371 7114	39
40	2.2080 3966	0.4528 9042	27.3554 7924	60.4019 8318	0.0365 5575	40
41	2.2522 0046	0.4440 1021	27.7994 8945	62.6100 2284	0.0359 7188	41
42	2.2972 4447	0.4353 0413	28.2347 9358	64.8622 2330	0.0354 1729	42
43	2.3431 8936	0.4267 6875	28.6615 6233	67.1594 6777	0.0348 8993	43
44	2.3900 5314	0.4184 0074	29.0799 6307	69.5026 5712	0.0343 8794	44
45	2.4378 5421	0.4101 9680	29.4901 5987	71.8927 1027	0.0339 0962	45
46	2.4866 1129	0.4021 5373	29.8923 1360	74.3305 6447	0.0334 5342	46
47	2.5363 4351	0.3942 6836	30.2865 8196	76.8171 7576	0.0330 1792	47
48	2.5870 7039	0.3865 3761	30.6731 1957	79.3535 1927	0.0326 0184	48
49	2.6388 1179	0.3789 5844	31.0520 7801	81.9405 8966	0.0322 0396	49
50	2.6915 8803	0.3715 2788	31.4236 0589	84.5794 0145	0.0318 2321	50

Table XIII (*continued*). 2 %

Number of periods n	Amount of 1 at compound interest $s = (1+i)^n$	Present value of 1 $v^n = \dfrac{1}{(1+i)^n}$	Present value of an annuity of 1 $a_{\overline{n}|} = \dfrac{1-v^n}{i}$	Amount of an annuity of 1 $s_{\overline{n}|} = \dfrac{(1+i)^n-1}{i}$	Annuity whose present value is 1 $\dfrac{1}{a_{\overline{n}|}} = \dfrac{1}{s_{\overline{n}|}} + i$	Number of periods n
51	2.7454 1979	0.3642 4302	31.7878 4892	87.2709 8948	0.0314 5356	51
52	2.8003 2819	0.3571 0100	32.1449 4992	90.0164 0927	0.0311 0909	52
53	2.8563 3475	0.3500 9902	32.4950 4894	92.8167 3746	0.0307 7392	53
54	2.9134 6144	0.3432 3433	32.8382 8327	95.6730 7221	0.0304 5226	54
55	2.9717 3067	0.3365 0425	33.1747 8752	98.5865 3365	0.0301 4337	55
56	3.0311 6529	0.3299 0613	33.5046 9365	101.5582 6432	0.0298 4656	56
57	3.0917 8859	0.3234 3738	33.8281 3103	104.5894 2961	0.0295 6120	57
58	3.1536 2436	0.3170 9547	34.1452 2650	107.6812 1820	0.0292 8667	58
59	3.2166 9685	0.3108 7791	34.4561 0441	110.8348 4257	0.0290 2243	59
60	3.2810 3079	0.3047 8227	34.7608 8668	114.0515 3942	0.0287 6797	60
61	3.3466 5140	0.2988 0614	35.0596 9282	117.3325 7021	0.0285 2278	61
62	3.4135 8443	0.2929 4720	35.3526 4002	120.6792 2161	0.0282 8643	62
63	3.4818 5612	0.2872 0314	35.6398 4316	124.0928 0604	0.0280 5848	63
64	3.5514 9324	0.2815 7170	35.9214 1486	127.5746 6216	0.0278 3855	64
65	3.6225 2311	0.2760 5069	36.1974 6555	131.1261 5541	0.0276 2624	65
66	3.6949 7357	0.2706 3793	36.4681 0348	134.7486 7852	0.0274 2122	66
67	3.7688 7304	0.2653 3130	36.7334 3478	138.4436 5209	0.0272 2316	67
68	3.8442 5050	0.2601 2873	36.9935 6351	142.2125 2513	0.0270 3173	68
69	3.9211 3551	0.2550 2817	37.2485 9168	146.0567 7563	0.0268 4665	69
70	3.9995 5822	0.2500 2761	37.4986 1929	149.9779 1114	0.0266 6765	70
71	4.0795 4939	0.2451 2511	37.7437 4441	153.9774 6937	0.0264 9446	71
72	4.1611 4038	0.2403 1874	37.9840 6314	158.0570 1875	0.0263 2683	72
73	4.2443 6318	0.2356 0661	38.2196 6975	162.2181 5913	0.0261 6454	73
74	4.3292 5045	0.2309 8687	38.4506 5662	166.4625 2231	0.0260 0736	74
75	4.4158 3546	0.2264 5771	38.6771 1433	170.7917 7276	0.0258 5508	75
76	4.5041 5216	0.2220 1737	38.8991 3170	175.2076 0821	0.0257 0751	76
77	4.5942 3521	0.2176 6408	39.1167 9578	179.7117 6038	0.0255 6447	77
78	4.6861 1991	0.2133 9616	39.3301 9194	184.3059 9558	0.0254 2576	78
79	4.7798 4231	0.2092 1192	39.5394 0386	188.9921 1549	0.0252 9123	79
80	4.8754 3916	0.2051 0973	39.7445 1359	193.7719 5780	0.0251 6071	80
81	4.9729 4794	0.2010 8797	39.9456 0156	198.6473 9696	0.0250 3405	81
82	5.0724 0690	0.1971 4507	40.1427 4663	203.6203 4490	0.0249 1110	82
83	5.1738 5504	0.1932 7948	40.3360 2611	208.6927 5180	0.0247 9173	83
84	5.2773 3214	0.1894 8968	40.5255 1579	213.8666 0683	0.0246 7581	84
85	5.3828 7878	0.1857 7420	40.7112 8999	219.1439 3897	0.0245 6321	85
86	5.4905 3636	0.1821 3157	40.8934 2156	224.5268 1775	0.0244 5381	86
87	5.6003 4708	0.1785 6036	41.0719 8192	230.0173 5411	0.0243 4750	87
88	5.7123 5402	0.1750 5918	41.2470 4110	235.6177 0119	0.0242 4416	88
89	5.8266 0110	0.1716 2665	41.4186 6774	241.3300 5521	0.0241 4370	89
90	5.9431 3313	0.1682 6142	41.5869 2916	247.1566 5632	0.0240 4602	90
91	6.0619 9579	0.1649 6217	41.7518 9133	253.0997 8944	0.0239 5101	91
92	6.1832 3570	0.1617 2762	41.9136 1895	259.1617 8523	0.0238 5859	92
93	6.3069 0042	0.1585 5649	42.0721 7545	265.3450 2094	0.0237 6868	93
94	6.4330 3843	0.1554 4754	42.2276 2299	271.6519 2135	0.0236 8118	94
95	6.5616 9920	0.1523 9955	42.3800 2254	278.0849 5978	0.0235 9602	95
96	6.6929 3318	0.1494 1132	42.5294 3386	284.6466 5898	0.0235 1313	96
97	6.8267 9184	0.1464 8169	42.6759 1555	291.3395 9216	0.0234 3242	97
98	6.9633 2768	0.1436 0950	42.8195 2505	298.1663 8400	0.0233 5383	98
99	7.1025 9423	0.1407 9363	42.9603 1867	305.1297 1168	0.0232 7729	99
100	7.2446 4612	0.1380 3297	43.0983 5164	312.2323 0591	0.0232 0274	100

Table XIV. 2½ %

Number of periods n	Amount of 1 at compound interest $s = (1+i)^n$	Present value of 1 $v^n = \dfrac{1}{(1+i)^n}$	Present value of an annuity of 1 $a_{\overline{n}\mid} = \dfrac{1-v^n}{i}$	Amount of an annuity of 1 $s_{\overline{n}\mid} = \dfrac{(1+i)^n-1}{i}$	Annuity whose present value is 1 $\dfrac{1}{a_{\overline{n}\mid}} = \dfrac{1}{s_{\overline{n}\mid}} + i$	Number of periods n
1	1.0250 0000	0.9756 0976	0.9756 0976	1.0000 0000	1.0250 0000	1
2	1.0506 2500	0.9518 1440	1.9274 2415	2.0250 0000	0.5188 2716	2
3	1.0768 9063	0.9285 9941	2.8560 2356	3.0756 2500	0.3501 3717	3
4	1.1038 1289	0.9059 5064	3.7619 7421	4.1525 1563	0.2658 1788	4
5	1.1314 0821	0.8838 5429	4.6458 2850	5.2563 2852	0.2152 4686	5
6	1.1596 9342	0.8622 9687	5.5081 2536	6.3877 3673	0.1815 4997	6
7	1.1886 8575	0.8412 6524	6.3493 9060	7.5474 3015	0.1574 9543	7
8	1.2184 0290	0.8207 4657	7.1701 3717	8.7361 1590	0.1394 6735	8
9	1.2488 6297	0.8007 2836	7.9708 6553	9.9545 1880	0.1254 5689	9
10	1.2800 8454	0.7811 9840	8.7520 6393	11.2033 8177	0.1142 5876	10
11	1.3120 8666	0.7621 4478	9.5142 0871	12.4834 6631	0.1051 0596	11
12	1.3448 8882	0.7435 5589	10.2577 6460	13.7955 5297	0.0974 8713	12
13	1.3785 1104	0.7254 2038	10.9831 8497	15.1404 4179	0.0910 4827	13
14	1.4129 7382	0.7077 2720	11.6909 1217	16.5189 5284	0.0855 3653	14
15	1.4482 9817	0.6904 6556	12.3813 7773	17.9319 2666	0.0807 6646	15
16	1.4845 0562	0.6736 2493	13.0550 0266	19.3802 2483	0.0765 9899	16
17	1.5216 1826	0.6571 9506	13.7121 9772	20.8647 3045	0.0729 2777	17
18	1.5596 5872	0.6411 6591	14.3533 6363	22.3863 4871	0.0696 7008	18
19	1.5986 5019	0.6255 2772	14.9788 9134	23.9460 0743	0.0667 6062	19
20	1.6386 1644	0.6102 7094	15.5891 6229	25.5446 5761	0.0641 4713	20
21	1.6795 8185	0.5953 8629	16.1845 4857	27.1832 7405	0.0617 8733	21
22	1.7215 7140	0.5808 6467	16.7654 1324	28.8628 5590	0.0596 4661	22
23	1.7646 1068	0.5666 9724	17.3321 1048	30.5844 2730	0.0576 9638	23
24	1.8087 2595	0.5528 7535	17.8849 8583	32.3490 3798	0.0559 1282	24
25	1.8539 4410	0.5393 9059	18.4243 7642	34.1577 6393	0.0542 7592	25
26	1.9002 9270	0.5262 3472	18.9506 1114	36.0117 0803	0.0527 6875	26
27	1.9478 0002	0.5133 9973	19.4640 1087	37.9120 0073	0.0513 7687	27
28	1.9964 9502	0.5008 7778	19.9648 8866	39.8598 0075	0.0500 8793	28
29	2.0464 0739	0.4886 6125	20.4535 4991	41.8562 9577	0.0488 9127	29
30	2.0975 6758	0.4767 4269	20.9302 9259	43.9027 0316	0.0477 7764	30
31	2.1500 0677	0.4651 1481	21.3954 0741	46.0002 7074	0.0467 3900	31
32	2.2037 5694	0.4537 7055	21.8491 7796	48.1502 7751	0.0457 6831	32
33	2.2588 5086	0.4427 0298	22.2918 8094	50.3540 3445	0.0448 5938	33
34	2.3153 2213	0.4319 0534	22.7237 8628	52.6128 8531	0.0440 0675	34
35	2.3732 0519	0.4213 7107	23.1451 5734	54.9282 0744	0.0432 0558	35
36	2.4325 3532	0.4110 9372	23.5562 5107	57.3014 1263	0.0424 5158	36
37	2.4933 4870	0.4010 6705	23.9573 1812	59.7339 4794	0.0417 4090	37
38	2.5556 8242	0.3912 8492	24.3486 0304	62.2272 9664	0.0410 7012	38
39	2.6195 7448	0.3817 4139	24.7303 4443	64.7829 7906	0.0404 3615	39
40	2.6850 6384	0.3724 3062	25.1027 7505	67.4025 5354	0.0398 3623	40
41	2.7521 9043	0.3633 4695	25.4661 2200	70.0876 1737	0.0392 6786	41
42	2.8209 9520	0.3544 8483	25.8206 0683	72.8398 0781	0.0387 2876	42
43	2.8915 2008	0.3458 3886	26.1664 4569	75.6608 0300	0.0382 1688	43
44	2.9638 0808	0.3374 0376	26.5038 4945	78.5523 2308	0.0377 3037	44
45	3.0379 0328	0.3291 7440	26.8330 2386	81.5161 3116	0.0372 6752	45
46	3.1138 5086	0.3211 4576	27.1541 6962	84.5540 3443	0.0368 2676	46
47	3.1916 9713	0.3133 1294	27.4674 8255	87.6678 8530	0.0364 0669	47
48	3.2714 8956	0.3056 7116	27.7731 5371	90.8595 8243	0.0360 0599	48
49	3.3532 7680	0.2982 1576	28.0713 6947	94.1310 7199	0.0356 2348	49
50	3.4371 0872	0.2909 4221	28.3623 1168	97.4843 4879	0.0352 5806	50

Table XIV (continued). 2½ %

Number of periods n	Amount of 1 at compound interest $s = (1 + i)^n$	Present value of 1 $v^n = \dfrac{1}{(1 + i)^n}$	Present value of an annuity of 1 $a_{\overline{n}} = \dfrac{1 - v^n}{i}$	Amount of an annuity of 1 $s_{\overline{n}} = \dfrac{(1+i)^n-1}{i}$	Annuity whose present value is 1 $\dfrac{1}{a_{\overline{n}}} = \dfrac{1}{s_{\overline{n}}} + i$	Number of periods n
51	3.5230 3644	0.2838 4606	28.6461 5774	100.9214 5751	0.0349 0870	51
52	3.6111 1235	0.2769 2298	28.9230 8072	104.4444 9395	0.0345 7446	52
53	3.7013 9016	0.2701 6876	29.1932 4948	108.0556 0629	0.0342 5449	53
54	3.7939 2491	0.2635 7928	29.4568 2876	111.7569 9645	0.0339 4799	54
55	3.8887 7303	0.2571 5052	29.7139 7928	115.5509 2136	0.0336 5419	55
56	3.9859 9236	0.2508 7855	29.9648 5784	119.4396 9440	0.0333 7243	56
57	4.0856 4217	0.2447 5956	30.2096 1740	123.4256 8676	0.0331 0204	57
58	4.1877 8322	0.2387 8982	30.4484 0722	127.5113 2893	0.0328 4244	58
59	4.2924 7780	0.2329 6568	30.6813 7290	131.6991 1215	0.0325 9307	59
60	4.3997 8975	0.2272 8359	30.9086 5649	135.9915 8995	0.0323 5340	60
61	4.5097 8449	0.2217 4009	31.1303 9657	140.3913 7970	0.0321 2294	61
62	4.6225 2910	0.2163 3179	31.3467 2836	144.9011 6419	0.0319 0126	62
63	4.7380 9233	0.2110 5541	31.5577 8377	149.5236 9330	0.0316 8790	63
64	4.8565 4464	0.2059 0771	31.7636 9148	154.2617 8563	0.0314 8249	64
65	4.9779 5826	0.2008 8557	31.9645 7705	159.1183 3027	0.0312 8463	65
66	5.1024 0721	0.1959 8593	32.1605 6298	164.0962 8853	0.0310 9398	66
67	5.2299 6739	0.1912 0578	32.3517 6876	169.1986 9574	0.0309 1021	67
68	5.3607 1658	0.1865 4223	32.5383 1099	174.4286 6314	0.0307 3300	68
69	5.4947 3449	0.1819 9241	32.7203 0340	179.7893 7971	0.0305 6206	69
70	5.6321 0286	0.1775 5358	32.8978 5698	185.2841 1421	0.0303 9712	70
71	5.7729 0543	0.1732 2300	33.0710 7998	190.9162 1706	0.0302 3790	71
72	5.9172 2806	0.1689 9805	33.2400 7803	196.6891 2249	0.0300 8417	72
73	6.0651 5876	0.1648 7615	33.4049 5417	202.6063 5055	0.0299 3568	73
74	6.2167 8773	0.1608 5478	33.5658 0895	208.6715 0931	0.0297 9222	74
75	6.3722 0743	0.1569 3149	33.7227 4044	214.8882 9705	0.0296 5358	75
76	6.5315 1261	0.1531 0389	33.8758 4433	221.2605 0447	0.0295 1956	76
77	6.6948 0043	0.1493 6965	34.0252 1398	227.7920 1709	0.0293 8997	77
78	6.8621 7044	0.1457 2649	34.1709 4047	234.4868 1751	0.0292 6463	78
79	7.0337 2470	0.1421 7218	34.3131 1265	241.3489 8795	0.0291 4338	79
80	7.2095 6782	0.1387 0457	34.4518 1722	248.3827 1265	0.0290 2605	80
81	7.3898 0701	0.1353 2153	34.5871 3875	255.5922 8047	0.0289 1248	81
82	7.5745 5219	0.1320 2101	34.7191 5976	262.9820 8748	0.0288 0254	82
83	7.7639 1599	0.1288 0098	34.8479 6074	270.5566 3966	0.0286 9608	83
84	7.9580 1389	0.1256 5949	34.9736 2023	278.3205 5566	0.0285 9298	84
85	8.1569 6424	0.1225 9463	35.0962 1486	286.2785 6955	0.0284 9310	85
86	8.3608 8834	0.1196 0452	35.2158 1938	294.4355 3379	0.0283 9633	86
87	8.5699 1055	0.1166 8733	35.3325 0671	302.7964 2213	0.0283 0255	87
88	8.7841 5832	0.1138 4130	35.4463 4801	311.3663 3268	0.0282 1165	88
89	9.0037 6228	0.1110 6468	35.5574 1269	320.1504 9100	0.0281 2353	89
90	9.2288 5633	0.1083 5570	35.6657 6848	329.1542 5328	0.0280 3809	90
91	9.4595 7774	0.1057 1296	35.7714 8144	338.3831 0961	0.0279 5523	91
92	9.6960 6718	0.1031 3460	35.8746 1604	347.8426 8735	0.0278 7486	92
93	9.9384 6886	0.1006 1912	35.9752 3516	357.5387 5453	0.0277 9690	93
94	10.1869 3058	0.0981 6500	36.0734 0016	367.4772 2339	0.0277 2126	94
95	10.4416 0385	0.0957 7073	36.1691 7089	377.6641 5398	0.0276 4786	95
96	10.7026 4395	0.0934 3486	36.2626 0574	388.1057 5783	0.0275 7662	96
97	10.9702 1004	0.0911 5596	36.3537 6170	398.8084 0177	0.0275 0747	97
98	11.2444 6530	0.0889 3264	36.4426 9434	409.7786 1182	0.0274 4034	98
99	11.5255 7693	0.0867 6355	36.5294 5790	421.0230 7711	0.0273 7517	99
100	11.8137 1635	0.0846 4737	36.6141 0526	432.5486 5404	0.0273 1188	100

Table XV. 3%

Number of periods n	Amount of 1 at compound interest $s = (1 + i)^n$	Present value of 1 $v^n = \dfrac{1}{(1+i)^n}$	Present value of an annuity of 1 $a_{\overline{n}} = \dfrac{1 - v^n}{i}$	Amount of an annuity of 1 $s_{\overline{n}} = \dfrac{(1+i)^n - 1}{i}$	Annuity whose present value is 1 $\dfrac{1}{a_{\overline{n}}} = \dfrac{1}{s_{\overline{n}}} + i$	Number of periods n
1	1.0300 0000	0.9708 7379	0.9708 7379	1.0000 0000	1.0300 0000	1
2	1.0609 0000	0.9425 9591	1.9134 6970	2.0300 0000	0.5226 1084	2
3	1.0927 2700	0.9151 4166	2.8286 1135	3.0909 0000	0.3535 3036	3
4	1.1255 0881	0.8884 8705	3.7170 9840	4.1836 2700	0.2690 2705	4
5	1.1592 7407	0.8626 0878	4.5797 0719	5.3091 3581	0.2183 5457	5
6	1.1940 5230	0.8374 8426	5.4171 9144	6.4684 0988	0.1845 9750	6
7	1.2298 7387	0.8130 9151	6.2302 8296	7.6624 6218	0.1605 0635	7
8	1.2667 7008	0.7894 0923	7.0196 9219	8.8923 3605	0.1424 5639	8
9	1.3047 7318	0.7664 1673	7.7861 0892	10.1591 0613	0.1284 3386	9
10	1.3439 1638	0.7440 9391	8.5302 0284	11.4638 7931	0.1172 3051	10
11	1.3842 3387	0.7224 2128	9.2526 2411	12.8077 9569	0.1080 7745	11
12	1.4257 6089	0.7013 7988	9.9540 0399	14.1920 2956	0.1004 6209	12
13	1.4685 3371	0.6809 5134	10.6349 5533	15.6177 9045	0.0940 2954	13
14	1.5125 8972	0.6611 1781	11.2960 7314	17.0863 2416	0.0885 2634	14
15	1.5579 6742	0.6418 6195	11.9379 3509	18.5989 1389	0.0837 6658	15
16	1.6047 0644	0.6231 6694	12.5611 0203	20.1568 8130	0.0796 1085	16
17	1.6528 4763	0.6050 1645	13.1661 1847	21.7615 8774	0.0759 5253	17
18	1.7024 3306	0.5873 9461	13.7535 1308	23.4144 3537	0.0727 0870	18
19	1.7535 0605	0.5702 8603	14.3237 9911	25.1168 6844	0.0698 1388	19
20	1.8061 1123	0.5536 7575	14.8774 7486	26.8703 7449	0.0672 1571	20
21	1.8602 9457	0.5375 4928	15.4150 2414	28.6764 8572	0.0648 7178	21
22	1.9161 0341	0.5218 9250	15.9369 1664	30.5367 8030	0.0627 4739	22
23	1.9735 8651	0.5066 9175	16.4436 0839	32.4528 8370	0.0608 1390	23
24	2.0327 9411	0.4919 3374	16.9355 4212	34.4264 7022	0.0590 4742	24
25	2.0937 7793	0.4776 0557	17.4131 4769	36.4592 6432	0.0574 2787	25
26	2.1565 9127	0.4636 9473	17.8768 4242	38.5530 4225	0.0559 3829	26
27	2.2212 8901	0.4501 8906	18.3270 3147	40.7096 3352	0.0545 6421	27
28	2.2879 2768	0.4370 7675	18.7641 0823	42.9309 2252	0.0532 9323	28
29	2.3565 6551	0.4243 4636	19.1884 5459	45.2188 5020	0.0521 1467	29
30	2.4272 6247	0.4119 8676	19.6004 4135	47.5754 1571	0.0510 1926	30
31	2.5000 8035	0.3999 8715	20.0004 2849	50.0026 7818	0.0499 9893	31
32	2.5750 8276	0.3883 3703	20.3887 6553	52.5027 5852	0.0490 4662	32
33	2.6523 3524	0.3770 2625	20.7657 9178	55.0778 4128	0.0481 5612	33
34	2.7319 0530	0.3660 4490	21.1318 3668	57.7301 7652	0.0473 2196	34
35	2.8138 6245	0.3553 8340	21.4872 2007	60.4620 8181	0.0465 3929	35
36	2.8982 7833	0.3450 3243	21.8322 5250	63.2759 4427	0.0458 0379	36
37	2.9852 2668	0.3349 8294	22.1672 3544	66.1742 2259	0.0451 1162	37
38	3.0747 8348	0.3252 2615	22.4924 6159	69.1594 4927	0.0444 5934	38
39	3.1670 2698	0.3157 5355	22.8082 1513	72.2342 3275	0.0438 4385	39
40	3.2620 3779	0.3065 5684	23.1147 7197	75.4012 5973	0.0432 6238	40
41	3.3598 9893	0.2976 2800	23.4123 9997	78.6632 9753	0.0427 1241	41
42	3.4606 9589	0.2889 5922	23.7013 5920	82.0231 9645	0.0421 9167	42
43	3.5645 1677	0.2805 4294	23.9819 0213	85.4838 9234	0.0416 9811	43
44	3.6714 5227	0.2723 7178	24.2542 7392	89.0484 0911	0.0412 2985	44
45	3.7815 9584	0.2644 3862	24.5187 1254	92.7198 6139	0.0407 8518	45
46	3.8950 4372	0.2567 3653	24.7754 4907	96.5014 5723	0.0403 6254	46
47	4.0118 9503	0.2492 5876	25.0247 0783	100.3965 0095	0.0399 6051	47
48	4.1322 5188	0.2419 9880	25.2667 0664	104.4083 9598	0.0395 7777	48
49	4.2562 1944	0.2349 5029	25.5016 5693	108.5406 4785	0.0392 1314	49
50	4.3839 0602	0.2281 0708	25.7297 6401	112.7968 6729	0.0388 6550	50

Table XV (continued). 3%

Number of periods n	Amount of 1 at compound interest $s = (1 + i)^n$	Present value of 1 $v^n = \dfrac{1}{(1 + i)^n}$	Present value of an annuity of 1 $a_{\overline{n}\rceil} = \dfrac{1 - v^n}{i}$	Amount of an annuity of 1 $s_{\overline{n}\rceil} = \dfrac{(1+i)^n - 1}{i}$	Annuity whose present value is 1 $\dfrac{1}{a_{\overline{n}\rceil}} = \dfrac{1}{s_{\overline{n}\rceil}} + i$	Number of periods n
51	4.5154 2320	0.2214 6318	25.9512 2719	117.1807 7331	0.0385 3382	51
52	4.6508 8590	0.2150 1280	26.1662 3999	121.6961 9651	0.0382 1718	52
53	4.7904 1247	0.2087 5029	26.3749 9028	126.3470 8240	0.0379 1471	53
54	4.9341 2485	0.2026 7019	26.5776 6047	131.1374 9488	0.0376 2558	54
55	5.0821 4859	0.1967 6717	26.7744 2764	136.0716 1972	0.0373 4907	55
56	5.2346 1305	0.1910 3609	26.9654 6373	141.1537 6831	0.0370 8447	56
57	5.3916 5144	0.1854 7193	27.1509 3566	146.3883 8136	0.0368 3114	57
58	5.5534 0098	0.1800 6984	27.3310 0549	151.7800 3280	0.0365 8848	58
59	5.7200 0301	0.1748 2508	27.5058 3058	157.3334 3379	0.0363 5593	59
60	5.8916 0310	0.1697 3309	27.6755 6367	163.0534 3680	0.0361 3296	60
61	6.0683 5120	0.1647 8941	27.8403 5307	168.9450 3991	0.0359 1908	61
62	6.2504 0173	0.1599 8972	28.0003 4279	175.0133 9110	0.0357 1385	62
63	6.4379 1379	0.1553 2982	28.1556 7261	181.2637 9284	0.0355 1682	63
64	6.6310 5120	0.1508 0565	28 3064 7826	187.7017 0662	0.0353 2760	64
65	6.8299 8273	0.1464 1325	28.4528 9152	194.3327 5782	0.0351 4581	65
66	7.0348 8222	0.1421 4879	28.5950 4031	201.1627 4055	0.0349 7110	66
67	7.2459 2868	0.1380 0853	28.7330 4884	208.1976 2277	0.0348 0313	67
68	7.4633 0654	0.1339 8887	28.8670 3771	215.4435 5145	0.0346 4159	68
69	7.6872 0574	0.1300 8628	28.9971 2399	222.9068 5800	0.0344 8618	69
70	7.9178 2191	0.1262 9736	29.1234 2135	230.5940 6374	0.0343 3663	70
71	8.1553 5657	0.1226 1880	29.2460 4015	238.5118 8565	0.0341 9266	71
72	8.4000 1727	0.1190 4737	29.3650 8752	246.6672 4222	0.0340 5404	72
73	8.6520 1778	0.1155 7998	29.4806 6750	255.0672 5949	0.0339 2053	73
74	8.9115 7832	0.1122 1357	29.5928 8106	263.7192 7727	0.0337 9191	74
75	9.1789 2567	0.1089 4521	29.7018 2628	272.6308 5559	0.0336 6796	75
76	9.4542 9344	0.1057 7205	29.8075 9833	281.8097 8126	0.0335 4849	76
77	9.7379 2224	0.1026 9131	29.9102 8964	291.2640 7469	0.0334 3331	77
78	10.0300 5991	0.0997 0030	30.0099 8994	301.0019 9693	0.0333 2224	78
79	10.3309 6171	0.0967 9641	30.1067 8635	311.0320 5684	0.0332 1510	79
80	10.6408 9056	0.0939 7710	30.2007 6345	321.3630 1855	0.0331 1175	80
81	10.9601 1727	0.0912 3990	30.2920 0335	332.0039 0910	0.0330 1201	81
82	11.2889 2079	0.0885 8243	30.3805 8577	342.9640 2638	0.0329 1576	82
83	11.6275 8842	0.0860 0236	30.4665 8813	354.2529 4717	0.0328 2284	83
84	11.9764 1607	0.0834 9743	30.5500 8556	365.8805 3558	0.0327 3313	84
85	12.3357 0855	0.0810 6547	30.6311 5103	377.8569 5165	0.0326 4650	85
86	12.7057 7981	0.0787 0434	30.7098 5537	390.1926 6020	0.0325 6284	86
87	13.0869 5320	0.0764 1198	30.7862 6735	402.8984 4001	0.0324 8202	87
88	13.4795 6180	0.0741 8639	30 8604 5374	415.9853 9321	0.0324 0393	88
89	13.8839 4865	0.0720 2562	30.9324 7936	429.4649 5500	0.0323 2848	89
90	14.3004 6711	0.0699 2779	31.0024 0714	443.3489 0365	0.0322 5556	90
91	14.7294 8112	0.0678 9105	31.0702 9820	457.6493 7076	0.0321 8508	91
92	15.1713 6556	0.0659 1364	31.1362 1184	472.3788 5189	0.0321 1694	92
93	15.6265 0652	0.0639 9383	31.2002 0567	487.5502 1744	0.0320 5107	93
94	16.0953 0172	0.0621 2993	31.2623 3560	503.1767 2397	0.0319 8737	94
95	16.5781 6077	0.0603 2032	31.3226 5592	519.2720 2569	0.0319 2577	95
96	17.0755 0559	0.0585 6342	31.3812 1934	535.8501 8645	0.0318 6619	96
97	17.5877 7076	0.0568 5769	31.4380 7703	552.9256 9205	0.0318 0856	97
98	18.1154 0388	0.0552 0164	31.4932 7867	570.5134 6281	0.0317 5281	98
99	18.6588 6600	0.0535 9383	31.5468 7250	588.6288 6669	0.0316 9886	99
100	19.2186 3198	0.0520 3284	31.5989 0534	607.2877 3270	0.0316 4667	100

421

Table XVI. 3½ %

Number of periods n	Amount of 1 at compound interest $s = (1 + i)^n$	Present value of 1 $v^n = \dfrac{1}{(1 + i)^n}$	Present value of an annuity of 1 $a_{\overline{n}|} = \dfrac{1 - v^n}{i}$	Amount of an annuity of 1 $s_{\overline{n}|} = \dfrac{(1+i)^n - 1}{i}$	Annuity whose present value is 1 $\dfrac{1}{a_{\overline{n}|}} = \dfrac{1}{s_{\overline{n}|}} + i$	Number of periods n
1	1.0350 0000	0.9661 8357	0.9661 8357	1.0000 0000	1.0350 0000	1
2	1.0712 2500	0.9335 1070	1.8996 9428	2.0350 0000	0.5264 0049	2
3	1.1087 1788	0.9019 4271	2.8016 3698	3.1062 2500	0.3569 3418	3
4	1.1475 2300	0.8714 4223	3.6730 7921	4.2149 4288	0.2722 5114	4
5	1.1876 8631	0.8419 7317	4.5150 5238	5.3624 6588	0.2214 8137	5
6	1.2292 5533	0.8135 0064	5.3285 5302	6.5501 5218	0.1876 6821	6
7	1.2722 7926	0.7859 9096	6.1145 4398	7.7794 0751	0.1635 4449	7
8	1.3168 0904	0.7594 1156	6.8739 5554	9.0516 8677	0.1454 7665	8
9	1.3628 9735	0.7337 3097	7.6076 8651	10.3684 9581	0.1314 4601	9
10	1.4105 9876	0.7089 1881	8.3166 0532	11.7313 9316	0.1202 4137	10
11	1.4599 6972	0.6849 4571	9.0015 5104	13.1419 9192	0.1110 9197	11
12	1.5110 6866	0.6617 8330	9.6633 3433	14.6019 6164	0.1034 8395	12
13	1.5639 5606	0.6394 0415	10.3027 3849	16.1130 3030	0.0970 6157	13
14	1.6186 9452	0.6177 8179	10.9205 2028	17.6769 8636	0.0915 7073	14
15	1.6753 4883	0.5968 9062	11.5174 1090	19.2956 8088	0.0868 2507	15
16	1.7339 8604	0.5767 0591	12.0941 1681	20.9710 2971	0.0826 8483	16
17	1.7946 7555	0.5572 0378	12.6513 2059	22.7050 1575	0.0790 4313	17
18	1.8574 8920	0.5383 6114	13.1896 8173	24.4996 9130	0.0758 1684	18
19	1.9225 0132	0.5201 5569	13.7098 3742	26.3571 8050	0.0729 4033	19
20	1.9897 8886	0.5025 6588	14.2124 0330	28.2796 8181	0.0703 6108	20
21	2.0594 3147	0.4855 7090	14.6979 7420	30.2694 7068	0.0680 3659	21
22	2.1315 1158	0.4691 5063	15.1671 2484	32.3289 0215	0.0659 3207	22
23	2.2061 1448	0.4532 8563	15.6204 1047	34.4604 1373	0.0640 1880	23
24	2.2833 2849	0.4379 5713	16.0583 6760	36.6665 2821	0.0622 7283	24
25	2.3632 4498	0.4231 4699	16.4815 1459	38.9498 5669	0.0606 7404	25
26	2.4459 5856	0.4088 3767	16.8903 5226	41.3131 0168	0.0592 0540	26
27	2.5315 6711	0.3950 1224	17.2853 6451	43.7590 6024	0.0578 5241	27
28	2.6201 7196	0.3816 5434	17.6670 1885	46.2906 2734	0.0566 0265	28
29	2.7118 7798	0.3687 4815	18.0357 6700	48.9107 9930	0.0554 4538	29
30	2.8067 9370	0.3562 7841	18.3920 4541	51.6226 7728	0.0543 7133	30
31	2.9050 3148	0.3442 3035	18.7362 7576	54.4294 7098	0.0533 7240	31
32	3.0067 0759	0.3325 8971	19.0688 6547	57.3345 0247	0.0524 4150	32
33	3.1119 4235	0.3213 4271	19.3902 0818	60.3412 1005	0.0515 7242	33
34	3.2208 6033	0.3104 7605	19.7006 8423	63.4531 5240	0.0507 5966	34
35	3.3335 9045	0.2999 7686	20.0006 6110	66.6740 1274	0.0499 9835	35
36	3.4502 6611	0.2898 3272	20.2904 9381	70.0076 0318	0.0492 8416	36
37	3.5710 2543	0.2800 3161	20.5705 2542	73.4578 6930	0.0486 1325	37
38	3.6960 1132	0.2705 6194	20.8410 8736	77.0288 9472	0.0479 8214	38
39	3.8253 7171	0.2614 1250	21.1024 9987	80.7249 0604	0.0473 8775	39
40	3.9592 5972	0.2525 7247	21.3550 7234	84.5502 7775	0.0468 2728	40
41	4.0978 3381	0.2440 3137	21.5991 0371	88.5095 3747	0.0462 9822	41
42	4.2412 5799	0.2357 7910	21.8348 8281	92.6073 7128	0.0457 9828	42
43	4.3897 0202	0.2278 0590	22.0626 8870	96.8486 2928	0.0453 2539	43
44	4.5433 4160	0.2201 0231	22.2827 9102	101.2383 3130	0.0448 7768	44
45	4.7023 5855	0.2126 5924	22.4954 5026	105.7816 7290	0.0444 5343	45
46	4.8669 4110	0.2054 6787	22.7009 1813	110.4840 3145	0.0440 5108	46
47	5.0372 8404	0.1985 1968	22.8994 3780	115.3509 7255	0.0436 6919	47
48	5.2135 8898	0.1918 0645	23.0912 4425	120.3882 5659	0.0433 0646	48
49	5.3960 6459	0.1853 2024	23.2765 6450	125.6018 4557	0.0429 6167	49
50	5.5849 2686	0.1790 5337	23.4556 1787	130.9979 1016	0.0426 3371	50

Table XVI (continued). 3½%

Number of periods n	Amount of 1 at compound interest $s = (1 + i)^n$	Present value of 1 $v^n = \dfrac{1}{(1 + i)^n}$	Present value of an annuity of 1 $a_{\overline{n}|} = \dfrac{1 - v^n}{i}$	Amount of an annuity of 1 $s_{\overline{n}|} = \dfrac{(1+i)^n - 1}{i}$	Annuity whose present value is 1 $\dfrac{1}{a_{\overline{n}|}} = \dfrac{1}{s_{\overline{n}|}} + i$	Number of periods n
51	5.7803 9930	0.1729 9843	23.6286 1630	136.5828 3702	0.0423 2156	51
52	5.9827 1327	0.1671 4824	23.7957 6454	142.3632 3631	0.0420 2429	52
53	6.1921 0824	0.1614 9589	23.9572 6043	148.3459 4958	0.0417 4100	53
54	6.4088 3202	0.1560 3467	24.1132 9510	154.5380 5782	0.0414 7090	54
55	6.6331 4114	0.1507 5814	24.2640 5323	160.9468 8984	0.0412 1323	55
56	6.8653 0108	0.1456 6004	24.4097 1327	167.5800 3099	0.0409 6730	56
57	7.1055 8662	0.1407 3433	24.5504 4760	174.4453 3207	0.0407 3245	57
58	7.3542 8215	0.1359 7520	24.6864 2281	181.5509 1869	0.0405 0810	58
59	7.6116 8203	0.1313 7701	24.8177 9981	188.9052 0085	0.0402 9366	59
60	7.8780 9090	0.1269 3431	24.9447 3412	196.5168 8288	0.0400 8862	60
61	8.1538 2408	0.1226 4184	25.0673 7596	204.3949 7378	0.0398 9249	61
62	8.4392 0793	0.1184 9453	25.1858 7049	212.5487 9786	0.0397 0480	62
63	8.7345 8020	0.1144 8747	25.3003 5796	220.9880 0579	0.0395 2513	63
64	9.0402 9051	0.1106 1591	25.4109 7388	229.7225 8599	0.0393 5308	64
65	9.3567 0068	0.1068 7528	25.5178 4916	238.7628 7650	0.0391 8826	65
66	9.6841 8520	0.1032 6114	25.6211 1030	248.1195 7718	0.0390 3031	66
67	10.0231 8168	0.0997 6922	25.7208 7951	257.8037 6238	0.0388 7892	67
68	10.3739 4129	0.0963 9538	25.8172 7489	267.8268 9406	0.0387 3375	68
69	10.7370 2924	0.0931 3563	25.9104 1052	278.2008 3535	0.0385 9453	69
70	11.1128 2526	0.0899 8612	26.0003 9664	288.9378 6459	0.0384 6095	70
71	11.5017 7414	0.0869 4311	26.0873 3975	300.0506 8985	0.0383 3277	71
72	11.9043 3624	0.0840 0300	26.1713 4275	311.5524 6400	0.0382 0973	72
73	12.3209 8801	0.0811 6232	26.2525 0508	323.4568 0024	0.0380 9160	73
74	12.7522 2259	0.0784 1770	26.3309 2278	335.7777 8824	0.0379 7816	74
75	13.1985 5038	0.0757 6590	26.4066 8868	348.5300 1083	0.0378 6919	75
76	13.6604 9964	0.0732 0376	26.4798 9244	361.7285 6121	0.0377 6450	76
77	14.1386 1713	0.0707 2827	26.5506 2072	375.3890 6085	0.0376 6390	77
78	14.6334 6873	0.0683 3650	26.6189 5721	389.5276 7798	0.0375 6721	78
79	15.1456 4013	0.0660 2560	26.6849 8281	404.1611 4671	0.0374 7426	79
80	15.6757 3754	0.0637 9285	26.7487 7567	419.3067 8685	0.0373 8489	80
81	16.2243 8835	0.0616 3561	26.8104 1127	434.9825 2439	0.0372 9894	81
82	16.7922 4195	0.0595 5131	26.8699 6258	451.2069 1274	0.0372 1628	82
83	17.3799 7041	0.0575 3750	26.9275 0008	467.9991 5469	0.0371 3676	83
84	17.9882 6938	0.0555 9178	26.9830 9186	485.3791 2510	0.0370 6025	84
85	18.6178 5881	0.0537 1187	27.0368 0373	503.3673 9448	0.0369 8662	85
86	19.2694 8387	0.0518 9553	27.0886 9926	521.9852 5329	0.0369 1576	86
87	19.9439 1580	0.0501 4060	27.1388 3986	541.2547 3715	0.0368 4756	87
88	20.6419 5285	0.0484 4503	27.1872 8489	561.1986 5295	0.0367 8190	88
89	21.3644 2120	0.0468 0679	27.2340 9168	581.8406 0581	0.0367 1868	89
90	22.1121 7595	0.0452 2395	27.2793 1564	603.2050 2701	0.0366 5781	90
91	22.8861 0210	0.0436 9464	27.3230 1028	625.3172 0295	0.0365 9919	91
92	23.6871 1568	0.0422 1704	27.3652 2732	648.2033 0506	0.0365 4273	92
93	24.5161 6473	0.0407 8941	27.4060 1673	671.8904 2073	0.0364 8834	93
94	25.3742 3049	0.0394 1006	27.4454 2680	696.4065 8546	0.0364 3594	94
95	26.2623 2856	0.0380 7735	27.4835 0415	721.7808 1595	0.0363 8546	95
96	27.1815 1006	0.0367 8971	27.5202 9387	748.0431 4451	0.0363 3682	96
97	28.1328 6291	0.0355 4562	27.5558 3948	775.2246 5457	0.0362 8995	97
98	29.1175 1311	0.0343 4359	27.5901 8308	803.3575 1748	0.0362 4478	98
99	30.1366 2607	0.0331 8221	27.6233 6529	832.4750 3059	0.0362 0124	99
100	31.1914 0798	0.0320 6011	27.6554 2540	862.6116 5666	0.0361 5927	100

Table XVII. 4%

Number of periods n	Amount of 1 at compound interest $s = (1 + i)^n$	Present value of 1 $v^n = \dfrac{1}{(1+i)^n}$	Present value of an annuity of 1 $a_{\overline{n}|} = \dfrac{1-v^n}{i}$	Amount of an annuity of 1 $s_{\overline{n}|} = \dfrac{(1+i)^n-1}{i}$	Annuity whose present value is 1 $\dfrac{1}{a_{\overline{n}|}} = \dfrac{1}{s_{\overline{n}|}} + i$	Number of periods n
1	1.0400 0000	0.9615 3846	0.9615 3846	1.0000 0000	1.0400 0000	1
2	1.0816 0000	0.9245 5621	1.8860 9467	2.0400 0000	0.5301 9608	2
3	1.1248 6400	0.8889 9636	2.7750 9103	3.1216 0000	0.3603 4854	3
4	1.1698 5856	0.8548 0419	3.6298 9522	4.2464 6400	0.2754 9005	4
5	1.2166 5290	0.8219 2711	4.4518 2233	5.4163 2256	0.2246 2711	5
6	1.2653 1902	0.7903 1453	5.2421 3686	6.6329 7546	0.1907 6190	6
7	1.3159 3178	0.7599 1781	6.0020 5467	7.8982 9448	0.1666 0961	7
8	1.3685 6905	0.7306 9021	6.7327 4487	9.2142 2626	0.1485 2783	8
9	1.4233 1181	0.7025 8674	7.4353 3161	10.5827 9531	0.1344 9299	9
10	1.4802 4428	0.6755 6417	8.1108 9578	12.0061 0712	0.1232 9094	10
11	1.5394 5406	0.6495 8093	8.7604 7671	13.4863 5141	0.1141 4904	11
12	1.6010 3222	0.6245 9705	9.3850 7376	15.0258 0546	0.1065 5217	12
13	1.6650 7351	0.6005 7409	9.9856 4785	16.6268 3768	0.1001 4373	13
14	1.7316 7645	0.5774 7508	10.5631 2293	18.2919 1119	0.0946 6897	14
15	1.8009 4351	0.5552 6450	11.1183 8743	20.0235 8764	0.0899 4110	15
16	1.8729 8125	0.5339 0818	11.6522 9561	21.8245 3114	0.0858 2000	16
17	1.9479 0050	0.5133 7325	12.1656 6885	23.6975 1239	0.0821 9852	17
18	2.0258 1652	0.4936 2812	12.6592 9697	25.6454 1288	0.0789 9333	18
19	2.1068 4918	0.4746 4242	13.1339 3940	27.6712 2940	0.0761 3862	19
20	2.1911 2314	0.4563 8695	13.5903 2634	29.7780 7858	0.0735 8175	20
21	2.2787 6807	0.4388 3360	14.0291 5995	31.9692 0172	0.0712 8011	21
22	2.3699 1879	0.4219 5539	14.4511 1533	34.2479 6979	0.0691 9881	22
23	2.4647 1554	0.4057 2633	14.8568 4167	36.6178 8858	0.0673 0906	23
24	2.5633 0416	0.3901 2147	15.2469 6314	39.0826 0412	0.0655 8683	24
25	2.6658 3633	0.3751 1680	15.6220 7994	41.6459 0829	0.0640 1196	25
26	2.7724 6978	0.3606 8923	15.9827 6918	44.3117 4462	0.0625 6738	26
27	2.8833 6858	0.3468 1657	16.3295 8575	47.0842 1440	0.0612 3854	27
28	2.9987 0332	0.3334 7747	16.6630 6322	49.9675 8298	0.0600 1298	28
29	3.1186 5145	0.3206 5141	16.9837 1463	52.9662 8630	0.0588 7993	29
30	3.2433 9751	0.3083 1867	17.2920 3330	56.0849 3775	0.0578 3010	30
31	3.3731 3341	0.2964 6026	17.5884 9356	59.3283 3526	0.0568 5535	31
32	3.5080 5875	0.2850 5794	17.8735 5150	62.7014 6867	0.0559 4859	32
33	3.6483 8110	0.2740 9417	18.1476 4567	66.2095 2742	0.0551 0357	33
34	3.7943 1634	0.2635 5209	18.4111 9776	69.8579 0851	0.0543 1477	34
35	3.9460 8899	0.2534 1547	18.6646 1323	73.6522 2486	0.0535 7732	35
36	4.1039 3255	0.2436 6872	18.9082 8195	77.5983 1385	0.0528 8688	36
37	4.2680 8986	0.2342 9685	19.1425 7880	81.7022 4640	0.0522 3957	37
38	4.4388 1345	0.2252 8543	19.3678 6423	85.9703 3626	0.0516 3192	38
39	4.6163 6599	0.2166 2061	19.5844 8484	90.4091 4971	0.0510 6083	39
40	4.8010 2063	0.2082 8904	19.7927 7388	95.0255 1570	0.0505 2349	40
41	4.9930 6145	0.2002 7793	19 9930 5181	99.8265 3633	0.0500 1738	41
42	5.1927 8391	0.1925 7493	20.1856 2674	104.8195 9778	0.0495 4020	42
43	5.4004 9527	0.1851 6820	20.3707 9494	110.0123 8169	0.0490 8989	43
44	5.6165 1508	0.1780 4635	20.5488 4129	115.4128 7696	0.0486 6454	44
45	5.8411 7568	0.1711 9841	20.7200 3970	121.0293 9204	0.0482 6246	45
46	6.0748 2271	0.1646 1386	20.8846 5356	126.8705 6772	0.0478 8205	46
47	6.3178 1562	0.1582 8256	21.0429 3612	132.9453 9043	0.0475 2189	47
48	6.5705 2824	0.1521 9476	21.1951 3088	139.2632 0604	0.0471 8065	48
49	6.8333 4937	0.1463 4112	21.3414 7200	145.8337 3429	0.0468 5712	49
50	7.1066 8335	0.1407 1262	21.4821 8462	152.6670 8366	0.0465 5020	50

Table XVII (*continued*). 4 %

Number of periods n	Amount of 1 at compound interest $s = (1 + i)^n$	Present value of 1 $v^n = \dfrac{1}{(1 + i)^n}$	Present value of an annuity of 1 $a_{\overline{n}\rvert} = \dfrac{1 - v^n}{i}$	Amount of an annuity of 1 $s_{\overline{n}\rvert} = \dfrac{(1+i)^n - 1}{i}$	Annuity whose present value is 1 $\dfrac{1}{a_{\overline{n}\rvert}} = \dfrac{1}{s_{\overline{n}\rvert}} + i$	Number of periods n
51	7.3909 5068	0.1353 0059	21.6174 8521	159.7737 6700	0.0462 5885	51
52	7.6865 8871	0.1300 9672	21.7475 8193	167.1647 1768	0.0459 8212	52
53	7.9940 5226	0.1250 9300	21.8726 7493	174.8513 0639	0.0457 1915	53
54	8.3138 1435	0.1202 8173	21.9929 5667	182.8453 5865	0.0454 6910	54
55	8.6463 6692	0.1156 5551	22.1086 1218	191.1591 7299	0.0452 3124	55
56	8.9922 2160	0.1112 0722	22.2189 1940	199.8055 3991	0.0450 0487	56
57	9.3519 1046	0.1069 3002	22.3267 4943	208.7977 6151	0.0447 8932	57
58	9.7259 8688	0.1028 1733	22.4295 6676	218.1496 7197	0.0445 8401	58
59	10.1150 2635	0.0988 6282	22.5284 2957	227.8756 5885	0.0443 8836	59
60	10.5196 2741	0.0950 6040	22.6234 8997	237.9906 8520	0.0442 0185	60
61	10.9404 1250	0.0914 0423	22.7148 9421	248.5103 1261	0.0440 2398	61
62	11.3780 2900	0.0878 8868	22.8027 8289	259.4507 2511	0.0438 5430	62
63	11.8331 5016	0.0845 0835	22.8872 9124	270.8287 5412	0.0436 9237	63
64	12.3064 7617	0.0812 5803	22.9685 4927	282.6619 0428	0.0435 3780	64
65	12.7987 3522	0.0781 3272	23.0466 8199	294.9683 8045	0.0433 9019	65
66	13.3106 8463	0.0751 2762	23.1218 0961	307.7671 1567	0.0432 4921	66
67	13.8431 1201	0.0722 3809	23.1940 4770	321.0778 0030	0.0431 1451	67
68	14.3968 3649	0.0694 5970	23.2635 0740	334.9209 1231	0.0429 8578	68
69	14.9727 0995	0.0667 8818	23.3302 9558	349.3177 4880	0.0428 6272	69
70	15.5716 1835	0.0642 1940	23.3945 1498	364.2904 5876	0.0427 4506	70
71	16.1944 8308	0.0617 4942	23.4562 6440	379.8620 7711	0.0426 3253	71
72	16.8422 6241	0.0593 7445	23.5156 3885	396.0565 6019	0.0425 2489	72
73	17.5159 5290	0.0570 9081	23.5727 2966	412.8988 2260	0.0424 2190	73
74	18.2165 9102	0.0548 9501	23.6276 2468	430.4147 7550	0.0423 2334	74
75	18.9452 5466	0.0527 8367	23.6804 0834	448.6513 6652	0.0422 2900	75
76	19.7030 6485	0.0507 5353	23.7311 6187	467.5766 2118	0.0421 3869	76
77	20.4911 8744	0.0488 0147	23.7799 6333	487.2796 8603	0.0420 5221	77
78	21.3108 3494	0.0469 2449	23.8268 8782	507.7708 7347	0.0419 6939	78
79	22.1632 6834	0.0451 1970	23.8720 0752	529.0817 0841	0.0418 9007	79
80	23.0497 9907	0.0433 8433	23.9153 9185	551.2449 7675	0.0418 1408	80
81	23.9717 9103	0.0417 1570	23.9571 0754	574.2947 7582	0.0417 4127	81
82	24.9306 6267	0.0401 1125	23.9972 1879	598.2665 6685	0.0416 7150	82
83	25.9278 8918	0.0385 6851	24.0357 8730	623.1972 2952	0.0416 0463	83
84	26.9650 0475	0.0370 8510	24.0728 7240	649.1251 1870	0.0415 4054	84
85	28.0436 0494	0.0356 5875	24.1085 3116	676.0901 2345	0.0414 7909	85
86	29.1653 4914	0.0342 8726	24.1428 1842	704.1337 2839	0.0414 2018	86
87	30.3319 6310	0.0329 6852	24.1757 8694	733.2990 7753	0.0413 6370	87
88	31.5452 4163	0.0317 0050	24.2074 8745	763.6310 4063	0.0413 0953	88
89	32.8070 5129	0.0304 8125	24.2379 6870	795.1762 8225	0.0412 5758	89
90	34.1193 3334	0.0293 0890	24.2672 7759	827.9833 3354	0.0412 0775	90
91	35.4841 0668	0.0281 8163	24.2954 5923	862.1026 6688	0.0411 5995	91
92	36.9034 7094	0.0270 9772	24.3225 5695	897.5867 7356	0.0411 1410	92
93	38.3796 0978	0.0260 5550	24.3486 1245	934.4902 4450	0.0410 7010	93
94	39.9147 9417	0.0250 5337	24.3736 6582	972.8698 5428	0.0410 2789	94
95	41.5113 8594	0.0240 8978	24.3977 5559	1012.7846 4845	0.0409 8738	95
96	43.1718 4138	0.0231 6325	24.4209 1884	1054.2960 3439	0.0409 4850	96
97	44.8987 1503	0.0222 7235	24.4431 9119	1097.4678 7577	0.0409 1119	97
98	46.6946 6363	0.0214 1572	24.4646 0692	1142.3665 9080	0.0408 7538	98
99	48.5624 5018	0.0205 9204	24.4851 9896	1189.0612 5443	0.0408 4100	99
100	50.5049 4818	0.0198 0004	24.5049 9900	1237.6237 0461	0.0408 0800	100

Table XVIII. 5 %

Number of periods n	Amount of 1 at compound interest $s = (1+i)^n$	Present value of 1 $v^n = \dfrac{1}{(1+i)^n}$	Present value of an annuity of 1 $a_{\overline{n}|} = \dfrac{1-v^n}{i}$	Amount of an annuity of 1 $s_{\overline{n}|} = \dfrac{(1+i)^n-1}{i}$	Annuity whose present value is 1 $\dfrac{1}{a_{\overline{n}|}} = \dfrac{1}{s_{\overline{n}|}} + i$	Number of periods n
1	1.0500 0000	0.9523 8095	0.9523 8095	1.0000 0000	1.0500 0000	1
2	1.1025 0000	0.9070 2948	1.8594 1043	2.0500 0000	0.5378 0488	2
3	1.1576 2500	0.8638 3760	2.7232 4803	3.1525 0000	0.3672 0856	3
4	1.2155 0625	0.8227 0247	3.5459 5050	4.3101 2500	0.2820 1183	4
5	1.2762 8156	0.7835 2617	4.3294 7667	5.5256 3125	0.2309 7480	5
6	1.3400 9564	0.7462 1540	5.0756 9206	6.8019 1281	0.1970 1747	6
7	1.4071 0042	0.7106 8133	5.7863 7340	8.1420 0845	0.1728 1982	7
8	1.4774 5544	0.6768 3936	6.4632 1276	9.5491 0888	0.1547 2181	8
9	1.5513 2822	0.6446 0892	7.1078 2168	11.0265 6432	0.1406 9008	9
10	1.6288 9463	0.6139 1325	7.7217 3493	12.5778 9254	0.1295 0458	10
11	1.7103 3936	0.5846 7929	8.3064 1422	14.2067 8716	0.1203 8889	11
12	1.7958 5633	0.5568 3742	8.8632 5164	15.9171 2652	0.1128 2541	12
13	1.8856 4914	0.5303 2135	9.3935 7299	17.7129 8285	0.1064 5577	13
14	1.9799 3160	0.5050 6795	9.8986 4094	19.5986 3199	0.1010 2397	14
15	2.0789 2818	0.4810 1710	10.3796 5804	21.5785 6359	0.0963 4229	15
16	2.1828 7459	0.4581 1152	10.8377 6956	23.6574 9177	0.0922 6991	16
17	2.2920 1832	0.4362 9669	11.2740 6625	25.8403 6636	0.0886 9914	17
18	2.4066 1923	0.4155 2065	11.6895 8690	28.1323 8467	0.0855 4622	18
19	2.5269 5020	0.3957 3396	12.0853 2086	30.5390 0391	0.0827 4501	19
20	2.6532 9771	0.3768 8948	12.4622 1034	33.0659 5410	0.0802 4259	20
21	2.7859 6259	0.3589 4236	12.8211 5271	35.7192 5181	0.0779 9611	21
22	2.9252 6072	0.3418 4987	13.1630 0258	38.5052 1440	0.0759 7051	22
23	3.0715 2376	0.3255 7131	13.4885 7388	41.4304 7512	0.0741 3682	23
24	3.2250 9994	0.3100 6791	13.7986 4179	44.5019 9887	0.0724 7090	24
25	3.3863 5494	0.2953 0277	14.0939 4457	47.7270 9882	0.0709 5246	25
26	3.5556 7269	0.2812 4073	14.3751 8530	51.1134 5376	0.0695 6432	26
27	3.7334 5632	0.2678 4832	14.6430 3362	54.6691 2645	0.0682 9186	27
28	3.9201 2914	0.2550 9364	14.8981 2726	58.4025 8277	0.0671 2253	28
29	4.1161 3560	0.2429 4632	15.1410 7358	62.3227 1191	0.0660 4551	29
30	4.3219 4238	0.2313 7745	15.3724 5103	66.4388 4750	0.0650 5144	30
31	4.5380 3949	0.2203 5947	15.5928 1050	70.7607 8988	0.0641 3212	31
32	4.7649 4147	0.2098 6617	15.8026 7667	75.2988 2937	0.0632 8042	32
33	5.0031 8854	0.1998 7254	16.0025 4921	80.0637 7084	0.0624 9004	33
34	5.2533 4797	0.1903 5480	16.1929 0401	85.0669 5938	0.0617 5545	34
35	5.5160 1537	0.1812 9029	16.3741 9429	90.3203 0735	0.0610 7171	35
36	5.7918 1614	0.1726 5741	16.5468 5171	95.8363 2272	0.0604 3446	36
37	6.0814 0694	0.1644 3563	16.7112 8734	101.6281 3886	0.0598 3979	37
38	6.3854 7729	0.1566 0536	16.8678 9271	107.7095 4580	0.0592 8423	38
39	6.7047 5115	0.1491 4797	17.0170 4067	114.0950 2309	0.0587 6462	39
40	7.0399 8871	0.1420 4568	17.1590 8635	120.7997 7424	0.0582 7816	40
41	7.3919 8815	0.1352 8160	17.2943 6796	127.8397 6295	0.0578 2229	41
42	7.7615 8756	0.1288 3962	17.4232 0758	135.2317 5110	0.0573 9471	42
43	8.1496 6693	0.1227 0440	17.5459 1198	142.9933 3866	0.0569 9333	43
44	8.5571 5028	0.1168 6133	17.6627 7331	151.1430 0559	0.0566 1625	44
45	8.9850 0779	0.1112 9651	17.7740 6982	159.7001 5587	0.0562 6173	45
46	9.4342 5818	0.1059 9668	17.8800 6650	168.6851 6366	0.0559 2820	46
47	9.9059 7109	0.1009 4921	17.9810 1571	178.1194 2185	0.0556 1421	47
48	10.4012 6965	0.0961 4211	18.0771 5782	188.0253 9294	0.0553 1843	48
49	10.9213 3313	0.0915 6391	18.1687 2173	198.4266 6259	0.0550 3965	49
50	11.4673 9979	0.0872 0373	18.2559 2546	209.3479 9572	0.0547 7674	50

Table XVIII (*continued*). 5 %

Number of periods n	Amount of 1 at compound interest $s = (1+i)^n$	Present value of 1 $v^n = \dfrac{1}{(1+i)^n}$	Present value of an annuity of 1 $a_{\overline{n}|} = \dfrac{1-v^n}{i}$	Amount of an annuity of 1 $s_{\overline{n}|} = \dfrac{(1+i)^n-1}{i}$	Annuity whose present value is 1 $\dfrac{1}{a_{\overline{n}|}} = \dfrac{1}{s_{\overline{n}|}} + i$	Number of periods n
51	12.0407 6978	0.0830 5117	18.3389 7663	220.8153 9550	0.0545 2867	51
52	12.6428 0826	0.0790 9635	18.4180 7298	232.8561 6528	0.0542 9450	52
53	13.2749 4868	0.0753 2986	18.4934 0284	245.4989 7354	0.0540 7334	53
54	13.9386 9611	0.0717 4272	18.5651 4556	258.7739 2222	0.0538 6438	54
55	14.6356 3092	0.0683 2640	18.6334 7196	272.7126 1833	0.0536 6686	55
56	15.3674 1246	0.0650 7276	18.6985 4473	287.3482 4924	0.0534 8010	56
57	16.1357 8309	0.0619 7406	18.7605 1879	302.7156 6171	0.0533 0343	57
58	16.9425 7224	0.0590 2291	18.8195 4170	318.8514 4479	0.0531 3626	58
59	17.7897 0085	0.0562 1230	18.8757 5400	335.7940 1703	0.0529 7802	59
60	18.6791 8589	0.0535 3552	18.9292 8952	353.5837 1788	0.0528 2818	60
61	19.6131 4519	0.0509 8621	18.9802 7574	372.2629 0378	0.0526 8627	61
62	20.5938 0245	0.0485 5830	19.0288 3404	391.8760 4897	0.0525 5183	62
63	21.6234 9257	0.0462 4600	19.0750 8003	412.4698 5141	0.0524 2442	63
64	22.7046 6720	0.0440 4381	19.1191 2384	434.0933 4398	0.0523 0365	64
65	23.8399 0056	0.0419 4648	19.1610 7033	456.7980 1118	0.0521 8915	65
66	25.0318 9559	0.0399 4903	19.2010 1936	480.6379 1174	0.0520 8057	66
67	26.2834 9037	0.0380 4670	19.2390 6606	505.6698 0733	0.0519 7757	67
68	27.5976 6488	0.0362 3495	19.2753 0101	531.9532 9770	0.0518 7986	68
69	28.9775 4813	0.0345 0948	19.3098 1048	559.5509 6258	0.0517 8715	69
70	30.4264 2554	0.0328 6617	19.3426 7665	588.5285 1071	0.0516 9915	70
71	31.9477 4681	0.0313 0111	19.3739 7776	618.9549 3625	0.0516 1563	71
72	33.5451 3415	0.0298 1058	19.4037 8834	650.9026 8306	0.0515 3633	72
73	35.2223 9086	0.0283 9103	19.4321 7937	684.4478 1721	0.0514 6103	73
74	36.9835 1040	0.0270 3908	19.4592 1845	719.6702 0807	0.0513 8953	74
75	38.8326 8592	0.0257 5150	19.4849 6995	756.6537 1848	0.0513 2161	75
76	40.7743 2022	0.0245 2524	19.5094 9519	795.4864 0440	0.0512 5709	76
77	42.8130 3623	0.0233 5727	19.5328 5257	836.2607 2462	0.0511 9580	77
78	44.9536 8804	0.0222 4512	19.5550 9768	879.0737 6085	0.0511 3756	78
79	47.2013 7244	0.0211 8582	19.5762 8351	924.0274 4889	0.0510 8222	79
80	49.5614 4107	0.0201 7698	19.5964 6048	971.2288 2134	0.0510 2962	80
81	52.0395 1312	0.0192 1617	19.6156 7665	1020.7902 6240	0.0509 7963	81
82	54.6414 8878	0.0183 0111	19.6339 7776	1072.8297 7552	0.0509 3211	82
83	57.3735 6322	0.0174 2963	19.6514 0739	1127.4712 6430	0.0508 8694	83
84	60.2422 4138	0.0165 9965	19.6680 0704	1184.8448 2752	0.0508 4399	84
85	63.2543 5344	0.0158 0919	19.6838 1623	1245.0870 6889	0.0508 0316	85
86	66.4170 7112	0.0150 5637	19.6988 7260	1308.3414 2234	0.0507 6433	86
87	69.7379 2467	0.0143 3940	19.7132 1200	1374.7584 9345	0.0507 2740	87
88	73.2248 2091	0.0136 5657	19.7268 6857	1444.4964 1812	0.0506 9228	88
89	76.8860 6195	0.0130 0626	19.7398 7483	1517.7212 3903	0.0506 5888	89
90	80.7303 6505	0.0123 8691	19.7522 6174	1594.6073 0098	0.0506 2711	90
91	84.7668 8330	0.0117 9706	19.7640 5880	1675.3376 6603	0.0505 9689	91
92	89.0052 2747	0.0112 3530	19.7752 9410	1760.1045 4933	0.0505 6815	92
93	93.4554 8884	0.0107 0028	19.7859 9438	1849.1097 7680	0.0505 4080	93
94	98.1282 6328	0.0101 9074	19.7961 8512	1942.5652 6564	0.0505 1478	94
95	103.0346 7645	0.0097 0547	19.8058 9059	2040.6935 2892	0.0504 9003	95
96	108.1864 1027	0.0092 4331	19.8151 3390	2143.7282 0537	0.0504 6648	96
97	113.5957 3078	0.0088 0315	19.8239 3705	2251.9146 1564	0.0504 4407	97
98	119.2755 1732	0.0083 8395	19.8323 2100	2365.5103 4642	0.0504 2274	98
99	125.2392 9319	0.0079 8471	19.8403 0571	2484.7858 6374	0.0504 0245	99
100	131.5012 5785	0.0076 0449	19.8479 1020	2610.0251 5693	0.0503 8314	100

Table XIX. 6%

Number of periods n	Amount of 1 at compound interest $s = (1 + i)^n$	Present value of 1 $v^n = \dfrac{1}{(1 + i)^n}$	Present value of an annuity of 1 $a_{\overline{n}|} = \dfrac{1 - v^n}{i}$	Amount of an annuity of 1 $s_{\overline{n}|} = \dfrac{(1+i)^n - 1}{i}$	Annuity whose present value is 1 $\dfrac{1}{a_{\overline{n}|}} = \dfrac{1}{s_{\overline{n}|}} + i$	Number of periods n
1	1.0600 0000	0.9433 9623	0.9433 9623	1.0000 0000	1.0600 0000	1
2	1.1236 0000	0.8899 9644	1.8333 9267	2.0600 0000	0.5454 3689	2
3	1.1910 1600	0.8396 1928	2.6730 1195	3.1836 0000	0.3741 0981	3
4	1.2624 7696	0.7920 9366	3.4651 0561	4.3746 1600	0.2885 9149	4
5	1.3382 2558	0.7472 5817	4.2123 6379	5.6370 9296	0.2373 9640	5
6	1.4185 1911	0.7049 6054	4.9173 2433	6.9753 1854	0.2033 6263	6
7	1.5036 3026	0.6650 5711	5.5823 8144	8.3938 3765	0.1791 3502	7
8	1.5938 4807	0.6274 1237	6.2097 9381	9.8974 6791	0.1610 3594	8
9	1.6894 7896	0.5918 9846	6.8016 9227	11.4913 1598	0.1470 2224	9
10	1.7908 4770	0.5583 9478	7.3600 8705	13.1807 9494	0.1358 6796	10
11	1.8982 9856	0.5267 8753	7.8868 7458	14.9716 4264	0.1267 9294	11
12	2.0121 9647	0.4969 6936	8.3838 4394	16.8699 4120	0.1192 7703	12
13	2.1329 2826	0.4688 3902	8.8526 8296	18.8821 3767	0.1129 6011	13
14	2.2609 0396	0.4423 0096	9.2949 8393	21.0150 6593	0.1075 8491	14
15	2.3965 5819	0.4172 6506	9.7122 4899	23.2759 6988	0.1029 6276	15
16	2.5403 5168	0.3936 4628	10.1058 9527	25.6725 2808	0.0989 5214	16
17	2.6927 7279	0.3713 6442	10.4772 5969	28.2128 7976	0.0954 4480	17
18	2.8543 3915	0.3503 4379	10.8276 0348	30.9056 5255	0.0923 5654	18
19	3.0255 9950	0.3305 1301	11.1581 1649	33.7599 9170	0.0896 2086	19
20	3.2071 3547	0.3118 0473	11.4699 2122	36.7855 9120	0.0871 8456	20
21	3.3995 6360	0.2941 5540	11.7640 7662	39.9927 2668	0.0850 0455	21
22	3.6035 3742	0.2775 0510	12.0415 8172	43.3922 9028	0.0830 4557	22
23	3.8197 4966	0.2617 9726	12.3033 7898	46.9958 2769	0.0812 7848	23
24	4.0489 3464	0.2469 7855	12.5503 5753	50.8155 7735	0.0796 7900	24
25	4.2918 7072	0.2329 9863	12.7833 5616	54.8645 1200	0.0782 2672	25
26	4.5493 8296	0.2198 1003	13.0031 6619	59.1563 8272	0.0769 0435	26
27	4.8223 4594	0.2073 6795	13.2105 3414	63.7057 6568	0.0756 9717	27
28	5.1116 8670	0.1956 3014	13.4061 6428	68.5281 1162	0.0745 9255	28
29	5.4183 8790	0.1845 5674	13.5907 2102	73.6397 9832	0.0735 7961	29
30	5.7434 9117	0.1741 1013	13.7648 3115	79.0581 8622	0.0726 4891	30
31	6.0881 0064	0.1642 5484	13.9290 8599	84.8016 7739	0.0717 9222	31
32	6.4533 8668	0.1549 5740	14.0840 4339	90.8897 7803	0.0710 0234	32
33	6.8405 8988	0.1461 8622	14.2302 2961	97.3431 6471	0.0702 7293	33
34	7.2510 2528	0.1379 1153	14.3681 4114	104.1837 5460	0.0695 9843	34
35	7.6860 8679	0.1301 0522	14.4982 4636	111.4347 7987	0.0689 7386	35
36	8.1472 5200	0.1227 4077	14.6209 8713	119.1208 6666	0.0683 9483	36
37	8.6360 8712	0.1157 9318	14.7367 8031	127.2681 1866	0.0678 5743	37
38	9.1542 5235	0.1092 3885	14.8460 1916	135.9042 0578	0.0673 5812	38
39	9.7035 0749	0.1030 5552	14.9490 7468	145.0584 5813	0.0668 9377	39
40	10.2857 1794	0.0972 2219	15.0462 9687	154.7619 6562	0.0664 6154	40
41	10.9028 6101	0.0917 1905	15.1380 1592	165.0476 8356	0.0660 5886	41
42	11.5570 3267	0.0865 2740	15.2245 4332	175.9505 4457	0.0656 8342	42
43	12.2504 5463	0.0816 2962	15.3061 7294	187.5075 7724	0.0653 3312	43
44	12.9854 8191	0.0770 0908	15.3831 8202	199.7580 3188	0.0650 0606	44
45	13.7646 1083	0.0726 5007	15.4558 3209	212.7435 1379	0.0647 0050	45
46	14.5904 8748	0.0685 3781	15.5243 6990	226.5081 2462	0.0644 1485	46
47	15.4659 1673	0.0646 5831	15.5890 2821	241.0986 1210	0.0641 4768	47
48	16.3938 7173	0.0609 9840	15.6500 2661	256.5645 2882	0.0638 9766	48
49	17.3775 0403	0.0575 4566	15.7075 7227	272.9584 0055	0.0636 6356	49
50	18.4201 5427	0.0542 8836	15.7618 6064	290.3359 0458	0.0634 4429	50

Table XIX (*continued*). 6%

Number of periods n	Amount of 1 at compound interest $s = (1 + i)^n$	Present value of 1 $v^n = \dfrac{1}{(1+i)^n}$	Present value of an annuity of 1 $a_{\overline{n}|} = \dfrac{1 - v^n}{i}$	Amount of an annuity of 1 $s_{\overline{n}|} = \dfrac{(1+i)^n - 1}{i}$	Annuity whose present value is 1 $\dfrac{1}{a_{\overline{n}|}} = \dfrac{1}{s_{\overline{n}|}} + i$	Number of periods n
51	19.5253 6353	0.0512 1544	15.8130 7607	308.7560 5886	0.0632 3880	51
52	20.6968 8534	0.0483 1645	15.8613 9252	328.2814 2239	0.0630 4617	52
53	21.9386 9846	0.0455 8156	15.9069 7408	348.9783 0773	0.0628 6551	53
54	23.2550 2037	0.0430 0147	15.9499 7554	370.9170 0620	0.0626 9602	54
55	24.6503 2159	0.0405 6742	15.9905 4297	394.1720 2657	0.0625 3696	55
56	26.1293 4089	0.0382 7115	16.0288 1412	418.8223 4816	0.0623 8765	56
57	27.6971 0134	0.0361 0486	16.0649 1898	444.9516 8905	0.0622 4744	57
58	29.3589 2742	0.0340 6119	16.0989 8017	472.6487 9040	0.0621 1574	58
59	31.1204 6307	0.0321 3320	16.1311 1337	502.0077 1782	0.0619 9200	59
60	32.9876 9085	0.0303 1434	16.1614 2771	533.1281 8089	0.0618 7572	60
61	34.9669 5230	0.0285 9843	16.1900 2614	566.1158 7174	0.0617 6642	61
62	37.0649 6944	0.0269 7965	16.2170 0579	601.0828 2405	0.0616 6366	62
63	39.2888 6761	0.0254 5250	16.2424 5829	638.1477 9349	0.0615 6704	63
64	41.6461 9967	0.0240 1179	16.2664 7009	677.4366 6110	0.0614 7615	64
65	44.1449 7165	0.0226 5264	16.2891 2272	719.0828 6076	0.0613 9066	65
66	46.7936 6994	0.0213 7041	16.3104 9314	763.2278 3241	0.0613 1022	66
67	49.6012 9014	0.0201 6077	16.3306 5390	810.0215 0236	0.0612 3454	67
68	52.5773 6755	0.0190 1959	16.3496 7349	859.6227 9250	0.0611 6330	68
69	55.7320 0960	0.0179 4301	16.3676 1650	912.2001 6005	0.0610 9625	69
70	59.0759 3018	0.0169 2737	16.3845 4387	967.9321 6965	0.0610 3313	70
71	62.6204 8599	0.0159 6921	16.4005 1308	1027.0080 9983	0.0609 7370	71
72	66.3777 1515	0.0150 6530	16.4155 7838	1089.6285 8582	0.0609 1774	72
73	70.3603 7806	0.0142 1254	16.4297 9093	1156.0063 0097	0.0608 6505	73
74	74.5820 0074	0.0134 0806	16.4431 9899	1226.3666 7903	0.0608 1542	74
75	79.0569 2079	0.0126 4911	16.4558 4810	1300.9486 7977	0.0607 6867	75
76	83.8003 3603	0.0119 3313	16.4677 8123	1380.0056 0055	0.0607 2463	76
77	88.8283 5620	0.0112 5767	16.4790 3889	1463.8059 3659	0.0606 8315	77
78	94.1580 5757	0.0106 2044	16.4896 5933	1552.6342 9278	0.0606 4407	78
79	99.8075 4102	0.0100 1928	16.4996 7862	1646.7923 5035	0.0606 0724	79
80	105.7959 9348	0.0094 5215	16.5091 3077	1746.5998 9137	0.0605 7254	80
81	112.1437 5309	0.0089 1713	16.5180 4790	1852.3958 8485	0.0605 3984	81
82	118.8723 7828	0.0084 1238	16.5261 6028	1964.5396 3794	0.0605 0903	82
83	126.0047 2097	0.0079 3621	16.5343 9649	2083.4120 1622	0.0604 7998	83
84	133.5650 0123	0.0074 8699	16.5418 8348	2209.4167 3719	0.0604 5261	84
85	141.5789 0449	0.0070 6320	16.5489 4668	2342.9817 4142	0.0604 2681	85
86	150.0736 3875	0.0066 6340	16.5556 1008	2484.5606 4591	0.0604 0249	86
87	159.0780 5708	0.0062 8622	16.5618 9630	2634.6342 8466	0.0603 7956	87
88	168.6227 4050	0.0059 3040	16.5678 2670	2793.7123 4174	0.0603 5795	88
89	178.7401 0493	0.0055 9472	16.5734 2141	2962.3350 8225	0.0603 3757	89
90	189.4645 1123	0.0052 7803	16.5786 9944	3141.0751 8718	0.0603 1836	90
91	200.8323 8190	0.0049 7928	16.5836 7872	3330.5396 9841	0.0603 0025	91
92	212.8823 2482	0.0046 9743	16.5883 7615	3531.3720 8032	0.0602 8318	92
93	225.6552 6431	0.0044 3154	16.5928 0769	3744.2544 0514	0.0602 6708	93
94	239.1945 8017	0.0041 8070	16.5969 8839	3969.9096 6944	0.0602 5190	94
95	253.5462 5498	0.0039 4405	16.6009 3244	4209.1042 4961	0.0602 3758	95
96	268.7590 3028	0.0037 2081	16.6046 5325	4462.6505 0459	0.0602 2408	96
97	284.8845 7209	0.0035 1019	16.6081 6344	4731.4095 3486	0.0602 1135	97
98	301.9776 4642	0.0033 1150	16.6114 7494	5016.2941 0696	0.0601 9935	98
99	320.0963 0520	0.0031 2406	16.6145 9900	5318.2717 5337	0.0601 8803	99
100	339.3020 8351	0.0029 4723	16.6175 4623	5638.3680 5857	0.0601 7736	100

Table XX. 7 %

Number of periods n	Amount of 1 at compound interest $s = (1 + i)^n$	Present value of 1 $v^n = \dfrac{1}{(1+i)^n}$	Present value of an annuity of 1 $a_{\overline{n}|} = \dfrac{1 - v^n}{i}$	Amount of an annuity of 1 $s_{\overline{n}|} = \dfrac{(1+i)^n - 1}{i}$	Annuity whose present value is 1 $\dfrac{1}{a_{\overline{n}|}} = \dfrac{1}{s_{\overline{n}|}} + i$	Number of periods n
1	1.0700 0000	0.9345 7944	0.9345 7944	1.0000 0000	1.0700 0000	1
2	1.1449 0000	0.8734 3875	1.8080 1817	2.0700 0000	0.5530 9179	2
3	1.2250 4300	0.8162 9788	2.6243 1604	3.2149 0000	0.3810 5166	3
4	1.3107 9601	0.7628 9521	3.3872 1126	4.4399 4300	0.2952 2812	4
5	1.4025 5173	0.7129 8618	4.1001 9744	5.7507 3901	0.2438 9069	5
6	1.5007 3035	0.6663 4222	4.7665 3966	7.1532 9074	0.2097 9580	6
7	1.6057 8148	0.6227 4974	5.3892 8940	8.6540 2109	0.1855 5322	7
8	1.7181 8618	0.5820 0910	5.9712 9851	10.2598 0257	0.1674 6776	8
9	1.8384 5921	0.5439 3374	6.5152 3225	11.9779 8875	0.1534 8647	9
10	1.9671 5136	0.5083 4929	7.0235 8154	13.8164 4796	0.1423 7750	10
11	2.1048 5195	0.4750 9280	7.4986 7434	15.7835 9932	0.1333 5690	11
12	2.2521 9159	0.4440 1196	7.9426 8630	17.8884 5127	0.1259 0199	12
13	2.4098 4500	0.4149 6445	8.3576 5074	20.1406 4286	0.1196 5085	13
14	2.5785 3415	0.3878 1724	8.7454 6799	22.5504 8786	0.1143 4494	14
15	2.7590 3154	0.3624 4602	9.1079 1401	25.1290 2201	0.1097 9462	15
16	2.9521 6375	0.3387 3460	9.4466 4860	27.8880 5355	0.1058 5765	16
17	3 1588 1521	0.3165 7439	9.7632 2299	30.8402 1730	0.1024 2519	17
18	3.3799 3228	0.2958 6392	10.0590 8691	33.9990 3251	0.0994 1260	18
19	3.6165 2754	0.2765 0832	10.3355 9524	37.3789 6479	0.0967 5301	19
20	3.8696 8446	0.2584 1900	10.5940 1425	40.9954 9232	0.0943 9293	20
21	4.1405 6237	0.2415 1309	10.8355 2733	44.8651 7678	0.0922 8900	21
22	4.4304 0174	0.2257 1317	11.0612 4050	49.0057 3916	0.0904 0577	22
23	4.7405 2986	0.2109 4688	11.2721 8738	53.4361 4090	0.0887 1393	23
24	5.0723 6695	0.1971 4662	11.4693 3400	58.1766 7076	0.0871 8902	24
25	5.4274 3264	0.1842 4918	11.6535 8318	63.2490 3772	0.0858 1052	25
26	5.8073 5292	0.1721 9549	11.8257 7867	68.6764 7036	0.0845 6103	26
27	6.2138 6763	0.1609 3037	11.9867 0904	74.4838 2328	0.0834 2573	27
28	6.6488 3836	0.1504 0221	12.1371 1125	80.6976 9091	0.0823 9193	28
29	7.1142 5705	0.1405 6282	12.2776 7407	87.3465 2927	0.0814 4865	29
30	7.6122 5504	0.1313 6712	12.4090 4118	94.4607 8632	0.0805 8640	30
31	8.1451 1290	0.1227 7301	12.5318 1419	102.0730 4137	0.0797 9691	31
32	8.7152 7080	0.1147 4113	12.6465 5532	110.2181 5426	0.0790 7292	32
33	9.3253 3975	0.1072 3470	12.7537 9002	118.9334 2506	0.0784 0807	33
34	9.9781 1354	0.1002 1934	12.8540 0936	128.2587 6481	0.0777 9674	34
35	10.6765 8148	0.0936 6294	12.9476 7230	138.2368 7835	0.0772 3396	35
36	11.4239 4219	0.0875 3546	13.0352 0776	148.9134 5984	0.0767 1531	36
37	12.2236 1814	0.0818 0884	13.1170 1660	160.3374 0202	0.0762 3685	37
38	13.0792 7141	0.0764 5686	13.1934 7345	172.5610 2017	0.0757 9505	38
39	13.9948 2041	0.0714 5501	13.2649 2846	185.6402 9158	0.0753 8676	39
40	14.9744 5784	0.0667 8038	13.3317 0884	199.6351 1199	0.0750 0914	40
41	16.0226 6989	0.0624 1157	13.3941 2041	214.6095 6983	0.0746 5962	41
42	17.1442 5678	0.0583 2857	13.4524 4898	230.6322 3972	0.0743 3591	42
43	18.3443 5475	0.0545 1268	13.5069 6167	247.7764 9650	0.0740 3590	43
44	19.6284 5959	0.0509 4643	13.5579 0810	266.1208 5125	0.0737 5769	44
45	21.0024 5176	0.0476 1349	13.6055 2159	285.7493 1084	0.0734 9957	45
46	22.4726 2338	0.0444 9859	13.6500 2018	306.7517 6260	0.0732 5996	46
47	24.0457 0702	0.0415 8747	13.6916 0764	329.2243 8598	0.0730 3744	47
48	25.7289 0651	0.0388 6679	13.7304 7443	353.2700 9300	0.0728 3070	48
49	27.5299 2997	0.0363 2410	13.7667 9853	378.9989 9951	0.0726 3853	49
50	29.4570 2506	0.0339 4776	13.8007 4629	406.5289 2947	0.0724 5985	50

Table XX (*continued*). 7 %

Number of periods n	Amount of 1 at compound interest $s = (1 + i)^n$	Present value of 1 $v^n = \dfrac{1}{(1+i)^n}$	Present value of an annuity of 1 $a_{\overline{n}|} = \dfrac{1 - v^n}{i}$	Amount of an annuity of 1 $s_{\overline{n}|} = \dfrac{(1+i)^n - 1}{i}$	Annuity whose present value is 1 $\dfrac{1}{a_{\overline{n}|}} = \dfrac{1}{s_{\overline{n}|}} + i$	Number of periods n
51	31.5190 1682	0.0317 2688	13.8324 7317	435.9859 5454	0.0722 9365	51
52	33.7253 4799	0.0296 5129	13.8621 2446	467.5049 7135	0.0721 3901	52
53	36.0861 2235	0.0277 1148	13.8898 3594	501.2303 1935	0.0719 9509	53
54	38.6121 5092	0.0258 9858	13.9157 3453	537.3164 4170	0.0718 6110	54
55	41.3150 0148	0.0242 0428	13.9399 3881	575.9285 9262	0.0717 3633	55
56	44.2070 5159	0.0226 2083	13.9625 5964	617.2435 9410	0.0716 2011	56
57	47.3015 4520	0.0211 4096	13.9837 0059	661.4506 4569	0.0715 1183	57
58	50.6126 5336	0.0197 5791	14.0034 5850	708.7521 9089	0.0714 1093	58
59	54.1555 3910	0.0184 6533	14.0219 2383	759.3648 4425	0.0713 1689	59
60	57.9464 2683	0.0172 5732	14.0391 8115	813.5203 8335	0.0712 2923	60
61	62.0026 7671	0.0161 2834	14.0553 0949	871.4668 1019	0.0711 4749	61
62	66.3428 6408	0.0150 7321	14.0703 8270	933.4694 8690	0.0710 7127	62
63	70.9868 6457	0.0140 8711	14.0844 6981	999.8123 5098	0.0710 0019	63
64	75.9559 4509	0.0131 6553	14.0976 3534	1070.7992 1555	0.0709 3388	64
65	81.2728 6124	0.0123 0423	14.1099 3957	1146.7551 6064	0.0708 7203	65
66	86.9619 6153	0.0114 9928	14.1214 3885	1228.0280 2188	0.0708 1431	66
67	93.0492 9884	0.0107 4699	14.1321 8584	1314.9899 8341	0.0707 6046	67
68	99.5627 4976	0.0100 4392	14.1422 2976	1408.0392 8225	0.0707 1021	68
69	106.5321 4224	0.0093 8684	14.1516 1660	1507.6020 3201	0.0706 6331	69
70	113.9893 9220	0.0087 7275	14.1603 8934	1614.1341 7425	0.0706 1953	70
71	121.9686 4965	0.0081 9883	14.1685 8817	1728.1235 6645	0.0705 7866	71
72	130.5064 5513	0.0076 6246	14.1762 5063	1850.0922 1610	0.0705 4051	72
73	139.6419 0699	0.0071 6117	14.1834 1180	1980.5986 7123	0.0705 0490	73
74	149.4168 4047	0.0066 9269	14.1901 0449	2120.2405 7821	0.0704 7164	74
75	159.8760 1931	0.0062 5485	14.1963 5933	2269.6574 1869	0.0704 4060	75
76	171.0673 4066	0.0058 4565	14.2022 0498	2429.5334 3800	0.0704 1160	76
77	183.0420 5451	0.0054 6323	14.2076 6821	2600.6007 7866	0.0703 8453	77
78	195.8549 9832	0.0051 0582	14.2127 7403	2783.6428 3316	0.0703 5924	78
79	209.5648 4820	0.0047 7179	14.2175 4582	2979.4978 3148	0.0703 3563	79
80	224.2343 8758	0.0044 5962	14.2220 0544	3189.0626 7969	0.0703 1357	80
81	239.9307 0471	0.0041 6707	14.2261 7351	3413.2970 6727	0.0702 9297	81
82	256.7259 5034	0.0038 9520	14.2300 6851	3653.2278 6198	0.0702 7373	82
83	274.6967 6686	0.0036 4038	14.2337 0889	3909.9538 1231	0.0702 5576	83
84	293.9255 4054	0.0034 0222	14.2371 1111	4184.6505 7918	0.0702 3897	84
85	314.5003 2838	0.0031 7965	14.2402 9076	4478.5761 1972	0.0702 2329	85
86	336.5153 5137	0.0029 7163	14.2432 6239	4793.0764 4810	0.0702 0863	86
87	360.0714 2596	0.0027 7723	14.2460 3962	5129.5917 9946	0.0701 9495	87
88	385.2764 2578	0.0025 9554	14.2486 3516	5489.6632 2543	0.0701 8216	88
89	412.2457 7558	0.0024 2574	14.2510 6089	5874.9396 5121	0.0701 7021	89
90	441.1029 7988	0.0022 6704	14.2533 2794	6287.1854 2679	0.0701 5905	90
91	471.9801 8847	0.0021 1873	14.2554 4667	6728.2884 0667	0.0701 4863	91
92	505.0188 0166	0.0019 8012	14.2574 2680	7200.2685 9513	0.0701 3888	92
93	540.3701 1778	0.0018 5058	14.2592 7738	7705.2873 9679	0.0701 2978	93
94	578.1960 2602	0.0017 2952	14.2610 0690	8245.6575 1457	0.0701 2128	94
95	618.6697 4784	0.0016 1637	14.2626 2327	8823.8535 4059	0.0701 1333	95
96	661.9766 3019	0.0015 1063	14.2641 3390	9442.5232 8843	0.0701 0590	96
97	708.3149 9430	0.0014 1180	14.2655 4570	10104.4999 1862	0.0700 9897	97
98	757.8970 4390	0.0013 1944	14.2668 6514	10812.8149 1292	0.0700 9248	98
99	810.9498 3698	0.0012 3312	14.2680 9826	11570.7119 5683	0.0700 8643	99
100	867.7163 2557	0.0011 5245	14.2692 5071	12381.6617 9381	0.0700 8076	100

Table XXI. 8 %

Number of periods n	Amount of 1 at compound interest $s = (1 + i)^n$	Present value of 1 $v^n = \dfrac{1}{(1 + i)^n}$	Present value of an annuity of 1 $a_{\overline{n}\rvert} = \dfrac{1 - v^n}{i}$	Amount of an annuity of 1 $s_{\overline{n}\rvert} = \dfrac{(1+i)^n - 1}{i}$	Annuity whose present value is 1 $\dfrac{1}{a_{\overline{n}\rvert}} = \dfrac{1}{s_{\overline{n}\rvert}} + i$	Number of periods n
1	1.0800 0000	0.9259 2593	0.9259 2593	1.0000 0000	1.0800 0000	1
2	1.1664 0000	0.8573 3882	1.7832 6475	2.0800 0000	0.5607 6923	2
3	1.2597 1200	0.7938 3224	2.5770 9699	3.2464 0000	0.3880 3351	3
4	1.3604 8896	0.7350 2985	3.3121 2684	4.5061 1200	0.3019 2080	4
5	1.4693 2808	0.6805 8320	3.9927 1004	5.8666 0096	0.2504 5645	5
6	1.5868 7432	0.6301 6963	4.6228 7966	7.3359 2904	0.2163 1539	6
7	1.7138 2427	0.5834 9040	5.2063 7006	8.9228 0336	0.1920 7240	7
8	1.8509 3021	0.5402 6888	5.7466 3894	10.6366 2763	0.1740 1476	8
9	1.9990 0463	0.5002 4897	6.2468 8791	12.4875 5784	0.1600 7971	9
10	2.1589 2500	0.4631 9349	6.7100 8140	14.4865 6247	0.1490 2949	10
11	2.3316 3900	0.4288 8286	7.1389 6426	16.6454 8746	0.1400 7634	11
12	2.5181 7012	0.3971 1376	7.5360 7802	18.9771 2646	0.1326 9502	12
13	2.7196 2373	0.3676 9792	7.9037 7594	21.4952 9658	0.1265 2181	13
14	2.9371 9362	0.3404 6104	8.2442 3698	24.2149 2030	0.1212 9685	14
15	3.1721 6911	0.3152 4170	8.5594 7869	27.1521 1393	0.1168 2954	15
16	3.4259 4264	0.2918 9047	8.8513 6916	30.3242 8304	0.1129 7687	16
17	3.7000 1805	0.2702 6895	9.1216 3811	33.7502 2569	0.1096 2943	17
18	3.9960 1950	0.2502 4903	9.3718 8714	37.4502 4374	0.1067 0210	18
19	4.3157 0106	0.2317 1206	9.6035 9920	41.4462 6324	0.1041 2763	19
20	4.6609 5714	0.2145 4821	9.8181 4741	45.7619 6430	0.1018 5221	20
21	5.0338 3372	0.1986 5575	10.0168 0316	50.4229 2144	0.0998 3225	21
22	5.4365 4041	0.1839 4051	10.2007 4366	55.4567 5516	0.0980 3207	22
23	5.8714 6365	0.1703 1528	10.3710 5895	60.8932 9557	0.0964 2217	23
24	6.3411 8074	0.1576 9934	10.5287 5828	66.7647 5922	0.0949 7796	24
25	6.8484 7520	0.1460 1790	10.6747 7619	73.1059 3995	0.0936 7878	25
26	7.3963 5321	0.1352 0176	10.8099 7795	79.9544 1515	0.0925 0713	26
27	7.9880 6147	0.1251 8682	10.9351 6477	87.3507 6836	0.0914 4809	27
28	8.6271 0639	0.1159 1372	11.0510 7849	95.3388 2983	0.0904 8891	28
29	9.3172 7490	0.1073 2752	11.1584 0601	103.9659 3622	0.0896 1854	29
30	10.0626 5689	0.0993 7733	11.2577 8334	113.2832 1111	0.0888 2743	30
31	10.8676 6944	0.0920 1605	11.3497 9939	123.3458 6800	0.0881 0728	31
32	11.7370 8300	0.0852 0005	11.4349 9944	134.2135 3744	0.0874 5081	32
33	12.6760 4964	0.0788 8893	11.5138 8837	145.9506 2044	0.0868 5163	33
34	13.6901 3361	0.0730 4531	11.5869 3367	158.6266 7007	0.0863 0411	34
35	14.7853 4429	0.0676 3454	11.6545 6822	172.3168 0368	0.0858 0326	35
36	15.9681 7184	0.0626 2458	11.7171 9279	187.1021 4797	0.0853 4467	36
37	17.2456 2558	0.0579 8572	11.7751 7851	203.0703 1981	0.0849 2440	37
38	18.6252 7563	0.0536 9048	11.8288 6899	220.3159 4540	0.0845 3894	38
39	20.1152 9768	0.0497 1341	11.8785 8240	238.9412 2103	0.0841 8513	39
40	21.7245 2150	0.0460 3093	11.9246 1333	259.0565 1871	0.0838 6016	40
41	23.4624 8322	0.0426 2123	11.9672 3457	280.7810 4021	0.0835 6149	41
42	25.3394 8187	0.0394 6411	12.0066 9867	304.2435 2342	0.0832 8684	42
43	27.3666 4042	0.0365 4084	12.0432 3951	329.5830 0530	0.0830 3414	43
44	29.5559 7166	0.0338 3411	12.0770 7362	356.9496 4572	0.0828 0152	44
45	31.9204 4939	0.0313 2788	12.1084 0150	386.5056 1738	0.0825 8728	45
46	34.4740 8534	0.0290 0730	12.1374 0880	418.4260 6677	0.0823 8991	46
47	37.2320 1217	0.0268 5861	12.1642 6741	452.9001 5211	0.0822 0799	47
48	40.2105 7314	0.0248 6908	12.1891 3649	490.1321 6428	0.0820 4027	48
49	43.4274 1899	0.0230 2693	12.2121 6341	530.3427 3742	0.0818 8557	59
50	46.9016 1251	0.0213 2123	12.2334 8464	573.7701 5642	0.0817 4286	50

Table XXI (*continued*).   8 %

Number of periods n	Amount of 1 at compound interest $s = (1+i)^n$	Present value of 1 $v^n = \dfrac{1}{(1+i)^n}$	Present value of an annuity of 1 $a_{\overline{n}|} = \dfrac{1 - v^n}{i}$	Amount of an annuity of 1 $s_{\overline{n}|} = \dfrac{(1+i)^n - 1}{i}$	Annuity whose present value is 1 $\dfrac{1}{a_{\overline{n}|}} = \dfrac{1}{s_{\overline{n}|}} + i$	Number of periods n
51	50.6537 4151	0.0197 4188	12.2532 2652	620.6717 6893	0.0816 1116	51
52	54.7060 4084	0.0182 7952	12.2715 0604	671.3255 1044	0.0814 8959	52
53	59.0825 2410	0.0169 2548	12.2884 3152	726.0315 5128	0.0813 7735	53
54	63.8091 2603	0.0156 7174	12.3041 0326	785.1140 7538	0.0812 7370	54
55	68.9138 5611	0.0145 1087	12.3186 1413	848.9232 0141	0.0811 7796	55
56	74.4269 6460	0.0134 3599	12.3320 5012	917.8370 5752	0.0810 8952	56
57	80.3811 2177	0.0124 4073	12.3444 9085	992.2640 2213	0.0810 0780	57
58	86.8116 1151	0.0115 1920	12.3560 1005	1072.6451 4390	0.0809 3227	58
59	93.7565 4043	0.0106 6592	12.3666 7597	1159.4567 5541	0.0808 6247	59
60	101.2570 6367	0.0098 7585	12.3765 5182	1253.2132 9584	0.0807 9795	60
61	109.3576 2876	0.0091 4431	12.3856 9613	1354.4703 5951	0.0807 3830	61
62	118.1062 3906	0.0084 6695	12.3941 6309	1463.8279 8827	0.0806 8314	62
63	127.5547 3819	0.0078 3977	12.4020 0286	1581.9342 2733	0.0806 3214	63
64	137.7591 1724	0.0072 5905	12.4092 6190	1709.4889 6552	0.0805 8497	64
65	148.7798 4662	0.0067 2134	12.4159 8324	1847.2480 8276	0.0805 4135	65
66	160.6822 3435	0.0062 2346	12.4222 0671	1996.0279 2938	0.0805 0100	66
67	173.5368 1310	0.0057 6247	12.4279 6917	2156.7101 6373	0.0804 6367	67
68	187.4197 5815	0.0053 3562	12.4333 0479	2330.2469 7683	0.0804 2914	68
69	202.4133 3880	0.0049 4039	12.4382 4518	2517.6667 3497	0.0803 9719	69
70	218.6064 0590	0.0045 7443	12.4428 1961	2720.0800 7377	0.0803 6764	70
71	236.0949 1837	0.0042 3558	12.4470 5519	2938.6864 7967	0.0803 4029	71
72	254.9825 1184	0.0039 2184	12.4509 7703	3174.7813 9805	0.0803 1498	72
73	275.3811 1279	0.0036 3133	12.4546 0836	3429.7639 0989	0.0802 9157	73
74	297.4116 0181	0.0033 6234	12.4579 7071	3705.1450 2268	0.0802 6989	74
75	321.2045 2996	0.0031 1328	12.4610 8399	4002.5566 2449	0.0802 4984	75
76	346.9008 9236	0.0028 8267	12.4639 6665	4323.7611 5445	0.0802 3128	76
77	374.6529 6374	0.0026 6914	12.4666 3579	4670.6620 4681	0.0802 1410	77
78	404.6252 0084	0.0024 7112	12.4691 0721	5045.3150 1056	0.0801 9820	78
79	436.9952 1691	0.0022 8835	12.4713 9557	5449.9402 1140	0.0801 8349	79
80	471.9548 3426	0.0021 1885	12.4735 1441	5886.9354 2831	0.0801 6987	80
81	509.7112 2101	0.0019 6190	12.4754 7631	6358.8902 6258	0.0801 5726	81
82	550.4881 1809	0.0018 1657	12.4772 9288	6868.6014 8358	0.0801 4559	82
83	594.5271 6818	0.0016 8201	12.4789 7489	7419.0896 0227	0.0801 3479	83
84	642.0893 4164	0.0015 5742	12.4805 3230	8013.6167 7045	0.0801 2479	84
85	693.4564 8897	0.0014 4205	12.4819 7436	8655.7061 1209	0.0801 1553	85
86	748.9330 0808	0.0013 3523	12.4833 0959	9349.1626 0105	0.0801 0696	86
87	808.8176 4873	0.0012 3633	12.4845 4592	10098.0956 0914	0.0800 9903	87
88	873.5554 6063	0.0011 4475	12.4856 9066	10906.9432 5787	0.0800 9168	88
89	943.4398 9748	0.0010 5995	12.4867 5061	11780.4987 1850	0.0800 8489	89
90	1018.9150 8928	0.0009 8144	12.4877 3205	12723.9386 1598	0.0800 7859	90
91	1100.4282 9642	0.0009 0874	12.4886 4079	13742.8537 0526	0.0800 7277	91
92	1188.4625 6013	0.0008 4142	12.4894 8221	14843.2820 0168	0.0800 6737	92
93	1283.5395 6494	0.0007 7910	12.4902 6131	16031.7445 6181	0.0800 6238	93
94	1386.2227 3014	0.0007 2138	12.4909 8269	17315.2841 2676	0.0800 5775	94
95	1497.1205 4855	0.0006 6795	12.4916 5064	18701.5068 5690	0.0800 5347	95
96	1616.8901 9244	0.0006 1847	12.4922 6911	20198.6274 0545	0.0800 4951	96
97	1746.2414 0783	0.0005 7266	12.4928 4177	21815.5175 9788	0.0800 4584	97
98	1885.9407 2046	0.0005 3024	12.4933 7201	23561.7590 0572	0.0800 4244	98
99	2036.8159 7809	0.0004 9096	12.4938 6297	25447.6997 2617	0.0800 3930	99
100	2199.7612 5634	0.0004 5459	12.4943 1757	27484.5157 0427	0.0800 3638	100

INDEX